C000229709

The
Brilliant
Stage

The *Brilliant* *Stage*

The Story of
Frances Walsingham

ANGELA McLEOD

Matador
9 Priory Business Park,
Wistow Road, Kibworth Beauchamp,
Leicestershire. LE8 0RX
Tel: (+44) 116 279 2299
Fax: (+44) 116 279 2277
Email: books@troubador.co.uk
Web: www.troubador.co.uk/matador

ISBN 978 1783064 717

British Library Cataloguing in Publication Data.
A catalogue record for this book is available from the British Library.

Typeset in 11pt Aldine401 BT Roman by Troubador Publishing Ltd, Leicester, UK
Printed and bound in the UK by TJ International, Padstow, Cornwall

Matador is an imprint of Troubador Publishing Ltd

ACKNOWLEDGEMENTS

I am grateful to so many people for their help in getting this book off the ground and into print.

Primarily, to my husband, David, for his heroic patience and encouragement. Then to my children who have brought their modern realism and candid opinions to the project.

Also to my Editor and great friend, Christopher Hanson-Smith for his precision and sharp eye for imperfections.

My thanks go as well to Anna Greening, archivist at All Hallows By The Tower for the help, time, and valuable information she gave me: to the Vicar of St.Olave's Church, Hart Street, who trustingly left me to rifle through some of his records and registers: to Mrs.Maisie Brown who supplied information on the history of Barn Elms: to Davyd Power, archivist for the Tonbridge Parish Church, St.Peter and St.Paul : to Mr.Scragg who took and sent the pictures of the "rain hoppers" at Somerhill: to the archivists at Portumna Castle for their assistance with the Irish questions: to Pamela Baker for her computer expertise and generous help: to Desmond Maxwell for his interest and knowledgeable advice. Lastly, to Matrix in Oban who twice saved material from my computer after being hit by the various natural disasters so common on the West Coast of Scotland.

CONTENTS

INTRODUCTION

The roar of fire or rushing water, both terrifying sounds, are very like the raging of an angry crowd. I have heard that noise twice and hope never to hear it again. The first time was on a hot August evening in Tokyo, four hundred years almost to the night when it reverberated through Paris during the worst atrocity in the history of European Christendom. The night was the Eve of St.Bartholomew, 24th August 1572, when the ringing of a church bell let loose night itself upon the city. Appalling scenes of violence and rivers of blood swept away three thousand Huguenots, their slaughter staining the Seine for days after.

While we lived in Tokyo, I had access to the library in Kanda which had a fascinating collection of historical books and references. I used to drop two of my children at the Lycée Franco Japonais which was a hectic forty minute drive across Tokyo, plunge into the library and read until I collected the youngest at noon. I would give anything to have those books with me now.

That particular August night I was reading a volume borrowed from Kanda by an open window and was deep in the happenings of St.Bartholomew's Eve when I became aware of background noise. An elemental roar was beginning to intrude, as if sounds from the past were insinuating themselves into the present.

I dropped the book and leaned out of the window. The sounds were real; not a ghost of the haunted past. Tens of thousands of people were demonstrating outside the American Embassy in protest against nuclear ships entering Yokosuka harbour, the American Naval Base. The roar came in waves, integrating past and present. Was I hearing the blood-soaked mob howling outside Sir Francis Walsingham's beleaguered Embassy in St.Germaine or the controlled demonstration of well-dressed Japanese. The situation soon became clear but the sound was probably very similar.

What remained in my mind was the fact that Sir Francis Walsingham's five year old daughter, his only child, was there in the house in Paris on St.Bartholomew's Eve with her parents, as was Sir Philip Sidney, her future husband. That coincidence sparked the interest I already had in this shadowy figure which has dogged me until it became imperative to know more about her and I have had the time to search for her.

My interest in Frances Walsingham began years ago when I first read Lytton Strachey's book "Elizabeth and Essex". It arose from one paragraph very near the end of the book, and brought to the surface the questions which, for me, had been rising throughout its length. After the execution of her husband Essex, and in response to a favour from Robert Cecil, we are told:

"A letter of thanks to Cecil gives us a momentary glimpse of the most mysterious of the personages in this tragic history. A shrouded figure, moving dubiously on that brilliantly lighted stage, Frances Walsingham remains utterly unknown to us. We can only guess, according to our fancy, at some rare beauty, some sovereign charm – and at one thing more; a superabundant vitality. For two years later, the widow of Sidney and Essex was married for the third time – to the Earl of Clanricarde. And so she vanishes".

Frances Walsingham, later Lady Philip Sidney, Countess of Essex and Countess of Clanricarde and St.Albans, is not an easy person to become acquainted with.

She moved in a vivid age in the company of the most illustrious men and women of her time, yet she remained as anonymous as her positions allowed. Apart from royalty, women were not much documented in the time of Elizabeth I, except where special notoriety connected them with the great and the good or, perhaps, the bad. Some women, either through force of character or because they wrote many letters reflecting the age in which they lived, have managed to leave their mark on history.

Few such letters have come to light and finding Frances Walsingham is not simple. She is referred to in biographies, but seldom in her own right. Dates of marriages, births and deaths can be found and can provide information on the structure of her life, but facts have to be traced through the lives of her father, her husbands and her better known children. It is almost as if she covered her traces in death as carefully as she shunned the limelight in her life. Yet she must have been an exceptional woman, possessed of great personal magnetism, beauty, or that elusive commodity, charm. Certainly she possessed the ability to survive.

Her father, Sir Francis Walsingham, one of the most brilliant and tactical brains of his age, achieved high positions in diplomacy and within the State, besides the ultimate trust of the Queen and Lord Burghley, no mean feat with two such complex characters. Intelligence, the gathering and distribution of it, was one of his prime tasks and secrecy was naturally a vital part of this. From him, Frances must have learned early the lessons of discretion and restraint. She did not, however, always choose to apply them.

She married, very young, one of the brightest of Elizabethan stars, Sir Philip Sidney. On his death, three brief years later, her genuine grief might well have given her every reason to retire, with her surviving child, to her father's house. Instead, she married, within three years, one of her husband's greatest admirers; an even brighter, though more intransigent star, the Earl of Essex. When he lost his head eleven years later on Tower Green, she married the Earl of Clanricarde, a man strangely similar to Essex though with less explosive tendences. With him, it is hoped, she passed a happy, comparatively peaceful twenty seven years in the beautiful houses they built together in Kent and in Ireland.

She bore Sidney two children, one posthumous, Essex seven children and Clanricarde three. Given the infant mortality rate in Elizabethan England, it is not surprising that only seven of these survived.

What we know of her suggests a woman of strength, capable, like the phoenix, of rising from the ashes of despair and defeat; no reed shaken by any Elizabethan blast. Also a woman able to delight, fulfil and support those within her circle. Where does the truth lie? Was she soft and confiding, was the steel well sheathed, or did she become, like Lady Bacon, a formidable matriarch?

Although it has been possible, from the facts available, to piece together the course of Frances Walsingham's life, I have not been able to write what should be a biography. Research has shown a lack of written material both on her and by her. It has been necessary, therefore, to construct her personality on the basis of what is truly known and recorded of her reactions to the historical events in which she was involved. I do not believe she was the passive, child-bearing wife history appears to have made her. I have, however, tried to portray her with the minimum amount of invention or supposition, fascinating though this can be, and working within the correct dates.

THE BEGINNING AND THE END

Ash Wednesday 1601

Frances, Countess of Essex, leant her forehead against the cold stone casement of her window in Walsingham House, her eyes fixed on the pennants that fluttered above the White Tower deep in the heart of the Tower of London.

It was Ash Wednesday, 1601, a bleak morning in February. She was waiting for the roar of a canon that would signal the end of her husband's life; the moments could be counted by the thud of her heart.

He would, after all the raging and religious hysteria that had prompted him to implicate his nearest and dearest, be completely composed; his courage, in all his thirty-three years, had never been questioned. That something so vital could be snuffed out in one moment was unimaginable.

He had not once asked for her, nor had he sent any word or letter. It was as though their hectic eleven years of marriage had never been. He had sent no message for his children.

What then, at this eleventh hour, was in his mind? Was it hope of reprieve from the old woman to whose tune he had finally and fatally refused to dance? Or had his thoughts closed like a fist, shutting out both his Queen and his family, leaving only conduct and the saving of his soul to consider?

The recent march of events, inexorable and violent, had realised to the full her own long-standing fears.

No man, however charismatic and powerful, could continue so ruinous a course without Nemesis laying a cold hand on his shoulder. Nemesis, in his case, came in the form of the old woman whose immovable will he had never fully understood, so often had he managed to bend it, but who, when it came down to the wire, held all the cards including her own omnipotence.

Standing on the sidelines of this strange conflict, Frances had had ample time to observe both combatants and she knew, in her soul, that there would be no reprieve for Essex. He had gone beyond the rules of their peculiar, adoring, and sometimes vicious contact.

1

There is often a point in the affairs of men and women, Kings and subjects, which draws a line in the sand beyond which there is neither return nor pardon. Frances had heard him utter words which could never be unsaid and knew with certainty that they would be repeated to the Queen.

The Earl of Essex, after his last long and painful banishment, had received a message from Her Majesty asking after his health. Conditions for his return to Court were mentioned and he had roared back: "Her conditions! Her conditions are as crooked as her carcase!" Those unforgivable words had been faithfully reported and the line had been drawn. No woman could forgive them least of all a Queen. They made a mockery of every protestation of love, every fulsome letter, every vow of admiration and eternal service. Cold rage and anguish would erase any delight she had once taken in him. Outrage too, because the words hinted that she was not as other women, could never properly know a man or bear children. Statements of this kind had been made in the past by doctors and diplomats when her marriage had been in question but never by her beloved Essex; his fate was sealed. It was the end for them both.

The Countess of Essex was long past tears. Her impassive face, one of her greatest assets throughout her life, showed none of the rampant hopes and fears of the last two months. Her remarkable eyes, now fixed on the pennant, gave nothing away; the down-swept lids with their dark lashes half lowered. She stood, still and straight as a dancer, facing the White Tower and her future.

Constantly running through her mind, as a mantra, were words written by him to soften the heart of a Queen:

"The restless swallow fits my restless minde, in still reviving still renewing wronges; her just complaintes of cruelty unkinde, are all the music that of my life prolonges."

They had been written on a full length portrait of herself, pregnant and in Persian dress, which he had commissioned Marcus Gheeradts to paint and planned to offer to the Queen at the annual Accession Day Tilt on November 17th 1600. It was a most bizarre idea and madness to present a portrait of Frances, always a thorn in the Queen's flesh, with a poem which amounted to a rebuke for unfair and harsh treatment and a reminder that his wife was again to present him with a child. She had managed, for once, to dissuade him and had hidden the portrait, which she disliked intensely: it was full of symbolism, the Devereux hart with tears in its eyes, the fruit tree shedding kernels. She knew he was capable of sending it anyway and she suspected his mind, at that time, was far from sound.

As for their marriage, they had loved and laughed despite the many other women in his life and the intense pace at which they lived, and it was to her that he had turned in the days of his disgrace and illness after the fateful return from Ireland and his long detention. She had born another child and nursed him back to health. This was a bitter ending that, for her, could be no end, but the beginning of a very different and restricted life. She and her children would lose everything; there would be no quarter given. Only beloved Barn Elms, curled in its sweep of the river, would still be theirs.

What would he wear? She hoped a warm velvet cloak this cold, grey, February morning, so that he would not shiver with what might be mistaken for fear. Would there be a bright doublet underneath, so that he stood out from those others on the scaffold? She was certain his pride would not permit them to bind his hands or to blindfold him. Neither would he allow a long harangue from any member of the Clergy in attendance.

What was there left for him to say to that select crowd, which had not already been said, as they gathered round the square of turf soaked by the blood of so many before him? The Queen would not risk a large gathering or a public place; despite all, he was still greatly loved by many in the city of London.

How would he die? With high courage, certainly; with humility, not so certainly. Would someone present have the fortitude to describe his last moments to her faithfully and without the kind of detail that could tear her apart, perhaps to settle a score, to see her reaction, or simply because it was irresistible not to do so? She knew the predatory nature of many at Court who would relish both his downfall and her own vulnerability.

She had written on 21st February to Robert Cecil Her Majesty's Secretary of State, a desperate last minute plea for intercession with the Queen for his life, saying: "I shall never wish to breathe one hour after." The answer was cold silence. He had been condemned on 19th February; now, on 25th February 1601, all hope had gone.

As the pounding of her heart increased and her breathing grew shorter, vivid memories of the last weeks jostled each other in a race towards these final moments.

The crisis had begun last October when the Queen had refused to renew his levy on the "Farm of Sweet Wines" which had been a large part of his income over the past ten years. Many other such sinecures which had arisen from his position at Court were denied him during the year of his banishment. He was looking ruin in the face and the desperation that went with it.

The birth of their last daughter, Dorothy, in December as the storm was gathering, had gone almost unnoticed by him. She was a quiet, unassuming baby who seemed to guess that her arrival was a minor event in the scheme of things and that she was a very small cog in the wheels of the fate engulfing her parents. Frances had gone to her mother at Walsingham House for her birth, but returned by Christmas, apprehensive of what she would find at Essex House.

From her bedchamber there Frances could sense the rising turmoil in the great house. There was clearly an unprecedented number of people arriving and departing, huge gatherings in the hall in the evenings and the level of noise higher than anything she could remember. With the stamping feet and ringing hooves in the courtyard, she could sense a surge of reckless urgency. There was an endless rumble of heavy laden carts; shouts, orders and more rumbles. A lot of weighty stuff was being unloaded into the house. Quick footsteps came and went past her door but few knocked except her beloved maid Jane.

Essex did visit her occasionally but was so tense that little could be got from him. She had questioned him about a small, black silk bag he wore night and day around his neck and against his chest. It seemed strange behaviour for a sane man and his replies were evasive and grudging. It appeared that James, King of Scotland, had sent it to him, for his eyes only, and it contained an assertion that he intended, with Essex's help, to claim the throne of England. They had corresponded regularly over the last few years but Essex refused to be drawn on whether this was to be before, or after, the Queen's death. Frances suspected it also contained a cypher; as Walsingham's daughter, she knew a certain amount about such things.

Frances also noticed that he no longer wore a ring given him by the Queen in the early days of their devotion and after one of their many quarrels. The ring, she said, had long ago spared her from the anger of her father, Henry Vlll, and it carried an assurance that if he ever sent it back to her, it would always bring him her forgiveness.

Her fears mounting, Frances left her room as early as she physically could and joined the now vast household for Christmas, strange and unnatural though it was this year; a lot of campfire singing but not much dancing and very little exchange of presents. The atmosphere was frankly belligerent and, apart from Essex's close circle, there was a concourse of strangers unknown to Frances. Young aristocrats with their pockets to let, soldiers of fortune who had been with Essex on the Spanish raids or in Ireland, and more sinister, many brought up from his Welsh estates; dark, incomprehensible little men quartered all over the district. Frances did not like the atmosphere. Her house was beginning to look like a barracks and much less the centre of arts and music it had always been.

The main mass of people began to disperse, though not far, after New Year but, with the arrival of Penelope Rich the Earl's still lovely sister and her children, the pace picked up again. She had been for many years now the mistress of Charles, Baron Mountjoy, and three of her seven children were his. Charles had taken over the Irish campaign from Essex and appeared to be making a success of an almost irredeemable mess. Penelope had written, at the beginning of the year, a most impertinent and arrogant letter to the Queen on her captive brother's behalf which had served only to stir the coals and infuriate Her Majesty. Since his release she appeared to have learnt no caution but continued to stir. Though devoted to her and normally able to restrain her flights, Frances felt that this time her meddling was becoming dangerous.

Anthony Bacon, gentle man that he was, and the mainspring of Essex's intelligence service, remained in his upstairs rooms, so crippled now that movement anywhere was difficult, but he knew well what had been recently stored in the armouries and stables of Essex House. He looked anxious and strained, but would only say that many of Essex's followers and friends had left only to foregather with the Earl of Southampton at Drury House, in Drury Lane. She guessed the reason was that it was too easy to keep a watch on Essex House and its many visitors. The house had long been a centre of power and action; any observation would go straight to the misshapen but perspicacious little Secretary of State, Robert Cecil, who had more than a fair idea of what was going on and was fully prepared to act. The bands of roistering swordsmen, many familiar faces from Essex's past campaigns and the hard-riding messengers in an out of Essex House, had not gone unnoticed.

Rumours were flying, put about by Essex and relayed to King James, that

5

Cecil and his faction were considering the Spanish Infanta as a possible successor to the English throne. Though quite untrue and designed as a goad to James and others, this was not so far-fetched as it sounded. John of Gaunt's daughter had inherited Spain through her mother, and King Philip had been consort to Mary Tudor, the Queen's sister. Essex was becoming increasingly unbalanced and seeing conspiracies and forces against himself behind every bush and Frances found it difficult to speak to him at all, let alone to reason with him. She was beginning to realise it was now too late to halt whatever hell-bent purpose he had in mind. Where was the joyous, confident friend she had married?

Events had quickened since New Year and, like a landslide, with very little control. Attempts had been made once more to embroil Charles Mountjoy in Ireland in order to bring his troops over to reinforce Essex's hotheads. With great good sense and inspite of their long friendship and Penelope's urging he refused categorically. How long had insurrection been in any of their minds?

Frances was too intelligent not to realise this was being planned and for the very near future. Her son Robert returned to Eton, having hardly exchanged two words with his father, and she sent her little daughters to her mother in nearby Walsingham House. Only these three of her seven Essex children now remained. Penelope's children were sent to their grandmother at Wanstead.

Two councils of war, she knew, had been held in Drury House under the auspices of the fiery young Earl of Southampton but God only knew what the outcome had been. All she could do was to remain by Essex's side and try to mitigate whatever new madness erupted. He had ordered her to remain in Walsingham House with the children but she had refused.

Then came the evening of 7th February. At the instigation of Southampton and several other followers of Essex a performance of Shakespeare's "Richard II" had been specially arranged at the Globe Playhouse across the river for an increased sum. The inference was perfectly clear and it was inflammatory stuff. The abdication of King Richard, a scene which had been banned, in favour of Henry Bolingbroke, the future Henry IV, was flagrantly near the bone and marrow of the here and now; a King being deposed in favour of a young, popular soldier of Royal blood was more than controversial.

Frances could remember the cold as they were rowed across, the broad grins and sly winks of the boatmen and the dark water like oiled silk hiding the imperfections of the day; then the large crowds in the Playhouse and their swaggering mood. There were cheers for Essex and Christopher Blount, his stepfather, Southampton, Rutland, Mounteagle and the others. As a piece of propaganda, it was a great success. Penelope was with them, dressed to kill, hugely enjoying herself and in the highest spirits. She was one who lived for the moment, unlike Frances, who thought well into the future and suffered because of it.

They had all returned to a late dinner little knowing that an emergency meeting of the Council was being held at the home of the Lord Treasurer. Then, like a skilled angler, Secretary Cecil cast his fly. Around midnight he summoned Essex to appear at once before the Privy Council. Prevarication followed, but the mischief was done. The deputation would return in the morning but, as Cecil intended, pandemonium broke out and the theatre supper party became a council of war. It was then after midnight but the fuse had been lit. They would have to act immediately.

Listening, horrified, Frances at last fully understood what was intended, how chaotic and still undecided were their plans and how unprepared were their resources. Men were still on the road to London, no sign of the Embassy promised by James of Scotland had materialised, and arms from the Continent had not yet arrived. They could not even establish whether first to turn left out of Essex House to Whitehall Palace, or right to raise the City where a Sheriff had purportedly promised support and armed men. Some were for immediate flight to Wales and to raise the rebellion from there. They had been outmanoeuvred and even the element of surprise had been taken from them.

Essex was blustering furiously that he could raise three hundred men by morning and win the day with support from the City. His sister Penelope, equally polemic, was urging them on and blaming them for dragging their feet even overnight. Others warned of leaving men like Raleigh unaccounted for. He loathed Essex with a deep and bitter loathing and was too dangerous to be left on the loose.

Frances did not sleep and Essex did not come to her chamber. All that night there were feet running in every direction, orders shouted and, towards dawn, the sound of men and horses gathering in the outer courtyard. She learnt, early in the morning, that Sir Charles Danvers, sent to reconnoitre the situation at Whitehall, had reported that the guard there had been doubled and there could be no taking the Court by surprise. Even so, he reckoned, there was a chance of storming it with three hundred men.

When Essex eventually came in to hastily change his clothes, Frances tried with every power of reason and persuasion she possessed to turn him away from the ruinous course he was set on. There was no way now, she said, in which he could depose the Queen and set James in her place. James was three days away, in Scotland; it was madness.

He looked at her, his hazel eyes hard and his face set like that of a fallen angel. Time was snapping at his heels, he said, the situation was desperate but all was not yet lost. He kissed her quickly and turned to the door as it opened with his frightened page, Henry Tracey, delivering the message that the deputation had arrived from Whitehall.

The Lord Keeper Egerton, who had been Essex's former kindly gaoler, Lord Chief Justice Popham, Sir William Knollys, Essex's uncle, and the Earl of Worcester, Essex's friend, were awaiting him. Egerton had with him the Great Seal of England and they were not paying a social call. With the greatest politeness, they asked what was the meaning of this gathering of armed men, to which Essex replied that his life was in danger and they were there to defend him. He invited them upstairs to his study to discuss the matter and they bowed as they passed Frances, now standing stiffly at the head of the stairs. With even greater politeness they then made it clear that if Essex did not immediately cease what he was about and disperse the armed crowd in the courtyard, and should he allow them to pass the gates into the streets, he would be outside the law.

As they went upstairs, there were yells of derision from below, fists raised and cries of "Kill them" and some of "Shop them up." If that was not enough, others shouted "They abuse you, My Lord. You lose time." All of which made it very clear that a rebellion was under way. Frances saw Rutland, Southampton, Mounteagle, Blount and Danvers close in behind the Councillors, but they left open the door to Essex's study.

"My Lords," said Essex, "be patient a while and stay here and I will go into London and take order with the Mayor and Sheriffs for the City and be here again within this half hour."

He then whisked himself and his friends out of the room, turned on his heel and gave orders for the Councillors to be locked in. He crammed his hat on his head and marched past Frances down to the shouting crowd of men. After a brief argument and some wild wavering, they turned west to the City instead of east to Whitehall, their swords drawn; the die was truly cast and in the wrong direction.

Frances did not see him again until dusk that evening when he came in through the garden via Essex Stairs whence he had fled by boat from the city. She was waiting for him in mounting terror at the end of the passage into the hall and could hear the sounds of arrival, the clunk of shipped oars, the sound of voices out of the dark and dragging footsteps. Dear God! Who and what was coming through that door? He was grey with fatigue, drenched in sweat and hardly recognisable. Mounteagle, behind him, had fallen in the river as they escaped and was shuddering with cold and dripping wet. Christopher Blount, leading an attack in the city, had been wounded and arrested there.

Frances had spent one of the worst days of her life, realizing he was not capable of rational thought and that his decisions were crazy and had no chance of success. She and Penelope had been left to explain to the Councillors why they had been locked in. To alleviate their anger and discomfort, they had ordered them food and wine and done their best to appear unconcerned. In the circumstances, polite conversation could hardly flourish, especially as they were guarded by two armed men. Even Penelope, who had been full of bravado to begin with, became subdued.

Just before dusk, Sir Ferdinand Gorges, never the bravest of the brave and determined to escape in one piece, arrived and ordered that the Councillors be freed before vanishing into the night. Moments later, Essex himself arrived, to find his last hope, his hostages, had gone and with them any bargaining power he may have had. Essex House was, by this time, almost surrounded by the Queen's most powerful and loyal subjects and it was only a matter of time before they broke into the house.

Tight-lipped and desperate, Essex pushed past Frances to the stairs, the events of the day written on his face, and began frantically to burn incriminating papers in the hearth of his study. She watched, unbelieving, while he wrenched the black silk bag from his neck and threw it on the blaze, then she turned to lock and bar the door so that he could have a few extra minutes to complete the task and so, perhaps, help save some of his friends. She could hear that those attacking the house were breaking through to the outer courtyard. There was gunfire and the sound of shattering glass, followed by the screams and shouts of the servants. There was clearly about to be a very ugly scene and much loss of life. For one brief moment he looked at her and smiled his old wicked smile.

He then left the room to join Southampton who, by this time, was shouting terms from the roof, interspersed with assurances that they had never intended to harm the Queen, only to defend themselves. Even to Frances, it sounded improbable.

At this point, the Queen's deputies sent Robert Sidney, Essex's great friend and the former brother-in-law of Frances, into the house to urge him to surrender rather than risk a massacre. Both he and Southampton were now yelling defiantly, that they would die like men, by the sword and not on the scaffold. The Queen's men agreed to take the women in the house to safety during a two hour ceasefire. Robert Sidney and his men returned to escort Frances and Penelope from the house together with all the servants.

As she left her house for the last time, Frances looked back to see Essex silhouetted against the flares, still on the rooftop, demanding fair treatment and a fair trial. She stood, unmoving, by the gates gazing at his tall form outlined against the torches until kind Robert Sidney wrapped a cloak around her and lifted her before him on to his horse. It was freezing hard. His left arm tightened round her as the force went out of her and her dark head rolled on his shoulder. It was over; she would never, in this world, see him again.

Now, this biting February morning, she had chosen to be alone; to share the hour with another soul would have been unbearable. How, from where they had started, had they managed to arrive at this moment?

The wind was blowing away from her and sight travels faster than sound. She saw the small cloud of smoke before she heard the cannon.

IN THE WINGS 1

1568-1570 – The Papey

The Papey, unlike many of the houses surrounding it, was old and stone built with turreted walls and an enclosed garden and orchard. It lay on the junction of Camomile Street and St.Mary Axe, close to London Wall. A former religious house belonging to a brotherhood of St. John and St. Charity, it had been founded in 1430 by three Charity priests and, not surprisingly, appeared somewhat monasterial. Because of its origins, it had its own water supply, a spring and a little stream running through the orchard. The religious orders were particularly adept at building over or near water, knowing their need of it in caring for the sick.

In March 1568 Francis Walsingham had bought a house in St.Giles Cripplegate which he used as an office, for the accomodation of staff and for the stabling of horses. He had, later, moved his family from his wife's estate in the Isle of Wight, to the Papey because it was a larger house with bigger rooms and had, for London, a beautiful garden. It was, however, a far cry from Appuldurcombe and the sea breezes of the Wight.

On a blisteringly hot morning in August a very small girl played happily in the stream by herself. She was busily employed in piling sticks into the water and watching the current gradually pick them up and carry them away. She then scooped up mud, squeezing it lingeringly through her fingers, and anchoring the sticks with it. On top she put a stone to hold the edifice down, squatting alongside and feeling the cool water seep into her shoes. There was a loud squawk behind her, two large hands grabbed her from her earthworks and swung her away from the water while Alice Poole, her nurse, scolding horribly, bore her off towards the house. She reacted like any self-respecting toddler by becoming alarmingly rigid and screaming furiously at the outrage. The nurse set her down on a stone step and tried to pull off her muddy little shoes. The baby put her head down on the step, stuck her rump in the air and really showed what she could do with her lungs. Her stiff skirt and the cotton shift beneath it

11

were soaking almost up to her waist. Her embroidered cap fell off and the soft dark curls tumbled around her face. Alice coaxed and cooed in vain.

Lady Ursula Walsingham, her mother, hurried down the stairs to put an end to a rumpus which might seriously disturb the interview being held in the large front room used by her husband for official visitors. Behind her, fussing and fuming, came her sister Edith Beale. They swept the bawling child up, carrying her across the stone hallway, deliciously cool and sweet smelling after the heat outside, up the stairs to Lady Ursula's dressing chamber and proceeded to stop the riot by turning her on her face and beating her with the flat of a hairbrush. Edith Beale, unable to resist the opportunity, self-righteously deplored such lack of discipline and wilfulness in her niece and criticised the indulgence of her upbringing. Odious though her carping was, there was some truth in what she said.

Frances Walsingham was her father's only chick and child and her mother's one remaining offspring, therefore unusually precious. Lady Ursula's two boys, sons of her first marriage to Sir Richard Worsley, Captain of the Isle of Wight, would now have been ten and eight. Time and the baby had helped to heal the shock of their death but, so far, no new arrivals appeared to be in the offing and Frances was being brought up as a treasured only child with some ambitious plans made for her.

The boys' death in the gatehouse at Appuldurcombe had been tragic and unnecessary. There were rumours of ships sighted in the Channel, a muster had been called and the children were helping servants dry gunpowder. It was a cold day and someone, with sad lack of intelligence, lit a fire. They were blown to pieces just three weeks before Frances was born on 28th September 1567.

By the following year, the strings attached to Walsingham's career began to tighten. Queen, Court and the corridors of power were beckoning and it was time to plunge into "the whirlpool of State" leaving the tranquility of beautiful Appuldurcombe.

Robert and Edith Beale lived next to the Papey in a contemporary house made of the usual timber and clay with two storeys, one overhanging the other. Like so many other London houses, its slate roof tiles were salvaged from the huge glut of material still left from the destruction of the monastries. The lives of the two families were destined to remain closely linked. Robert Beale, though bluff and sometimes irritating, was an intelligent and capable man who dealt extremely well with Walsingham and was to be invaluable to him; the sisters remained close despite Edith's tendency to grumble and endlessly fear the worst.

Their two daughters, Margaret and Catherine, detested Frances and considered her a spoilt brat. They were several years older, rather plain, and sly enough to make trouble for her when they could. She was far too young to be aware of this, but as aware as a young animal that she did not like them, and there was cause for their jealousy. Frances was an attractive child, small and delicate with a born sense of timing.

The men esconced in Walsingham's front room got an echo of the fracas going on outside and permitted themselves a brief grin of empathy, their attention only momentarily drawn from their discussion. Like the hall, the room was cool and comfortable. Lady Ursula was a skilled needlewoman and chairs, window seats and stools were well-padded with tapestry and embroidered cushions. Rush mats, new and fragrant, lay on the stone floor and the big fireplace with logs piled neatly into an embrasure in the wall beside it lay swept and clean. The Papey was at its best in summer; the cold could bite through the stone walls and floors in winter and the wind could whistle through and round the rather narrow stained glass windows

Nicholas Throckmorton stood with his back to the fireplace, a glass of Walsingham's excellent Rhenish wine in hand, and surveyed his old friend with interest and affection. He was a good looking man in his fifties and a cousin of King Henry VIII's last wife, Katherine Parr. He had shared exile with Walsingham during Mary Tudor's reign, Throckmorton's through a degree of employment and Walsingham's self-imposed. Both were rigidly Protestant, their friendship stemming from shared opinions, mutual respect and a knowledge that each had the brain and the courage to back the other up in a crisis. Sir Nicholas had an Ambassadorship in Paris under his belt and was now pouring diplomatic oil on the troubled waters of Scotland. He was counting on Walsingham's support today in approaching the wonderfully devious Secretary of State, Sir William Cecil, soon to be Lord Burghley, on the subject of a Royal audience.

The hopeful recipient of the audience was the third man in the room, Robert Stewart, and the subject of the audience was the proposed marriage between the Queen and Henri Duc d'Anjou, the third and favourite son of Catherine de Medici's Valois brood.

Large, redhaired and, today, rather pink about the jowls, Robert Stewart sat opposite Walsingham, drinking cold water from the spring. He was the representative of the two main leaders of the Huguenots in France, the Prince de Condé and Admiral Gaspard de Coligny. This morning of the 19th August they were discussing Walsingham's letter to Cecil written on the 18th, the postscript of which read "Touching these matters wherein you appoint me to deal, I will tomorrow in the morning attend upon your Lordship". This he had duly done and was now reporting the outcome of a preliminary chat the two had shared earlier in the day. The Duc was proving a reluctant contender and had made some disparaging remarks about Her Majesty's age and appearance which did not augur well. The French Queen Mother, much given to the occult, had conveniently dreamed that each and every one of her sons would wear a crown and was offering them up to a variety of European Royal houses. She still had Anjou's younger brother, Francois Duc D'Alençon, up her sleeve.

Elizabeth's prevarications on the subject of marriage were well known to her Ministers, most of her Court and a great many of her subjects. These were now being reviewed in retrospect, with a certain amount of jocularity, by the three in the cool dimly lit room. Walsingham's pale, rather austere face was alight with laughter, his grey eyes, penetrating but impenetrable, were creased with mirth, some of it self-directed. He told a story with bite and a bone dry wit.

Under discussion were the princely wooings of King Philip of Spain, the Queen's brother-in-law who, soon after her accession, had offered "brotherly" support and spiritual guidance as well as marriage, which she rightly interpreted as a veiled effort to reinstate Catholicism in England. She politely, but firmly, turned him down. His son, Don Carlos, was then proposed, though it was common knowledge by 1564 that he was far from normal, having pitched down a flight of stone steps in amorous pursuit of a gardener's daughter, landing "upon his noddle." This resulted in swelling of the head, blindness and raging fever, accompanied in due course by raging madness. Adding insult to injury, he had formerly been suggested as a husband for Mary Queen of Scots.

Don Carlos was followed in 1566 by Prince Erik of Sweden whose intellect was not of the strongest either. The Earl of Leicester, the Queen's favourite and best-beloved, in a fit of pique, described him as a "half-wit". Elizabeth's resulting anger was spurious and efforts to bring Erik to England for inspection quietly fizzled out, despite a deputation from his sister, Princess Cecilia, to further his chances.

He was followed in 1567 by the Archduke Charles of Austria. Glowing descriptions, portraits and gifts had been exchanged and delight expressed on both sides. With familiar intransigence, however, the Queen was, yet again, dragging her feet. Yes, the Archduke's birth was sufficiently elevated; he was brave, handsome, had wonderful legs and was a brilliant horseman, but there remained the hurdle of his religion. As befitted the brother of the Holy Roman Emperor, he was a dedicated Catholic who expected to be able to practice his religion with freedom when and how he chose. The English marriage terms (as they had been with Mary Tudor and Philip of Spain), were that he should not do so in public. Things had faltered on until the Archduke Charles eventually married his niece, the Duchess of Bavaria (despite Rome's strict notions on consanguinity). Elizabeth declared herself "insulted and rejected."

And now here was Henri of Anjou, the most intelligent and least pleasant of the Valois Princes, put forward by both Catherine de Medici and the Huguenot leaders as a bridegroom for an English Queen sixteen years his senior; their thinking being that an Anglo-French alliance would minimize future Spanish expansion. The French were still reeling from the aftermath of the Second Religious War and the peace that followed it was proving very much bloodier than the war. Walsingham's opinion was that a Third Religious War was about to erupt. He neither admired nor trusted the French Queen Mother and Robert Stewart agreed with him. He said Catherine de Medici was being characteristically devious. Her deepest instinct, jealous, maternal fear for her brood, had been outraged by a Huguenot attempt to seize the young King Charles IX at Meaux in September 1567. This did not appear to have bothered Charles, who was given a lark pie of such succulence by his captors that he pardoned them all and asked for the receipt.

The conversation then became more serious as Robert Stewart gave his opinions on both French and Dutch affairs. The Duke of Alva's occupation of the Low Countries the year before had left the Spanish Field Army a mere two hundred miles from London where it was even less welcome than in France. Catherine de Medici had refused to allow the Spanish to march through France and had no wish to see their growth of power in the Low Countries though she fell short of actually assisting the suffering Dutch.

At this point, Lady Ursula knocked on the door ushering in a maid carrying a fresh flagon of wine and leading a clean, tidy, smiling child.

Frances led a very sheltered life at this age, mostly within the confines of The Papey and its walls and attended day and night by Alice or one of her minions. Alice was a senior member of the household having come with Lady Ursula on her first marriage as a waiting woman.

There were shopping expeditions with her mother, often to The Royal Exchange, a form of mall with many tradesmen of every description under one roof or certainly in one street. Their wares were dazzling and diverse and anything could be bought from silks and velvets to oil for lamps, harness for horses, dolls for Frances, jewelry and trinkets and sherbet or lemon drinks served from comfortable stalls where a good gossip could be enjoyed with friends. It was a great meeting place for fashionable London. Lady Ursula had her own sedan chair with four stout men to carry it and two more to walk beside it, clearing the way and looking out for any possible trouble.

Having had two boys before her, she revelled in dressing Frances beautifully. As soon as she could toddle, she wore small replicas of Ursula's own clothes; tiny ruffs, slashed and puffed sleeves, silk hose and satin slippers.

There were other treats as well as she grew up. Visits to Footscray and Scadbury, the Walsingham family homes in Kent where there were dogs, cats and cousins to play with, of all ages and sizes. The three Walsingham boys at Scadbury were older than Frances, but Thomas, the youngest, six years her senior, was surprisingly willing to carry her off to the kennels or the stables and entertain her. She needed no entertainment in fact; young as she was, she loved all animals and was alarmingly fearless among them. She particularly loved Thomas's ferrets, his pride and joy, with which he terrorized the rabbit population. When she was older, he would take her out with him and a couple of small lurchers, to spend hours in the hedgerows and the corners of woods, bolting rabbits and learning the patience needed to coax the ferrets back from the burrows. At her present age, however, she was happy just to handle them, feeling their sleek, sinuous little bodies, questing noses and soft fur. That they had an odour all their own did not worry her in the least or that they sometimes forgot themselves and nipped her.

Walsingham's stepson by his first marriage, Christopher Carleill, erupted occasionally into the Papey family circle. Now seventeen, he was finishing his education in the University of Cambridge and straining at the academic leash. He kicked up his heels very effectively both at Cambridge and in London and

Walsingham had several times to bail him out of trouble as a result of his roistering. Fond though he was of him, he was encouraging a naval or a military career for Christopher, the two being conveniently interchangeable, rather than a stately progression through Gray's Inn. Christopher's love of adventure and action needed to be channelled.

All little girls idolise big brothers and Frances adored him. He would sweep into the house, swing her up into the air, catching her at the last moment and spinning her round like a top, her little legs flying out horizontally. It was the sort of affectionate rough housing she lacked and she could not get enough of it.

Walsingham had brought him up together with his elder sister, Alice, since their mother, Anne Carleill, died in 1564. His marriage to her had been brief but happy and the children were left well provided for. Christopher had been a handful but Alice, good and quiet, had suitably married Christopher Hoddeson of her father's Muscovy Company taking with her a substantial dowry.

In a normal Elizabethan household Frances would have lived a nursery existence with a horde of siblings and without a great deal of contact with her parents. The children ate together, played together and slept together; often several to a bed if space was short. Frances, however, slept in a cradle on rockers with a canopy over her head and Alice on a "trundle bed" beside her. No one slept unattended.

As an only child, she spent more time with her parents, received far more attention than was usual and, up to a point, was very much indulged. To Lady Ursula she was the balm that had helped heal the trauma caused by the violent death of her two sons. To Walsingham she was his hope for the future of his name and nothing was too good for her.

Very much a part of the household and of Frances's life, was Francis Milles, her father's Personal Secretary and Assistant. This faithful man, much more than a Secretary or an Assistant was a lynch pin to their existence. He had begun his service to Walsingham in an office capacity which quickly diversified as family, property, and public and Court office increased. He arranged the staffing of Appuldurcombe and the London houses. He supervised travel arrangements, horses, coaches, grooms and overnight stays at hostelries or with friends. He ran Walsingham's offices at Cripplegate and in the Papey.

William Cecil, quickly realising Walsingham's talents in the spheres of diplomacy and intelligence and the many valuable contacts that went with them, began a close collaboration with him and to hand him assignments in rapid succession. His intelligence service was already developing and his contacts becoming a cohesive collection of agents. As time went on, Francis Milles became more and more involved with Walsingham's intelligence work, paying and directing agents and correlating the material they brought in; sometimes taking part himself in covert operations. Walsingham's trust in him was absolute.

Lady Ursula rose to the occasion on the domestic front also as her husband's career unfolded and grew. There were greater demands made on her also. The family's boot-faced steward, Leander, was her great ally. He was a man of awe-inspiring size whose grandeur of manner would have done credit to any of the Royal Courts of Europe and he could quell pretension with a glance. He also knew precisely who was who in the Elizabethan hierachy. Physically, he was well able to bundle out any unwelcome or rowdy visitor and he guarded Frances like a mastiff.

Frances's education started early. From the age of two she learned her Catechism, her numbers and her letters. In these matters, discipline was strict and the rod was not spared if she defaulted or failed. No child escaped beatings except Royal children when they were diverted to a "whipping boy". After a particularly painful experience, Margaret Beale made sure she was told of this manifestly unfair and unhealthy practice. Mocking Frances's stinging seat and outraged dignity, she failed to tell her that the children at the wrong end of the Royal rod were very well rewarded in later life.

With Margaret and Catherine she learned dancing and by the age of four it was apparent that in this she would excel. Carefully imitating the steps and following the older girls, she quickly found her feet and discovered a natural sense of rhythm and time. It was one of her greatest pleasures and long after the lesson was over, she would practise in front of the polished steel mirror in Lady Ursula's bedchamber, strutting out the steps with her head held high. These mirrors had become fashionable and Robert Dudley, Earl of Leicester, one of the first to do so, had installed "three great glasses, two of steel and one of crystal" in Leicester House. The Earl was wont to do himself extremely well in most respects and years later Frances was destined to dance again before those very mirrors.

Her father, a first class linguist, also insisted that she learn French. He was looking through his fingers at the future, perhaps guessing where fate was to take him but knowing already that children destined for Court life needed languages, music, dancing and horsemanship. Well born girls as young as eleven or twelve were accepted as Maids of Honour to the Queen.

By the time Frances was three, she was beginning to read and write and could speak a little basic French. Lessons were so hard, unforgiving and regular that when she escaped from them and when play with a large family would have followed naturally, she was forced to entertain herself and invent the companions who were not there. Alice Poole and the nursery maids could be amusing up to a point, but they were no substitute for a pack of brothers and sisters and they did not enter into the imaginative games and characters so absorbing to small children that they cannot, or do not want, to explain them. Frances belonged to the "do not want to" company. She preferred to keep her play world to herself and, at a very early age, began to evade the inevitable questions and intrusions of older parents with only one child and their wish to probe into every facet of her life. She became adept at disappearing. Escaping the supervision of the nursery, she would scuttle down a back stair and roam the house, acting out imaginary happenings and creating another world into which, if she was really lucky, some interesting stranger could be persuaded to enter and amuse her. She was equally adept at re-appearing before the alarm went up and a search began.

Frances was no fool. She knew her father had a great many visitors and she knew where they were likely to be found while waiting to see him. It became a habit to peep into this ante-room and the hall beyond it, provided the majestic bulk of Leander was elsewhere. As a result she had managed to meet a number of extremely interesting men from early childhood. Some of these came from other countries and their strange accents, scents and clothes were fascinating. To men awaiting what promised to be a difficult or intimidating interview with Walsingham, it was a relief to have the company of a small girl who danced in and prattled away with unshadowed friendliness. Stories were sometimes told on both sides to while away the time. Who would think that the child might remember tales told to her which, at the time, constituted no more than entertainment?

In October 1569, a portly Florentine with an unquenchable sense of humour, spent a months enforced sojourn in The Papey being questioned by

Walsingham on the subject of a plot that became known as the "Enterprise of England". Roberto Ridolphi had been required by Pope Pius V to channel money from the Vatican to English Catholics in order to finance the overthrow of the English Queen. Walsingham's Italian was well up to the task of extracting information from him and Ridolphi admitted to financing both the Bishop of Ross, Mary Queen of Scots envoy in London, and the Duke of Norfolk, England's premier nobleman and, like all his family, a committed Catholic. Ridolphi's brief included encouraging Norfolk to consider marriage with Mary, Queen of Scots and generally stirring up the already restive and rebellious North.

Inspite of his nefarious doings, and the fact that he was virtually a prisoner, Ridolphi enchanted Lady Ursula with his beautiful manners and obvious admiration of Frances who, having spent only five minutes in his company could hardly bear to be parted from him. He was Saint Nicholas and every indulgent uncle known rolled into one and he possessed the Italian's genuine adoration of children which made him irresistible to them. Sitting by a huge log fire in the hall, firelight glinting on his many ornate rings, he played spillikins with Frances and did tricks with silk handkerchiefs. Watching his antics, nobody would have guessed that the Tower, the rack and execution might well have been his next step. He was under house arrest until 11th November when he was mysteriously released on the orders of Cecil and Leicester. That, however, was by no means the end of his activities.

Another friendship arising from Frances's secret visits to the ante chamber was to bring memorable trouble to her.

One day she found a young man, well dressed but travel stained, enjoying a glass of wine and awaiting her father, who was meeting Leicester that morning and had gone to Whitehall early by barge. He had an acquiline nose and a slightly bored, patrician face, but when he smiled at Frances, a change took place and his narrow, twinkling eyes became quite magnetic. He sat gracefully on his heels to talk to her and she knew at once that this was a lucky day.

George Fitzwilliam was the product of a noble house, but his arrival was, unfortunately, on the wrong side of the blanket. That was the only unfortunate thing about him. He grasped life with both hands and wrung the last ounce of adventure and excitement from it. His was the same spirit that had sent Hawkins and Drake careering round the world in tiny ships and he possessed the same quick wit and physical stamina that had brought them home again. He was a true soldier of fortune and he was blessed with a golden tongue.

He talked to Frances as if to an equal and expected her to understand. She did because what he told her was so graphic and enthralling.

He had just come from the court of King Philip II of Spain having completed the first part of a dangerous and important mission, the results of which he was about to lay before Walsingham. Sitting companionably on a step beside her, he described to Frances the Monarch, his family and his courtiers, their manners, their clothes and their enormous New World jewels. He enlarged upon the Spaniards dislike of sunlight and the whiteness of their skin, the long shadowy galleries of the Escorial Palace and the scented shady gardens with water flowing ornately through them. He dwelt upon the magnificence of their horses and he mentioned the constant presence of the sombre, black clad men of the Church who chanted the Holy Offices almost round the clock.

He should have been a writer but his mission had been verbal. By most standards it had also been suicidal, but he did not give Frances any reason why he had been in Spain. He merely drew spell-binding word pictures. She could smell the gardenia hedges, watch the splendour of hidalgo horsemanship and the great Andalucian stallions circling and curvetting to music; she could taste the yellow dust rising from their hooves.

He described too the horrors of the Auto da Fé; the long chanting procession, the condemned in hideous hooded yellow robes, some hardly able to limp; the many stakes planted in a circle, oil-soaked wood stacked at their bases and the cowled members of the Inquisition, carrying huge crosses and swinging incense. Englishmen had perished at those stakes, he said; the Spanish were a cruel race. Frances listened in fascinated terror. Elizabethan children were not shielded from the realities of their world. Before George had got as far as the torches being thrust into the pyres, the smoke, the stench and the shrieks, Walsingham arrived home. His anger was intense and it was directed at Frances for encroaching into his world and for talking to an agent of such importance. It was unjust; circumstance had made the encounter possible but he shook her like a rabbit, called a servant and sent her straight to bed. Later, when his anger had cooled, he came upstairs and talked gently to her, explaining that she was never to speak to strangers in the house unless he told her to. If they spoke to her, she was to remember and tell him exactly what they said. He most specifically asked her what Fitzwilliam had talked about, extracting the last detail from her. This was not difficult and he was astonished. Her earnest little face and big hazel grey eyes fixed on his, she gave a minute description, young as she was. He realised that she had inherited a very great asset from him; an almost perfect memory.

From that day, and very gradually, began a working relationship. As she grew older, her eyes and ears and, more than either, her memory, began to be used as a corroborating tool to his own.

George Fitzwilliam's mission to Spain was one of barefaced effrontery and extreme danger. He was perfectly suited to such an assignment and relished the idea of marching into any lion's den particularly a Spanish one. He knew the country well, spoke Spanish and had several times been included in diplomatic representations; also others, much less reputable.

This mission had been instigated by John Hawkins, one of England's greatest seamen and was part of an attempt to rescue seventy three of his men, captured by the Spaniards in 1567. They had been taken to Spain to languish in the Archbishop of Seville's prisons. Most were tortured, several were burnt in the Autos da Fé and the rest were starving to death. There was not much love lost between Spain and English seamen. With William Cecil's approval and, later, Walsingham's help, a plan was formulated and Hawkins appealed to the Spanish Ambassador in London, Don Guerau d'Espés, an incurable plotter and busybody, complaining so bitterly of his treatment by his own Queen that D'Espés felt he had found an ally. The Ambassador wrote to the Duke of Alva in the Netherlands suggesting that to free the seamen would put Hawkins firmly in their camp after which good use could be made of him. This coincided with the arrival of Roberto Ridolphi in England and the hatching and failure of the plot foiled by Cecil and Walsingham. The Duke of Alva had refused to move in support of any uprising until he knew that Elizabeth had been assassinated.

Time passed and nothing transpired. Hawkins went a step further and assured D'Espés that he was quite disillusioned with the Queen's ingratitude and would prefer to serve the King of Spain, together with the seamen he hoped to see freed. Not only that but he would bring with him further sailors and ships. Both Alva and D'Espés were delighted and passed the messages to Spain. Hawkins and Walsingham then almost overreached themselves and sent George Fitzwilliam direct to the Duke and the English Duchess de Feria in Spain, from whence he gained interviews with King Philip himself. Fitzwilliam assured the King that not only did Hawkins intend to defect, but also to convert to Catholicism. When asked for his credentials and whether he was in touch with the imprisoned Queen of Scots, Fitzwilliam replied that Hawkins name was credential enough and that all he required in exchange for part of the English fleet was the release of these few miserable seamen. His sangfroid was astonishing and his powers of deception were such that King Philip, a careful man and not one easy to dupe, sent him back with a letter for Mary Queen of Scots (written in invisible ink) appraising her of a plan to rescue her and giving his assurance that the bill for equipping Hawkins's contribution from the English fleet would be paid for from his own pocket.

Fitzwilliam hastened to Mary, then imprisoned at Sheffield, carrying King Philip's letter and presents from her old friends, the Duke and Duchess de Feria. He begged her to intercede for the prisoners so that the grand plan to use the ships and rescue her could be advanced. This was to coincide with the threatened Catholic rising in the North. Mary replied that she "Must pity the prisoners for she was used as one herself." And that she "would do any pleasure she could to an Englishman." She had no hesitation and wrote immediately to Philip on the seamen's behalf.

Considering the depredations made by Hawkins on Spanish shipping over the years, it was amazing that the King should have been so naïve and not at all in his character. Given the charms of Fitzwilliam, however, all things were possible.

At the time of his meeting with Frances, George was on his way back to Spain, carrying messages from Mary Stuart and Hawkins, which included an apology to His Majesty for his many misdemeanours together with the promise of 16 ships, 1,600 men and 400 guns of his command. Coinciding with the imminent Northern Rising, he airily proposed to sail up the Humber, rescue Mary, now at Tutbury, to the assured delight and acclaim of the populace, and to get rid of the heretic Queen. What could be easier?

To enter Spain a second time needed resolution, even for a brazen rover such as George Fitzwilliam. The stakes were high and could have landed him lashed to one, but before long he was beguiling the Spanish establishment once more and suggesting a date in late summer for the enterprise. The English prisoners were released with ten dollars apiece in their pockets. Hawkins received a pardon for his woeful wrongdoings and £40,000. All this left him in possession of the Spanish plans to support an uprising, money to equip English ships and his seamen returned. Game, set and match. Little could King Philip have guessed what havoc Hawkins would cause amidst his Armada eighteen years later.

Sadly, Frances never set eyes on Fitzwilliam again. When he returned, her father was in France and he was never able to tell her what had become of him; he merely remarked that he was unlikely to have died in his bed.

Ridolphi remained an incorrigible intriguer. His future reappearance was no surprise to anyone on the security side of government circles. His first efforts having been nipped in the bud (he may have been persuaded that a double agent's life could be profitable), the unfolding drama in the largely Catholic North of England put him temporarily out of mind. On 14th November, under the Earls of Northumberland, Westmorland, Arundel and Lord Dacre, the Northern Lords marched on Durham.

Even in 1568 the rumblings of revolt were beginning to be heard. The arrival of the beautiful and destitute Queen of Scots and her subsequent imprisonment gave the Northern Earls a focus for their intrigues. It was the first of those deadly and feared stabs from Elizabeth's thorn in the flesh, Mary Stuart, and the first of several spirited attempts to remove the Protestant Queen and install Mary as Monarch with the reinstatement of the old religion.

The Duke of Norfolk was a cousin of the Queen and one of the richest men in England. Having recently lost his third wife in childbirth he was again a matrimonial prize and he was greatly attracted by a suggestion that he should marry the Queen of Scots. They had met at Tutbury Castle under the eye of Lord Shrewsbury, at that time her guardian, and Mary's undoubted charm had been at work. When he found himself embroiled in a plot to put her on the throne, ably assisted by the Bishop of Ross, and the meddlesome Spanish Ambassador, Don Guerau d'Espés, and backed by the Northern Earls, the thought of becoming King Consort was too much for him. When questioned on the subject, this dilatory and witless peer whose ambition was unmatched by perception or powers of organisation, protested that:

"He would prefer to remain unmarried but if the Queen of Scots were to accept him, he would be content to sacrifice himself for the welfare of his country."

His own Queen, well aware how volatile were the Northern Lords and of Norfolk's connection with them, asked him point blank after dinner one night, after having "given him a nip", what his marriage plans were. His nerve completely shattered, he replied that the Queen of Scots was a wicked and adulterous woman and that:

"I love to sleep upon a safe pillow and count myself as good a prince at home in my bowling alley in Norwich as she is though she were in Scotland. And if I should go about to marry her, knowing as I do that she pretendeth to the present possession of your Majesty's crown, your Majesty might justly charge me with seeking your own crown upon your head."

Her Majesty did indeed think exactly that and ordered him straitly to abandon any such idea. Norfolk fled back to the bowling alley in Norwich pleading an ague but was subsequently arrested and taken to the Tower on 1st October 1569 by Sir Francis Knollys. By that time, however, there was no stopping the Northern Lords.

They ransacked Durham Cathedral, overturned the Communion table and celebrated Catholic Mass on Catholic altars. They then turned south towards Tutbury in order to release Mary. Her guardians, Lord Shrewsbury and the Earl of Huntingdon, hustled her forthwith to Coventry. The Northern Army, realising how heavily they were outnumbered by Elizabeth's forces advancing from the south, began to disperse and flee, many over the border to Scotland where they were pursued. Retribution followed, grisly, savage and swift. Hundreds were caught and swung from mass gallows, villages were sacked and homes burned. Those caught sheltering or helping the rebels suffered the same fate. Particularly bizarre and brutal was the case of a woman who was "pressed to death" for aiding an insurgent. Economically, it would take a long time for the North to recover and prosper. The Queen was badly shaken by their treachery and in no mood for mercy.

Undaunted, Ridolphi resumed his machinations immediately the hapless Duke of Norfolk was released from the Tower of London and his second attempt to marry him to Mary, raise the English Catholics and dispose of Elizabeth, known as "The Ridolphi Plot", resulted in the Duke's slow, undignified march to the scaffold in June 1572 where he died with great courage and humility, asking only that clemency should be shown to his children and his servants. The Florentine banker escaped any prosecution whatsoever and returned to live out a long life of limitless wealth in his home city.

Walsingham, by that time, had succeeded Sir Henry Norris as Ambassador to Paris and had taken up his appointment in early January 1571. Frances and Lady Ursula were to follow him in the spring. His brother in law, large, competent Robert Beale accompanied him as Principal Secretary and left in London was the equally competent Francis Milles to hold the fort and to deal with all intelligence matters in London.

During the time of their separation, Lady Ursula wrote to Walsingham every other day, her letters often accompanied by blotchy little missives from Frances.

IN THE WINGS 2

1572 – Paris

On June 8th 1572, a party of Englishmen came within sight of Paris and pulled in their sweating horses to rest and to view their destination. They were richly dressed but dusty and they had been on the road from Boulogne for almost a week. A train of spare horses, pack horses and servants followed them for theirs was a mission which would require the maximum amount of show and finery.

They were bound for the Palace of the Louvre as guests of the young King Charles IX, his new wife and his formidable mother, the Dowager Queen Catherine de Medici. The Earl of Lincoln led them and their purpose was to sign the Treaty of Blois which had been completed in March of that year and was designed to ensure that neither England nor France would assist an enemy of the other; between the lines, the enemy was Spain. The treaty was to be signed in each country by special embassies and on the same day.

Bringing up the rear of the party a group of young men rode together. Their elders were sagging somewhat in the saddle but they were in tearing spirits, having relished the journey to the full and now wildly excited at what lay before them in Paris. There was speculation and laughter and many jokes.

One of them immediately drew the eye. He rode a spectacular bay horse as if he were a part of it; never moving when it danced and sidled and, apart from his looks, he had a presence which belied his years. The other boys seemed to vie for his attention, calling his name when they pointed something out.

Philip Sidney, at seventeen, was a junior member of the delegation and a representative of his uncle, the Earl of Leicester. The Earl would have been only too delighted to do the honours of this mission himself, but his Queen had no intention of letting him our of her sight at this point. He was therefore eager for his nephew and heir to be present and with his ear firmly to the ground. For Philip, there were to be much wider chances of travel once the embassy had done its duty and he had leave to be out of England for two years. Life was good. He was to stay with the other members of the delegation at the Louvre for the first few weeks but, tucked into his doublet, he carried letters from Leicester to the English Ambassador, Francis Walsingham, with instructions to deliver them as soon as possible. One was a personal missive which he knew would ensure an invitation to stay at the Embassy when Lord Lincoln returned to England.

The party and its train dusted themselves down and rode on into the city, across the river bridge and along the further bank until they reached the huge entrance to the Palace and made themselves known to the Royal guard at the gate. Passing into the main courtyard, the Place de la Basse-cour, they gasped at the dimensions of this Valois Palace. Accustomed as they were to the many established residences inhabited by their Queen in and around London, built mainly by Henry VII and Henry VIII, the Louvre, to them, resembled a vast building site interspersed with medieval ruins. Elizabeth I, with her penchant for thrift, had seen no point in further monumental building but sank gratefully into those palaces erected by her forbears. In 1564, Catherine de Medici, weary of the noise and stinks of the city, had begun work on the Tuileries Palace a short distance to the West. Through this maze, old and new, the visitors were now conducted to their apartments and wine and water brought for their refreshment.

Travelling with Philip Sidney were a companion and three servants chosen by his father as a suitable entourage to accompany him, in due course, through Europe. Lodowick Bryskett, his main companion, was partly Genoese, a linguist and extremely well connected on the Continent. The servants were the very Welsh Griffin Maddox, an established retainer of Sir Henry Sidney, Harry White, and a young groom named John Fisher.

That evening the delegation was presented to the Valois Royal Family at a brief audience, being conducted down countless corridors by Sir Thomas Smith who had been in Paris some time, working on the Treaty and promoting the possible marriage between his Queen and the Duc d'Anjou. He was looking a little worn and harassed and confessed he would be delighted to be going home.

Philip wore a magnificent crimson doublet with a high, ornate gold-laced collar and a neat ruff above it. His heavy dark gold hair had been brushed free of dust and his tawny eyes were alert and bright as he made the necessary bows with smiling grace.

Charles IX was not a very prepossessing Sovereign. Like two of his brothers, he suffered from tuberculosis and, like all of them, from a subtle and domineering mother. Above his jewelled ruff, a sensitive face regarded the visitors. His wife, Elizabeth of Austria, the daughter of the Emperor Maximilian II, seemed sweetly serious, her long Hapsburg face giving her easy identity. Despite his properly downcast eyes, Philip made sure he got a long look at the Queen Mother. The plain, ill-complexioned little widow of Henry II appeared very Italian and resembled a lizard. She spoke quickly, on one note and with very little expression, her hooded eyes flicking sideways, never resting on those she addressed, and her black dress was quietly sumptuous.

Philip was particularly interested in the King's two younger brothers. Henri Duc d'Anjou was barely twenty and Francois Duc d'Alençon, seventeen. The Duc d'Anjou, proposed as a bridegroom for his Queen, was not an alluring prospect. He was thin, scented and effeminate, his face painted and unhealthy looking and his stare dismissive. Report made him highly intelligent, having inherited his mother's tortuous cunning rather than his father's flamboyant enjoyment of life and his nature was a compound of debauchery and repentance, impiety and superstition. His given reason for not encouraging his betrothal to Elizabeth was that he was so devout a Catholic that nothing would do for him but the celebration of the highest of Masses in public and that, in turn, would never do for Protestant England. He had also stipulated that he was to be crowned King with joint powers to rule the day after any marriage. Sir Henry Killigrew and Sir Thomas Smith, sent out in January this year to further the negotiations, could make no impression on the impasse. It was Sir Thomas's view that the younger Duc d'Alençon would be hauled into the breach as an alternative groom. Ambassador Walsingham had already sent a masterly and diplomatic description of the young prince to London but privately did not think that he was likely to capture the Queen's imagination. He was a somewhat weedy specimen with a badly pockmarked complexion but he had a merry face and a delightful smile. Elizabeth's reservation was that the world would make an even greater mock of their age difference but, contrary to all expectation, this proposed match was to come closer to fulfilling Catherine de Medici's dreams than any other.

Also present at this initial audience was Prince Henry of Navarre and he immediately caught Philip's attention. There could be no greater contrast between this large, forthright young man and the effete, sickly Valois princes.

He looked what he was, a man of action and a lover of women. His heavy-lidded eyes held a distinct twinkle, his large mouth curled upwards beneath the beard and his eyebrows had a tendency to shoot up and down. He appeared permanently amused and inclined to live by his motto: "sword in the hand and arse in the saddle". He was a Bourbon; his father, King Antoine of Navarre had been the nation's leading Huguenot and his mother, the widowed Queen Jeanne d'Albret had carried his mantle. At his birth, it was reputed, his maternal grandfather had rubbed garlic on his lips, poured wine down his throat and, seeing that his newborn grandson gulped it down greedily, exclaimed "You are a true Bearnais."

Realising the absolute necessity of reconciling Catholic and Huguenot before the country was torn apart by yet another religious war, and to the horror of the Catholic faction at court, Catherine de Medici had arranged his betrothal to her daughter, Marguerite de Valois. The King's sister, steeped in Catholicism from the cradle, had no wish to marry a Protestant, however attractive, and there was tension in the Royal household. She was not present that evening but the wedding was to take place on 18ᵗʰ August and, Pope Gregory XIII having refused the marriage his permission, it was with difficulty that the Cardinal de Bourbon had been persuaded to perform the ceremony.

As the English visitors took their leave, Henry of Navarre looked directly at Philip and slowly drooped one eyelid.

The following day, June 9ᵗʰ, news arrived that Jeanne d'Albret had died, leaving Henry King of Navarre. She had been a matriarch of the first order, a zealot and a great leader of Protestantism. He departed at once for Pau and Montauban leaving the Court plunged into mourning.

Philip, hurriedly calling Griffin Maddox and Harry White to assist him, donned a suit of black clothes, obtained directions from Sir Thomas Smith and taking with him Lodowick Bryskett, set out for the English Embassy on the Quai des Bernadines in Faubourg St.Germaine. It was not far; just across the river from the Louvre and its beautiful 12ᵗʰ Century Parish Church, St.Germaine L'Auxerrois.

Paris was still a walled city with, compared to London, a medieval ambience. Being more contained, it also seemed more densely populated and its streets were packed. This was a particularly hot summer accompanied by what Walsingham had described as a "dearth"; a want of food and supplies due to years of civil strife which had brought in its train a shifting population, lack of harvests and deep economic depression. Despite his interest and excitement, Philip felt uneasy. The crowds were not good natured. There was shouting, swearing and spitting. He saw fighting and the dirt was appalling.

They reached the house, set behind a wall and standing in a courtyard. It was large and light with a garden at the rear. A servant went to find Walsingham, the horses were led away and they entered the Embassy. Accompanied by Robert Beale, his brother-in-law, he soon joined them, greetings and introductions followed and the letters were handed over. Walsingham, never easily impressed, surveyed this nephew of Leicester and son of Sir Henry Sidney with speculation. He had heard tell of him from several sources and was interested to judge for himself if such reported excellence could be true. His hard enigmatic grey eyes, which made so many fidget, took in every detail. He saw an exceptionally good-looking boy gravely returning his scrutiny. His face was slightly pockmarked but not enough to detract from his general appearance. His education and courtesy were evident from every word he spoke and though he was clearly accustomed to move with ease in any society, he was primarily a polished product of the English aristocracy, both presentable and articulate. But Philip was also a Dudley. His mother, Lady Mary Dudley, was the daughter of the disgraced and executed Duke of Northumberland and the sister of the Earl of Leicester. They were a much older family than the Sidneys and Philip might have been expected to exhibit all the flaunting arrogance that characterised them. He did not, but cast a very different kind of spell over many that met him so that once seen, he was seldom forgotten. Walsingham knew that he had already caught the eye of William Cecil who realised, like Leicester, that his gifts could be used to win over opposition and charm difficult birds out of trees on his behalf. More than that, Cecil's daughter, Anne, was of marriageable age and the wily Secretary of State had designs on Philip as a son in law. Fulsome letters had passed between the two fathers and negotiations were going well when Cecil was created Lord Burghley and realised he could look higher for a bridegroom. He determined that his daughter should become a Countess and betrothed her to the dissolute Earl of Oxford who made her miserably unhappy. The marriage did not last and accounted for the fact that Philip and Oxford were at daggers drawn for the remainder of their lives. Having now met him, it flickered through

Walsingham's forward thinking mind that Philip, unless he had been snapped up in the interim, might be a suitable husband for Frances when she grew up. The fact that he was twelve years older mattered not a jot.

The letter from Leicester was a request to Walsingham to stand "in loco parentis" to Philip, to guide and advise him on account of his inexperience and youth and to supervise his future travel plans. Few people were better qualified to do so. He immediately invited Philip and his entourage to move to St.Germaine when the delegation returned to London.

The Court emerged from mourning with unseemly alacrity, however, and by 13th June, the Englishmen were being lavishly wined and dined all over Paris particularly on 15th June when the Treaty of Blois was ratified and they were entertained by the King and Queen and the Queen Mother. This was a sumptuous occasion beginning with representatives from both sides of the Treaty meeting within the Louvre, proceeding to the Church of St.Germaine L'Auxerrois where oaths were sworn and then repairing to the Queen Mother's completed apartments in the new Tuilleries Palace for supper. Walsingham was present throughout and during the proceedings Philip had ample opportunity to observe in action a master of diplomatic intricacy who knew exactly how to "draw men out".

For the occasion, Philip had been pinned, buttoned and coaxed into a doublet of dull gold brocade, embroidered in gold thread and with rows of gold and blue enamel buttons; his breeches, heavily padded and slashed gave way to gold stockings, embroidered with blue rosettes. He complained that he could hardly move, but was told sharply by Griffin Maddox to hold his peace while he threw a chain of sapphires and gold over his head. The result had nothing of the country cousin about it; he looked the complete courtier, French or English.

After 15th June, their hosts included the Duc d'Anjou, the Duc d'Alençon, the charming Admiral Gaspard de Coligny with Robert Stewart in train, and the Duc de Nevers who gave a delightful al fresco party under the trees. A splendid time was had by all, but the heat rose by the day.

Having completed their mission, the Earl of Lincoln's delegation said their farewells and departed, and Philip moved into the Embassy in Faubourg St.Germaine. This was a welcome change from the rigid formality and endless corridors of the Louvre and he relaxed immediately as he was warmly greeted by Lady Ursula and by a small dark child named Frances. Lady Ursula was again pregnant and viewing Paris with a slightly jaundiced eye but she was delighted with this guest.

She had arrived in Paris on 18th March 1571 after what had been, to Frances, a magical journey, and in time to see the new Queen crowned at St.Denis on 25th March, after which she had been entertained at an audience given by Catherine de Medici. The promptness with which she was invited to Court suggested that the Queen Mother may have been trying to placate Walsingham in some way, perhaps with a eye to the intended marriage or because Anjou, in a temper, had jibed that Elizabeth "was not only an old creature, but had a sore leg," and this piece of rudeness had found its way back to the English Queen who was, understandably, furious.

After the joy of being reunited with her father who met them at Clermont and escorted them to their new home, Frances had proceeded to absorb France, the French people and the French language like a sponge. She already spoke enough French to find her way around and the rest was enchanting; the food, above all the bread, the foreign smells and the fact that Walsingham had found a small, fat, grey pony on which she was allowed to accompany him when he rode out in the Bois du Boulogne. Though only five, she could manage quite well and was completely unafraid; though she raged at the indignity of a leading rein. The pony was a stolid individual and the current love of her life. There was access to the stables through the gardens, the whole being enclosed by a wall so that Frances could scuttle down to visit her beloved whenever she escaped from lessons. They had long conversations and the amused grooms were their allies. As a result of this, Frances's mastery of the French tongue became a little tainted; Walsingham was stunned by some of the oaths that tripped off his daughter's tongue.

He had had no wish to accept the post of Ambassador, knowing that the strains upon his purse would be severe. There had been some hard bargaining between him and his Sovereign before departure which had resulted in a raise in allowances but he was still hard pressed. The cost of constantly entertaining guests, both social and diplomatic, was compounded in his case by the payment of agents connected with his espionage and counter-espionage activities, already established in England and now enlarged in France. He had taken with him the stout and opinionated Robert Beale as Secretary, well proven by him as a rock of constant efficiency.

Lady Ursula needed all her skills as a hostess and provider to feed and entertain a very wide variety of folk. In this she had assistance from the faithful Leander who had accompanied her from England and whose talents as armed guard on the journey had been a boon. His French was good enough to grapple with the social structure of fashionable Paris but his accent was appalling.

She found Philip a very welcome addition to her household. In her absence, he was more than capable of entertaining guests, he quickly became a favourite with the household especially with Frances for whom he took the place of Christopher Carleill, teasing and playing with her and, better than anything, riding out with her in the company of John Fisher and two armed men of the household. His own horsemanship lacked nothing, but he, too, refused to relent on the subject of the leading rein.

Lodowick Bryskett and Philip's servants were housed in a separate wing and Walsingham disliked them. Returning Leicester's letter he wrote of them: "the evil practice of your said nephew's servants… the young gentleman, your nephew shall be in danger of a very lewd practice which were great pity in respect of the rare gifts that are in him." Whether he meant that he thought they were homosexual and might corrupt Philip or whether they were disorderly and addicted to wine, women and song, remained obscure. "lewd practice " meant any of these, or possibly, gambling. He may have mistrusted Lodowick because of his Italian parentage.

Philip had taken to life in Paris with seamless ease. The intellectual world opened to him around Walsingham's dinner table. There he met many who were to influence his life and thinking. Among them were Hubert Languet, the Ambassador for Saxony, Gaspard de Schomberg, the French Ambassador to Germany, both old friends of Walsingham, besides the well known Protestant humanist, Petrus Ramus, famous for his anti-Aristotelian logic, to whom Philip was instantly drawn. These men and many others were active Protestant intellectuals who, like Walsingham, were determined to defend the Huguenots and further their cause. Philip, who had been exceptionally well educated at Shrewsbury and Oxford and was naturally studious, had now found a cause of his own and was immediately precipitated into their culture, just as his Uncle had hoped.

Almost his own age was the historian Jacques-Auguste De Thou whose quick wit and Gallic humour made a pleasant contrast to the older men. Philip had met him in the Hall of the Caryatids, a huge chamber in the Louvre where a group of lawyers had been summoned to finalise the marriage settlements of Marguerite de Valois and Henry of Navarre. De Thou, destined for the Catholic Church and at present a Canon of Notre Dame, had preferred to study law and was shortly to form part of a delegation to the Italian Courts. There was much he could tell Philip at his own level about Court customs and behaviour.

He was looking at two worlds. The predominantly Catholic French Court opened its doors to him as widely as the Protestants had done. He was received everywhere as the son of Sir Henry Sidney, well known in France, and the nephew of Leicester and Warwick. Thanks to his father his French was perfect as were his manners and on 9th August, a bare two months after his arrival, King Charles IX made him a Gentleman of the Royal Bedchamber with the title "Baron de Sidenay" and with considerable material advantages. This elevation, remarkable for a young Englishman, gave him the opportunity, not only to attend the young Valois Princes and Princesses but to further his acquaintance with King Henry of Navarre on his return from the funeral of his mother. Their friendship grew quickly, Henry had a riotous sense of humour, and Philip was asked to attend as a gentleman of honour at his forthcoming marriage. Such honours spoke volumes for Philip's polished personality which was found, by those who looked deeper, to be no veneer but the outward sign of true greatness. His lifelong friend, Fulke Greville, commented on his friendship with Henry, that Navarre: "having measured and mastered all the spirits in his own nation, found out this master spirit among us and used him like an equal in nature and, so, fit for friendship with a King."

By 14th August, Walsingham's Embassy had other visitors to look after. Young Lord Wharton, preparing to do a Continental tour, even younger Thomas Walsingham, Frances's cousin from Kent and Nicholas Faunt, several years older, an enigmatic character who had been at the same school and University as Christopher Marlowe, the brilliant young poet and playwright, though several years ahead of him. (All three, Thomas, Marlowe and Faunt were to serve Walsingham and Philip in the years to come at home and abroad.) They were an added responsibility for Walsingham and Lady Ursula on top of the ceaseless round of parties going on at the time. For Frances, they were added entertainment, particularly Thomas despite the lack of ferrets.

Preparations for the Valois – Navarre wedding were in full swing. Huguenots from greatest to least were pouring into Paris for such an historic occasion and contributing to the crowds in the streets of the city. To the predominantly Catholic residents this caused rumbling friction. They were not, in any case, at all enthusiastic about their Valois Princess marrying a Huguenot, even if he was a King. The excruciating heat, unrelieved and intense, continued to rise which sparked men's tempers and added to their thirst. Walsingham was obliged to forbid any further riding out for Frances, much to her grief, (she was longing to show her pony off to Thomas.) He did not like the temper of the city and had already written to Cecil, now Lord Burghley: "I fear there will follow fearful effects unless God put to His helping hand."

The lavish wedding parties and ceremonials, a testimony to Royal indulgence, were in shameless contrast to the conditions in the streets. There were many undercurrents to this marriage and a sense of writhing unrest throughout Paris.

Philip was often in attendance at the Louvre and at the daily fetes, picnics and ceremonies. He knew his way around the labyrinth by now and had a fair idea of the Royal hierarchy and protocol. He had been obliged to order more clothes for the festivities inspite of Leicester's generosity, and to buy another horse.

A secular betrothal took place in the Louvre on 17th August. Marguerite de Valois looked pale and distraught which was put down to the heat and Philip, well within view, felt pity for her obvious misery. What pressure her mother had put on her to accept such a marriage could only be guessed. She had no wish to exchange her luxurious and frivolous life in Paris for the wilds of Pau and Montauban.

The following day Philip accompanied Henry of Navarre to the Cathedral of Notre Dame where a pavilion had been set up outside for the wedding ceremony only, to be followed by the celebration of mass and a Catholic blessing inside, to which the bridegroom and other Protestant guests would not be admitted. Henry of Navarre looked magnificent and was greeted by cheers from the many Huguenots in the crowds. The bride looked even paler. During the marriage vows, the only sign she gave of acquiescence was to nod briefly when her brother, Charles, pushed her head down in a gesture of submission. The groom and his Huguenot followers, Philip among them, then walked up and down outside the Cathedral waiting for her to emerge from the Catholic service held inside. It was a thoroughly uneasy occasion.

The wedding celebrations that followed were extravagant in the extreme. Spectacles, fireworks, allegorical plays and bearbaiting followed in quick succession, not to mention incessant hunting for which the King had an unbridled passion. Even Frances was allowed to attend the jousting as a member of the "corps diplomatique". This was the most exciting event of her life. She sat, dressed in pale blue satin, with her parents and other ambassadors in a window seat overlooking the Place de la Basse-Cour which had been transformed into a tilt yard. Yards of brightly coloured silk swathed the buildings, tiered seats were set up and the whole panoply of the joust unfolded before her round eyes. The Royal brothers with the Duc de Guise and others, dressed as Amazons, were pitted against Henry of Navarre and his followers dressed as infidel Turks. This was far too near the bone of what was pleasing. It was clearly a case of evil against good or heretic against Christian. The poor Turks in slipping turbans and flowing robes came off worse. Philip rode with the King of Navarre's men and, forgetting any implications, thoroughly enjoyed himself, as did Frances transfixed in the window seat, too excited even to clap but with her nails dug into her palms, gasping when there was a spill and drinking in the sound, the colour, the snorting, stamping horses and the skill of the horsemen.

Admiral Gaspard de Coligny, a leader of the Huguenots and a jovial, clever man, who had become a close friend and advisor to the King (though greatly distrusted by his mother), remained in the capital after the wedding. Despite their collaboration in the matter of Anjou's nuptials, the Queen Mother cordially loathed him. She feared that he would persuade Charles into a war with Spain in support of the Dutch in the Netherlands. Worse still, she feared the growing influence he exerted over her son, excluding her own. She had not forgotten the events at Meaux in 1567. The Peace of St.Germaine was still fragile; the extreme Catholic faction being much opposed to it and their jealous fury aroused by Coligny having been admitted to the King's Council.

On the morning of Friday 22nd August the Admiral was walking back to his house in the Rue de Bethisy, after watching the King play tennis with the Guise brothers in the Louvre, when he was fired upon by a would-be assassin. The shot shattered his left arm but failed to dispatch him. The poor man tottered home helped by his servants while the culprit, a man named Maurevert, escaped but not before it was seen that he had fired the shot from a house that belonged to the Dowager Duchess of Guise and had been recently occupied for the wedding by Madame de Nemours, an implacable enemy of the Admiral and a confidante of the Queen Mother. The Guise family also owned the horse which was held in readiness by one of their own servants for the escape. The piece fired came from the armoury of Anjou. The Guise undoubtedly had a score to settle; they had always maintained that Coligny ordered the murder of their father, Francis Duc de Guise ten years earlier.

Anjou had written shortly before the attempt that he and his mother were: "All but certain that it was the Admiral who had given the King some sinister opinion of us and we were determined then and there to be rid of him."

The King, apparently horrified by the attack on the Admiral, and having already sent his own doctor to delve for the bullets, went to his house that evening, accompanied, at their insistence, by the Queen Mother, Anjou and Alençon. Their over-solicitude, Judas-like, masked their fear that the Admiral, suspecting their involvement in the attack, would try to turn the King more violently against them. It was as they thought; Coligny did indeed ask to speak privately to the King but they hustled him away as soon as they decently could.

Meanwhile, downstairs in the Rue de Bethisy, Henry of Navarre and his cousin the Prince de Condé were taking stock of the situation and wondering what course they should follow. Any impulse to flee the city at that point was allayed by the King's outburst against the attempted murder. He swore: "By God's death, I protest and promise you I will have justice done for this outrage."

The following morning, the King sent a string of enquiries to the Admiral's house to see how he fared and Marguerite, the newly married Queen of Navarre, visited him in person, an action well received by the many Huguenots in the street that morning, Philip Sidney and Lodowick Bryskett among them. They had been sent by Walsingham to get what news they could of the Admiral. The Protestant Comte de Mongomery had rushed in the previous evening with news of the attempted murder and assured the English delegation of the King's concern and his resolve to arrest the culprits. Rumours were flying and had reached the Embassy from several sources.

The Queen Mother was loud in her demands for justice and extreme punishment for the outrage but Huguenot voices too, were beginning to demand a reckoning and threatening to act promptly and drastically if nothing was done. They knew that Coligny's brother-in-law was encamped outside

Paris with armed men; reprisals could come fast. Should the Guise be interrogated, the Royal Family would almost certainly be implicated. Fingers began to point and whispers ran like rats along the walls.

In the city, fear and tension rose unbearably, shops started to close and armed bands of angry Huguenots roamed the streets demanding vengeance as incriminating details of the bungled assassination circulated. Philip, riding back to Faubourg St. Germaine in the dust and heat, found his way blocked by armed guards sent to maintain order in the Place de Greve. He turned his frightened, snorting horse and rode back another way, for the first time feeling almost tangibly a sense of impending danger. At seventeen, physical fear is almost unknown unless there is good reason, but even Philip felt a strange pricking in his thumbs.

Like a drumbeat, events were inexorably gathering pace and pointing in one direction. Rumour raced through the thronged, humid city and tension continued to mount. Wine flowed on account of the wedding and the heat and dust had created a horrible miasma.

From the Valois viewpoint, there was not a moment to lose and the city forces went into action. The constabulary and armed men of the Swiss Guard were posted at points around the city. The city gates were closed, boats on the river were chained to their moorings to prevent escape that way. More chains and barricades were dragged across the entrances to known Huguenot streets. A comprehensive list of Huguenot dwellings, inns and shops was circulated to the city constabulary, the Royal armed forces, Catholic citizens and the criminal underworld for whom there would be rich pickings. It was a swift, merciless operation strongly suggesting that the whole of the undertaking was, in fact, premeditated. All these preparations could not have been organised in twenty four hours and the aim was clearly the destruction of, not just one or two prominent Huguenots but hundreds of ordinary citizens. Plans had been made and orders given to carry them out. By whom, and when?

The young historian, De Thou, himself in Paris that night, wrote later that the Duke of Guise was "Put in full command of the enterprise." Also that: "the signal to commence the massacre should be given by the bell of the Palace, and the marks by which they (Catholics) should recognize each other in the darkness were a bit of white linen tied around the left arm and a white cross on the hat." He was perfectly certain by whom the orders had been given.

There remained one person among the Royal inner circle who still did not know the full story or the grisly plans now under way. Catherine de Medici and her third and favourite son had yet to tell the hapless young King the whole story of their own implication and that of the Guise and to convince him that the Huguenots were about to lay the charge, not only at their door but at that of Charles himself; that they planned to rise that very night and seize both him and his crown. The Admiral must be killed immediately and around fifty leading Huguenots with him. (Henry of Navarre and the Prince de Condé were to be spared for political reasons and because of the recent marriage.)

They called a meeting of their closest advisors and then, behind closed doors, they disclosed the full state of affairs, ratchetting up the urgency and the danger. Charles, at first, flew into a terrible rage and refused to harm the Admiral. What pressure and arguments they then used upon him were never known but Anjou wrote later that: "Pacing the floor and silencing us, he said, swearing by "Le Mort de Dieu", that since we wished the Admiral to be killed, he consented, but then every Huguenot must die, not one must remain to reproach him and that we must give the command promptly."

Anjou, understandably, wished to shift the blame from himself to his brother, saying that the ultimate order came from the King himself. However, the necessary orders had already been given according to the plan that had already been made and it needed only the King's word to set the whole ghastly chain of events in motion. He was the last and weakest link in the chain, so weak that the Queen Mother, terrified that he would relent, visited him again at midnight to stiffen his resolve, her black robes hushing through the dark corridors. In her fear, she advanced the signal to proceed. It was the Eve of St.Bartholomew's Day.

Walsingham, with his many contacts, had by now a fairly good idea of what was going on. He was apprehensive and increasingly watchful. By the time Philip rode in with his friends, other more fearful souls were beginning to arrive. His houses was already full, he had a pregnant wife and small daughter to protect and he was responsible for the safety of English subjects in Paris and any other Protestant seeking sanctuary. "The fearful effects" seemed all too imminent and Walsingham forbade any of the household to go out of the house and grounds again. The big gates to the courtyard were closed and barred and all the able-bodied men and boys available were set to work erecting barricades at any weak point in the walls and gates enclosing the garden and the stables. A watch was kept at the gates in order to admit any seeking sanctuary. These soon began to arrive; Italian, Dutch, German, French and English Protestants, some with women and children and all in a state of apprehensive terror. They had seen men dragging barricades across their streets, erecting gibbets or sharpening swords and knives, and some had heard people shouting "Death to Huguenots." There appeared to be a horribly jovial atmosphere abroad which made the preparations even more terrifying.

Frances and her French nurse had been shut and locked into an upper room, up a second flight of stairs, in which there was a window looking down into the courtyard. Frances was not pleased at being thus removed but she pressed her nose to the window and could see people and torches approaching the house, the while keeping up a commentary in French to her nurse. Looking towards the river and the palace, her view was obscured by a dusty looking haze, which glowed murky red where lights shone behind it. Her mother had told her not to be frightened and, above all, to be quiet. A servant brought up supper for them, big with news about who had arrived and what reports they had given. To a man, these refugees had described the mounting hysteria and fear throughout Paris. A young friend of Mr. Philip had just ridden in, Timothy Bright, a Cambridge scholar, who said the mood in the city was very ugly and that he had been trying to find some English friends and persuade them to accompany him. He had been chased off by a knife-wielding bunch of thugs and he was extremely agitated, gratefully gulping down the wine offered him. The servant eventually departed, forgetting to lock the door.

These accounts did nothing to reassure Frances. She did not like being shut away upstairs, she could not eat or sleep, so she remained glued to the window, watching the courtyard. The nurse was beginning to say the rosary repeatedly, interspersed with tears and fears. She was one of the few Catholics in a mainly Protestant household.

And so the terrible night wore on until, at three o'clock in the morning the great bells of St.Germaine L'Auxerrois began to toll across the river. They were taken up by church after church. Carried on the hot night air came the sound of gunfire from the direction of the Louvre followed by the smell of smoke. Very soon after, a group of Protestants, mainly German, frantically beat at the gates asking for shelter. Their clothes were torn and dirty and some of them

41

were covered in blood. They told of a massacre of Huguenots in the city by the Catholic population and the Swiss Guard. Some said that Admiral Coligny had been brutally murdered.

Almost immediately after, Frances was roused from a light sleep by the clatter of hooves in the courtyard and urgent calls. She crept to the window again and saw it full of armed men, some with drawn swords, grand uniforms and gold braid. She could not know it, but the Huguenot General, Francois de Beauvais, Sieur de Briquemault, had just taken refuge in the Embassy.

Philip Sidney, together with Robert Beale, Lodowick, Nicholas Faunt, Lord Wharton, and Leander, had armed himself and stood watchfully behind Walsingham, listening intently to the accounts of the incoming refugees. It was becoming increasingly clear that the sounding of the Church bells, inconceivable though it was, had been a signal for mass murder. The nightmare had begun in earnest.

The Sieur de Briquemault, alarmingly well informed, described how the Duc de Guise and the King's bastard brother, d'Angoulême, had gone to the Admiral's house at 4.00am with a group of mercenaries, who broke in and repeatedly stabbed him while at prayer with his chaplain. (According to de Thou, writing later, the Admiral died with incredible courage and calm, having first ordered his companions to escape over the roof as he did not want them to die with him. His body was hurled out of an upstairs window into the courtyard where it was literally butchered and dragged through the streets until it was hung on the gibbet at Montfaucon, minus its hands and genitals which had been put up for sale. The head had been cut off with the amiable intention of sending it to the Pope.)

That had set the mood and with unbelievable and animal savagery, Catholic turned upon Huguenot. Every possible grudge that had been building up was translated into blood lust; every vestige of humanity or civilised behaviour was forgotten. Huguenots were hunted down by armed gangs of both citizens and mercenaries. They were not difficult to find and they could not escape though some were armed and managed to fight their way to safety. Moneylenders, regardless of their creed, were popular prey as debts were wiped out with them; women, children and babies were dragged by the hair into the street and cut to pieces, their screams turning to gurgles as their blood flowed on the cobbles and in the gutters. Not many were armed with guns and knives were the common tool. No one was safe and the first orgy of butchery left over two thousand people dead, their bodies lying in scarlet heaps until they were dragged to the river and thrown in. An unholy party spirit was abroad.

As the Embassy enclave listened, besides the peeling of the bells, they could make out a deep roar accompanied by louder gunfire. It was a terrible, bestial sound and it was drawing nearer. Soon they could see the glow and flicker of torches and make out a moving wall of people silhouetted against the lights. It was clear the Embassy was about to be attacked.

Lady Ursula, already busy with water, wine and the tearing of sheets into bandages, shepherded the women, children and wounded to the back of the house. She did not notice a small figure creep down the stairs and perch halfway, stiff with fright but unable to remain in that upstairs room.

Minutes later, piercing screams for help brought them out into the courtyard, swords drawn. A group of people hurled themselves against the gates, imploring them to open and let them in. The mob were on their heels and there was not a moment to lose. As they fumbled with locks and chains, the crowd appeared, torches flaring and howling like hounds on a scent. The pursued were dragged inside, but not before those at the head of the mob flung themselves forward and managed also to enter.

This was Philip's first experience of lethal hand to hand fighting; all the hours spent fencing and jousting had not prepared him for the savagery of the moment. Now it was kill or be killed and he saw Walsingham grab a young Italian employee and shove him to the rear as he himself thrust forward and killed his attacker. After that adrenalin sent him into action with a force and his skill gave him confidence. He had no trouble with the leaders of a drunken mob. Out of the corner of his eye, he saw, with horror, that the Huguenot General had been surrounded after his first impetuous rush well into the forefront of the crowd and was being dragged out of the courtyard as they began to retreat. Someone had put a rope around his neck and he had been disarmed. He disappeared with horrible speed and Walsingham gave the order to close the gates. Leander put his massive shoulder to one gate and a group of young men to the other and ground them shut, pushing the mob back and shooting the bolts.

Frances, shivering on the stairs, heard the stamping feet and the shouting. With the yells of the frustrated mob resounding in her ears, she watched the wounded being brought in and heard their disjointed, sobbing accounts, some more sickening than their hurts. Many had gaping knife wounds, one a severed arm and others could barely walk. There were bodies and pools of blood in the courtyard and she could clearly see her father, Philip and others of the household helping and carrying the refugees in. Her mother, running out of the back regions, calling for more water and directing them where to lay the wounded, caught sight of Frances and promptly ordered her to go to the kitchens and bring as much water as she could carry. This practicality broke the frozen horror that gripped her and she jumped to her feet and rushed off, bringing back a large earthenware jug, having told a kitchen boy to work both pumps for all he was worth. Lady Ursula, trying to staunch the blood from wounds, had no time to waste on the sensibilities of her daughter and kept her fetching, carrying and rolling bandages. Bringing yet more wine for those rescued, Philip collided with her on a journey to the kitchens and seeing the tears pouring down her cheeks, set down his burden and, with the innate kindness that characterised him, gathered the shuddering child up, wiped her face and kissed her, soothing and banishing the fright in her shocked eyes. She turned in his arms, put her own around his neck and buried her wet little face in his shoulder.

As red dawn was breaking, fresh turmoil erupted outside and the ringing of many hooves was heard beyond the locked gates, renewed yelling and screaming and the clash of arms. The Duke de Nevers, sent by the Queen Mother, was driving the mob from the gates of the Embassy in no uncertain fashion. After he had posted men of the Royal Guard around the house, he came in to report to Walsingham. This was doubly ironic, though Walsingham had no notion of it at the time, because their charming host of the al fresco dinner a bare week ago had been one of the inner circle who, with the Royal Family, had planned the massacre, a rabid Catholic sent to protect Protestants. He had been riding round the city and had much to tell. Three Englishmen had been murdered by the mercenaries, the Place de la Basse-Cour was piled with the bodies of Huguenot guests staying for the wedding (the final word in hospitality), Henry of Navarre and the Prince de Condé were incarcerated somewhere within the Palace, powerless to help their friends and servants, who had been killed to a man. Paris looked like a slaughterhouse and he had seen General Francois de Beauvais jerking at the end of a rope on a gibbet as he made his way to the Embassy.

When asked by Walsingham how and why this atrocity had been perpetrated, he became evasive and would only say that a Huguenot plot to kill the Royal Family had been discovered and that events had become out of hand, that the King had tried to stop the murder of Admiral Coligny but his message arrived too late, after which they had "let the enterprise run its course." The enterprise of St.Bartholomew's Eve.

Listening, Philip thought that the only reason de Nevers had been sent to protect them was the Queen Mother's obsession with the hope of an English Royal marriage. He went out to look for the men he had killed during the attack and found it impossible; it had happened so fast but he thought he had accounted for three. He remembered that he had not yet wiped his rapier.

Going back into the house, he found servants mopping blood from the floor and Frances curled in a small heap asleep in a corner like an exhausted puppy, the hem of her clothes also covered in blood. He found an embroidered tapestry table cover, wrapped her in it and carried her to a sofa. He then went in search of Timothy Bright and found him with the young Italian, Pietro Bizari, a history student from Perugia, presently working for Walsingham. Both were deeply grateful for the protection they had been given, but still horrified by what they had seen. Bizari was to write later that he owed his life to Walsingham who physically rescued him when "exposed to the swords of a rabid mob and entrapped by armed men, he, at that time, ambassador to the Queen, freed me from the brink of death."

With the dawn, the horror continued unabated. What darkness had hinted at stood revealed as hideous reality; the stacks of bodies, some streets impassable and reeking, the maimed and wounded being ruthlessly sought and finished off. The slaughter in Paris went on for days, despite the King's efforts to stop it and over three thousand men, women and children died in the city; the massacre then spread to the provinces where a further seven to ten thousand perished. The Seine was blocked with bodies and ran red as did the Loire where wolves came down to gorge themselves. No fish were caught or eaten out of either river for months.

The beleaguered English Embassy suffered greatly. There were too many people crammed inside, every room in the house and in the stables was full, and the water and food supplies were running low. Catholic bands continued to stalk around the house, despite de Nevers' Guard, and all around them was the stench of death.

Amid the carnage, the King attempted to justify and establish an official version of events at the Paris Parlement. On 26th August he called a "Lit de Justice" at which he admitted to ordering the massacre with the purpose of thwarting a Huguenot uprising and a plot to murder the Royal Family. Unbelievably, this was followed by a procession and a jubilee celebration through streets which had to be cleared of bodies and where his people were still being butchered. When not so occupied, he continued his furious hunting. He was twenty-two, his brothers, the Duc d'Anjou and the Duc d'Alençon, were twenty and seventeen. The Duc de Guise was twenty and the Duc d'Angoulême nineteen. Henry of Navarre and his cousin the Prince de Condé were nineteen and twenty respectively. It was not surprising that these, so principally involved in events, lost their heads and caused so many others to lose theirs.

After that first night, Frances was not allowed out of her upstairs room unless she was accompanied. Her sturdy cousin, Thomas, only eleven years old was very shaken and came up to visit and divert her. He took her down to the stables to visit her pony, but there was a man dying from a stomach wound in the harness room and the sounds of his suffering were terrible. She hugged the pony and fled.

Many of Walsingham's friends and colleagues were in danger. Among those who died were Petrus Ramus who, having hidden in a cellar, deemed it safe to return to his house. Like the Admiral, he was stabbed, thrown out of a window and dismembered. Hubert Languet, despite his diplomatic standing was seized and hauled before a Councillor of State who fortunately released him. He lived to become Philip's close friend and mentor.

Walsingham was becoming increasingly anxious about the future of his guests and their safety. Calling Philip in to discuss this, he suggested that he should travel as soon as he could to Heidelberg, the Calvinist capital of the Palatinate, where the Elector, Frederick III, would ensure the safety of all Protestants and where there was a humanist University. Besides Philip's own party there were several in the Embassy willing to make up a larger group to ensure the safety of all. He charged them to report the massacre wherever they happened to be. He found himself unwilling to part with the boy, whose behaviour and support he had much appreciated and of whom he had become extremely fond. He realised that Philip would be recalled by his family as soon as news of the massacre reached them and letters from England could be got through in return and he particularly wanted him to have the chance to travel independently in Europe as he himself had done. A letter did indeed arrive dated 9th September from the Privy Council containing a sharp request from Leicester for his nephew's return, but by that time the bird had flown and was winging its way around Europe.

His main concern, of course, was to get Frances and Lady Ursula back to England as soon as he safely could. Lady Ursula was now five months pregnant, the baby being due in late December, and despite her heroic behaviour during the massacre, she was quite worn out with providing for so many and taking care of the wounded. Frances was becoming extremely truculent and bored with her incarceration and he, himself, was beginning to feel most unwell.

He, therefore, arranged with de Nevers for an armed guard to escort them through Paris and some distance further on, sending with them several of his own household, including Leander, who could ill be spared, as protection for the remainder of the journey. Even the country districts were far from stable. As the coach rumbled through Paris, Lady Ursula held Frances's head on her knee, with a cover over her face to prevent her seeing sights that might horrify her, but the sounds she could hear told their story and she could not resist the odd mesmerised peep when her mother's attention was elsewhere. What she saw made her retreat into herself and become very quiet for a long time afterwards. At the Northern city gate, there was a fracas and two of their escort were attacked by the troops guarding it. Leander with his imposing size and fractured French, managed to persuade them to let them pass. He had no opinion whatever of Frenchmen. Frances, in her mother's arms, could feel her shaking with fear.

Walsingham was left with the task of getting his official despatch to London as soon as possible and this was awkward. During the first days of the massacre it was extremely dangerous and difficult to get anything or anybody out of the embassy. He did not want the despatch delivered to the Royal Guard who, though supposedly guarding the house would, he deemed, have orders to intercept any form of message and take it directly to the Queen Mother for scrutiny and he did not wish to risk those leaving for England under escort being searched and a despatch found. The Queen Mother would not want a derogatory report of her actions to reach the Queen of England so soon and before her own representative could explain her case. He, therefore, entrusted it to the memories of two of the young men among those first to leave. The ubiquitous Nicholas Faunt, whose education was well up to the task and his own assistant and messenger, Walter Williams. For thirty six hours, as he wrote it, shut in with him in the library, they exhaustively read and re-read his report, clutching their heads in their hands, pouring with sweat and wiping all other thought from their minds.

He had picked his envoys well. By 11th September, the Queen had Walsingham's version of events. She received the news of the massacre at Kenilworth with anger and distress but she did not receive La Motte Fénelon, the French Ambassador, for a further three days, only admitting him at Woodstock. He entered to find her and the entire Court dressed in deepest black and forming an aisle down which he was obliged to walk. He was then called to a window seat by the Queen and subjected to a difficult interview in which he lamely explained that the King had discovered a Protestant plot to assassinate himself and his family and was forced to take drastic action. The Queen knew better.

Those who lived through the shocking days in Paris in August 1572 never forgot them and suffered accordingly. Walsingham's health began to deteriorate because of them, Languet was haunted by them, Bright re-lived them constantly, Philip Sidney never wrote about them but detested the Valois from that time, putting his career on the line to prevent his Queen from marrying Anjou. Little Frances Walsingham became very quiet and withdrawn for a while, a lifetime of inscrutability gradually developing unnoticed. She smiled, she laughed, but who knew what she was thinking. Strangely, this added to her confidence and she was able to live her later life fully and with zest.

Other reactions to the massacre were varied. Pope Gregory XIII rejoiced unashamedly. He sent Charles IX a golden rose, he ordered a Te Deum to be sung at a special celebration service and he had a medal struck depicting an angel bearing a cross and sword standing over the bodies of slaughtered Huguenots. Not content with that, he commissioned the painting of three frescoes by the artist Giorgio Vasari to be hung in the Sala Regia in the Vatican showing the murder of Coligny and other atrocities.

The King of Spain "laughed for the only time recorded". The Emperor

Maximillian ll, on the other hand, described the massacre as shameful. Even the Tsar, Ivan the Terrible, whose own track record was outlandish, professed himself appalled in a letter to the Emperor.

Much later, the poet Christopher Marlowe wrote a play called "Massacre in Paris" on the subject of St.Batholomew's Eve. It was not one of his greater works, lacking the singing fluency of poetry in some of his other dramas, but was very accurate where the characters and their actions were concerned. His patron and friend was then Thomas Walsingham who had indeed witnessed the happenings in Paris.

Walsingham himself was not recalled to England until 1573, so ending his Ambassadorship in France. Kind Sir Thomas Smith, writing in January 1573 to Burghley in an effort to get him replaced said: "… The poor gentleman there was undone, having been at so great charge, all things waxing so dear, and his wife being here and great with child." He added that Lady Ursula was in floods of tears; reaction, worry and pregnancy had taken its toll.

Walsingham returned to London in April, to his wife, his daughter, Frances and his second child, Mary, born in late December 1572.

ACT ONE 1

1581 – Barn Elms

It was the year 1581, and early autumn was stealthily gilding the trees on the Surrey side of the River Thames.

Barn Elms was a fair sized manor of about nine hundred acres, the lease of which had been passed to Sir Francis Walsingham by the Queen in February 1579. Remote from the village of Barnes, it was approachable mainly by river, being surrounded on three sides by a great bend in the Thames, but it was within easy reach of London and accessible from Whitehall, Richmond and Hampton Court. Most of the meadows surrounding the house ran straight down to the river but around the gardens and the landing stage there was a sturdy wall.

On the wall, a child was sitting, the river slipping and sliding beneath her feet. But was she a child? Her hair and clothes proclaimed a young lady but the flower like face and tiny form belonged to childhood. There was little to suggest a woman except the thoughts which raced behind the passive face. In fact, there was nothing to suggest thought at all because throughout her short life she had been schooled to hide her emotions and conceal what was going on in her mind. Her face, as a result, appeared perpetually tranquil except for a rare and joyous smile that started in her eyes and was so arresting that a recipient would blink.

Frances Walsingham was not quite fourteen years old and her confusion was absolute. Her years, until this time, had been a curious mixture of the cherished and protected and the untoward and violent.

She was, once more, an only child of rather older parents, as she had been from her birth until the arrival of a sister five years later. This she had greeted with unmixed delight; jealousy was not in her nature and she viewed Mary's appearance as she would a new kitten; something small and friendly to be looked after and played with. As Mary grew, in form the image of their mother, including the red hair, the years between them shrank and Frances had, at last, a longed for playmate to banish the loneliness of her early childhood.

To be an only child in an Elizabethan household was an anomaly. Most families consisted of between six and twelve children. In the absence of servants, the older ones shared, with parents, the care and upbringing of the younger ones. Ages could vary between eighteen and a new baby, many of whom shared bed as well as board.

Frances had slept alone with Alice Poole wheezing gently in a corner since she graduated from her cradle.

Mary had changed that. Once past babyhood, they shared a bed, their toys, their dogs and their ponies. They played in the streams at Barn Elms, fished with jars in the fishponds and picked fruit from the trees they climbed; all with the joyful abandon of city children let loose in the country. Mary had been bold and active for her six years with a temper that matched her hair and a determination to keep up with her elder sister. She had died two years ago, burning and flushed with fever; crying out to begin with, then strangely quiet and limp, an ivory doll made stranger by the contrast with the vivid auburn hair spread out upon her pillows. Frances learnt, from the hushed voices after, and between her mother's choking sobs, that it was one of the deadly summer agues so common in London, called by the Italians "mala aria". Mary had been buried in the church in Barnes; a little ghost who had healed the hurts inflicted on Frances by the terrible events in Paris in August 1572 which had so scarred her father and his Embassy there.

The family had moved from the Papey to a much larger house in Seethng Lane, opposite St.Olave's Church and not very far from the Tower of London. It was now known as "Walsingham House" just as the other great houses on the Thames were named after their owners and was a measure of the respect in which the Secretary of State was held.

Frances's thoughts, adrift with the river, flitted from past arrivals at Barn Elms, the greetings and embraces, scamperings to and from the stables and dairies, to the being the river had brought her only a few weeks ago.

For what had stepped out of Sir Francis Walsingham's barge was a young man who was a joy to behold by any standard and who had, above all, looked at Frances and found himself unable to look away. Of this she was perfectly aware and it did not need so much as a peep to know that whatever pleasantries his tongue might be uttering, his eyes were on her alone. He was a boy of about nineteen whose eyes crinkled when he smiled so that he already had laughter lines around them and beside his full-lipped curling mouth. He was brown and rosy and wholesome and he had taken Frances's breath away. She could think of nothing but his laughing face and she lost her heart, her head and her ingrained caution in one dizzy moment. Caution was not only an inherited part of Frances's nature, but it had been drilled into her by her father from a very early age who, because of the nature of his work, had taught her discretion and the value of concealed thought to the degree that she had developed an already powerful memory and committed very little to paper.

First love is a shattering experience and fourteen is no age to deal with it. For Frances, there were no painful doubts about reciprocation. She had read his eyes and knew her own reflected what she saw. There was no hope for her.

As an employee of her father, he would be staying somewhere within the manor and she would make her curtsey to him that evening with downcast eyes, give him her hand and bid him welcome as she would to any guest.

It was, in fact, quite a large gathering. Her Aunt and Uncle Beale had come over from their nearby house at Mortlake bringing their daughters, Margaret and Catherine, two of Frances's less favourite cousins. They had grown into large, cumbersome girls, favouring their father, and their jealousy of Frances had not dimmed with the years. Their mother, Edith, was working hard to find them husbands and finding it a heavy task. They would make trouble if possible and could be relied on not to miss any opportunity to discomfort Frances. An added guest was Dr. John Dee, another neighbour and a close friend of her father. He was a kindly and intricately erudite man with an aesthetic face and long, delicate fingers. He was a mathematician, astrologer, navigator and alchemist, an occasional advisor to the Queen and a follower of the Neo-Platonist, Marsilio Ficino. He was always kind to Frances to whom he gave the run of his enormous library whenever she wanted it. Also present was the shortsighted Thomas Phelippes, who had come down in the barge from London, a small blond man employed by Walsingham as a codebreaker and messenger; shortsighted, perhaps, because of constant perusal of cyphers. With him was Francis Milles, her father's right hand man.

Throughout supper in the dining hall Frances had kept her gaze on her plate, not daring to look at the paragon down the table from her in case others watched. The "smothered" rabbit, capons in orange sauce, the cheese tart and sweetmeats went by her almost untouched.

In the morning she opened her eyes with John Wickerson's face before her and the warmth of knowing that a friend awaited her. From then on her waking moments were spent devising ways to meet him and to be alone with him before fate or his duty should whisk him away from her. She had no doubts either that this was going to happen whether by fate or by her own machinations. Further than that she did not think and, in fact, their moment came not forty eight hours later.

They had been lucky, or clever enough to come upon each other in a corner of the knot garden early one morning when the dew was heavy on the ground and the scent of late flowering roses spread from the formal beds like a benediction. Both had risen soon after dawn with this unspoken plan in mind. Frances knowing that Alice, asleep in her room, awoke much later, had chosen a simple day dress that required no help to put on.

The knot garden was in full view of the back of the house and John, taking one look at her, seized her hand and pulled her through the arched opening cut in the yew hedge bordering it. This led, via a dewy grass walk, to the walled garden. Down it they fled, opening the wooden door in the wall and leaning against it laughing with complicit glee like naughty children and there, among the fan-trained peaches and nectarines ripening on the walls, they fell into each others arms.

An Elizabethan kiss of greeting could go on for a very long time and the sun was warm by the time they could bear to let each other go.

From then on, Frances used her quick wits and her local knowledge of every quarter of Barn Elms to find safe and secret meeting places. The house itself, built of brick and timber contained around thirty wainscotted rooms and besides these there were kitchens, butteries, dairies, wash houses and stabling for over seventy horses. The Home Farm included orchards, fishponds and a mixture of arable and pasture land which supplied the needs of the household. Frances loved it and knew every inch of it, inside and out. Sometimes she chose the dovecotes, where the happy noise of the birds provided a cover for voices, sometimes the orchards or outbuildings near the stables. This needed a close study of where those working in these places were likely to be and when. There was also the importance of not appearing with muddy slippers from unlikely quarters and, above all, the avoidance of questioning by Alice or her mother. She began to lead a double life and the stakes were high. At each encounter, they tumbled more deeply into love. Frances felt that her whole life had been leading to this; all the vague longings were personified in this carefree, brown young man. She was perfectly certain that she wanted to spend her life with John and inevitably this led to talk of marriage. Both knew that Walsingham would never willingly bestow his daughter on the son of a minor Staffordshire landowner. He had far grander plans for her though he would not have considered either of them too young to marry by the standards of the day. They were, in fact, too intoxicated with each other and the moment to think very far ahead.

Frances, despite her childlike figure, had ripened early, her body keeping pace with her astute mind and she knew full well what she was doing. No child of that age remained an innocent. Very perturbing, now, were the promptings of her body and soul which violently shouldered aside every other consideration.

She knew that John was employed by her father as a courier but Sir Francis Walsingham, now Secretary of State to the Queen, and one of a triumverate with Lord Burghley and the Earl of Leicester, was not one to encourage discussion among those who worked for him. John had told her he acted as a messenger and travelled a great deal, no more, and she would not ask her father for fear that he would instantly question her interest and forbid her to see or speak to him. Luckily for her, he had much on his mind at the time. He had been appointed a Privy Councillor and one of two of the Queen's Principal Secretaries of State on 29th December 1573, although Her Majesty had grudgingly made him wait for Knighthood until 1st December 1577. His workload since then had been increasingly heavy. He had recently returned from France and a complex visit to King Henri III (His brother, Charles IX having died, appropriately, in a sea of his own blood, the uncharitable putting it down to excessive use of the hunting horn though tuberculosis was, in fact, the culprit.)

Certainly, Walsingham had his only daughter's marriage in mind and no Elizabethan father could dream of allowing such precious merchandise to be spoilt. Virginity was an absolute necessity in the brokerage of matrimony and her mother, Lady Ursula, was well aware that Frances was of marriageable state and age. Their hopes for her were high.

Imagine a scene such as had heralded the downfall of the lovely, but lascivious Catherine Howard, fifth wife of King Henry VIII, who had romped her way through several lovers before her marriage. A block and a sharp French sword had been the last things she saw and Walsingham was very mindful that his uncle, Sir Edmund, Henry's Lieutenant of the Tower, had arranged her departure from this world. Henry's anguish and bitter vengefulness had almost wrecked his mind. His "rose without a thorn" had turned out to be full-blown and lewd and one who knew well "how to meddle with a man".

Despite his ambition for Frances, Walsingham had, so far, resisted the temptation of proposing her as a Maid of Honour to the Queen. Well born and pretty girls of her age were granted these coveted posts by Her Majesty and were thus expected to acquire the polished manners, customs and etiquette required in Court circles, and, more importantly, they were given the chance to mix with the great and the rich with a view to being picked out by a suitable husband.

Walsingham's hesitation came from the knowledge that his family's origins lay in trade, not the established aristocracy, and his pride could not risk being turned down for this reason. He came of stock which had progressed through seven generations from London tradesmen to county landowners. In the Walsinghams' case shoemakers and cordwainers had become vintners and gentlemen. His father, William Walsingham, having joined the Inns of Court and become a senior barrister at Gray's Inn, ended his career as Under Sheriff of London and, at his death, his mother had married Sir John Carey whose brother was the husband of the flighty Mary Boleyn. Frances, therefore, did not have an aristocratic background, but one amply endowed with city, legal, county and Court connections. Her blood was by no means blue but she was well qualified to follow her father from the wings to the centre of the bright stage on which the Elizabethan saga was played.

The Queen, herself, was extremely strict with all her Ladies in Waiting. (Maid of Honour was the term given to the unmarried girls). She would stand no unseemly conceit, would permit no flirtation in her presence and no marriage could be arranged without her permission. In fact, she made herself responsible for their behaviour and their progress and her rages were terrifying, especially if prompted by jealousy. Misconduct was followed by dismissal, disgrace and, at worst, a nasty sojourn in the Tower of London.

John had far less caution than Frances. He had loved before, but never very deeply and never such a creature as Frances. What drew his gaze unerringly to that small figure, as it was to draw many another gaze, was her grace. Every move she made was a pleasure to watch. In today's idiom, she would have made the ideal model, one perfect gesture or attitude following another so that, had she been in the eye of a camera, not one image would have been bad. Her carriage was that of a dancer; back straight, head and neck a curve of elegance, and movement so fluid that each shifting stance was there to be enjoyed. She was unaware of her gift and searched, instead, her face for signs of beauty. Hers did not conform to the present fashion. Her skin was not white, her hair was not golden and her lips were not particularly red, but her eyes caused men to look and look again. They were large, darkly lashed and enigmatic. Their whites were intense and the irises were ringed on the outer edge with a dark circle. Their colour was indefinable, grey, gold and hazel and they were set in her little face like jewels. She had just begun to notice that heads turned when she entered a room but thought it was either because she was her father's daughter or that her great age now allowed her to wear much richer clothes. She had envied Mary her ideal colouring; the red hair and flawless white skin then so much admired because it was the Queen's, but Mary would have grown far larger than Frances and missed her delicacy. Not so immediately apparent was her vitality. Behind the passive face was an unquenchable energy inherited from her mother which was to see her through the many challenges in her life.

Her horizon was now entirely filled by John Wickerson and between their trysts her mood rushed from joy to dread; joy in finding such unlooked-for happiness and dread that they might be discovered and he would be taken from her. For one terrible week, he had been sent on a mission to London and she feared that he had been banished, but there was a reply to the mission and back he came to Barn Elms, after which luck had smiled on them and John had stayed, housed in the manor, for a further two weeks. They lived for each moment together and each moment to the full, completely absorbed in their own enchantment and oblivious to fears for the future.

She never looked at him or acknowledged his presence within the house beyond a courteous nod, for most of the servants had known her since childhood, particularly the steward, Leander, and Alice, and there was little that they would miss. Her inexpressive face stood her in good stead and even Lady Ursula had, as yet, no fears. Once they had been caught handfast in a doorway leading to the stable courtyard, but the intruder was Giles, a blacksmith, and a devoted friend to Frances who had held her on the back of her first pony and Mary after her. He drooped one bloodshot eye and made a throat-cutting motion with his forefinger. This happy state could not last.

She came into the house one golden afternoon, crossed the polished, herb strewn floor, trailing a hand along the oak table running down its centre and mounted the wide, shallow stairs where shafting sunlight streamed through the huge paned window overlooking the staircase. She had spent the last two hours locked in John's arms beneath a festooning apple tree, heavy with fruit and still full of friendly sheltering leaf. The branches came down to the ground and apart from their whispers and low laughter, it would have been hard to find them. She was unaware of the glow in her eyes and face or that her lips were slightly swollen from the increasing intensity of their kisses. It was becoming harder and harder to keep their physical need for each other within bounds. She looked up, in the full light of the window, and saw her mother standing at the top of the stairs staring down at her. Her upturned face told more than she knew and John had pushed a buttercup behind her ear. Lady Ursula had seen that look on many a girl's face after love making, including her own.

The questioning that followed in her mother's dressing chamber was forceful and hard and very particular. In a large family, she might well have got away with it, but the cherished only child was not allowed to have secrets or to cover her traces. While Mary lived this situation had been made easier; united they had stood. Over the years, Frances had learned how to keep a part of herself completely private, to avoid hurt and the scrutiny of her parents. This she had done with a certain amount of success and she was a master of the light answer and the turned subject. She did not lie because she was intelligent enough to know that lies lead to other lies and that her father could read one like a book. She stood, therefore, her eyes fixed fully on her mother, holding the back of an oak chair and simply did not answer any question that could incriminate or identify John. Yes, a young man had casually kissed her this afternoon. No, she did not want to name him for fear of getting him into trouble. No, she did not know him well. It was no more than a kiss, in fact, her first. Yes, she rather thought she had enjoyed it. Had not her mother enjoyed her first kiss; when had it been and where? Who was the lucky man? And so on, her answers getting more and more vague and interrogative. Her mother's hard hazel stare gradually softened, but Frances knew well she was unconvinced and would mentally review any young man within the domain and, worse, would consult her father as soon as she was able. This would speedily lead them to John who would, in turn, be questioned and far more ruthlessly.

Beneath her farthingale and stiff kirtle, her knees were shaking and her heart racing, but her wits did not desert her. Haste was needed and a plan.

Once in her own room, blessedly empty, she flung herself down on the bed and forced her mind to concentrate. The comfort of her bed was a balm; it had been given her after Mary died because the one they shared was large and had felt horribly empty. The frame was made of carved chestnut wood, rope interlaced to make a springy base and two mattresses to cushion any discomfort. The linen sheets and wool blanket were covered with a silk bedcover, the initial "F" embroidered on it. This bed was her refuge and once the curtains had been drawn round it at night, she could forget that Alice slept in the corner of the room and lose herself in dreams.

No time for dreams now, however, she had to use every wit God had given her and do it quickly. If only Christopher Carleill were here to help her, as he always did, but he was away in Antwerp, serving with the Prince of Orange, and there was no knowing when he might reappear. This half brother by marriage had always been her ally despite the sixteen years between them. Walsingham's stepson by his first marriage was no blood relation to Frances but much loved by Walsingham. His life was one of high adventure and now, in his twenties, he was worldly wise and would always lend an ear to the troubles and confidences of a small sister.

The enormity of her present dilemma did not overwhelm Frances as it would have done, perhaps, had she known better what the outcome might be.

She had heard that a couple could contract themselves in marriage, particularly if one party was going to be away for a time and wished to be sure of the other, thus making another subsequent offer of marriage harder to arrange and enforce, but she had no idea if this was in any way legal or binding or how easily it could be overturned. Neither did she know if it could be done without parental permission. Any person she could persuade to draw up a document to this effect and sign it on her behalf would incur her father's extreme wrath. Who would be safe? Her father would not harm a member of the clergy but what priest would sign an illicit contract, knowing that it was instigated by a wilful daughter who was in no mind to accept the authority of her parents? Frances had been brought up in the strictest Protestant traditions and she knew perfectly well that it was a sin to defy or deceive a father and mother, especially if a child were loved as she was loved.

Her mind seethed and slowly the unthinkable began to emerge. Could she ask John to run the enormous risk of taking her to a church, small and unknown among the hundreds in the City of London, and there persuade the incumbent to marry them? By the time they revealed what they had done, and the marriage had been consummated, her father would be powerless, in the face of an impending scandal, to tear them apart. He would then have to make the best of it and accept the marriage. Frances knew, however, that this would destroy him and the bond between them. His health, since those terrible weeks in Paris, had not been good and from time to time he was obliged to retire to his bed for days on end. She could not cause him such ultimate distress. Besides, it would be almost impossible to leave Barn Elms undetected.

Alternatively, she could pledge herself to John, before witnesses, but again, who to ask who would not immediately run to Walsingham?

Slowly, she climbed from the bed, went to her writing table, prepared her pen and ink and began to write.

Before supper that evening, just as heavy dark cloud was beginning to draw across what would have been a beautiful evening, and the sun's last rays were slanting on the glowing wainscot, Walsingham entered his library to find a lamp lit and his daughter standing before the fire with her back to him. He came up behind her, put his hands on her slender shoulders and gently turned her round to face him, smiling as he did so. She was holding something in her hands and she was not smiling. The blackness of the approaching thundercloud cut off the last rays of sun and the room went very dark.

The following morning, Frances Walsingham leant her head against the blurred panes of her window, the tears pouring down her face as fast as the sluicing rain driving against them. She had not been able, therefore, to see clearly the group of men walking in a clumped, unnatural way, down to the landing stage. In their midst was one man round whom they crowded and the manner in which he walked was not natural either. He moved in a constrained, awkward way as if he could not use his arms and Frances knew at once that they were tied behind his back. Although she could not see his face, she also knew that it was John.

There was no defence against the pain, the sickening fear, or the terrible sense of loss. It was, for this moment, unendurable. Few things in her life were to leave her so helpless; she had no weapons to fight with. Experience and a knowledge of her world would build defences round her as she grew older but on this bitter morning the hurt was raw; as was the sense of injustice. Above all, the cold horror of John's fate and her own ignorance of what that would be, made her writhe.

She had written, herself, and signed, a pledge to a contract of marriage with John Wickerson, without his knowledge and at her own instigation. The marriage, she proposed, was to happen at some time in the future and with her father's approval. She had explained to Walsingham that John had no hand in her action because she wanted no blame attached to him. It was the only way she could think of to protect him and to persuade her father that their intentions were not clandestine. She had not been able to see or speak to John before she acted, but she knew full well how fast Walsingham would move once her mother had voiced her suspicions and there must be some prior step on her part to forestall his anger and to assure him that marriage was indeed their intent.

It had come as a shock but she now understood how coldly ruthless this loving and indulgent father could be. He explained, in painstaking detail, how unsuitable a match John would be, how disgraced her parents and family would appear, what plans he was carefully laying for her future and ended by expressing his disappointment in her behaviour and forbidding her absolutely to think of John again. He did not raise his voice or applaud the honesty of her contract. He threw it on the fire and ordered her to her room in which she was now locked.

Lady Ursula had railed at her, accusing her of duplicity, then, seeing her distress, burst into tears and took her in her arms. This did not prevent her interrogating Frances again and again on the nature of her dealings with John. She wanted assurance that she had not lost more than her heart and her questions left her daughter feeling besmirched and as though love was in some way illicit and dirty.

She was never to see John again although he was to see her. The next stage of her life was already mapped out and he was not going to be allowed any part in it. Walsingham had relented enough to assure her that John would not be harmed but more than that he would not tell her and she could not bring herself to believe him.

Released later from her room, Frances resumed her perch on the wall above the landing stage, no longer confused but with a very sharp idea of reality and a hardening resolve never to trust to authority. The last of her childhood had gone downstream that stormy morning with a boy and a barge and a very young woman sat contemplating the bright coloured leaves now swirling in the surge of water left by the tempest. She wished she had the courage to join them.

So ended the autumn idyll that had begun with love and laughter and ended in a cold veil of rain and tears.

John Wickerson was to spend two long years in the Marshalsea prison, a terrible place of fear, cold and hunger. Walsingham had no intention of risking his reappearance until his daughter was safely and suitably married.

ACT ONE 2

1581-1582 – Penshurst, Wilton

While Frances Walsingham was gazing bleakly into the swirling waters of the Thames, Philip Sidney was staring out of the library windows at Penshurst across the grassy quadrangle to the two Tudor ranges built by his father and the magnificent new Italianate loggia inspired by his own travels in Europe. He was seeing, not the carved, honey-coloured stone but the honey-coloured hair and bright black eyes of a girl whom he might have married and who was now beyond his reach. Running through his mind and written on the paper before him were the first sonnets of "Astrophil and Stella" which were to number, eventually, one hundred and eight, sprinkled with eleven "songs" and would rank as his greatest work. Begun in May, it had been a relief to pour out love and longing in this way. His unattainable "Stella" was Lady Penelope Devereux, daughter of the Earl of Essex, and the unrequited "Astrophil" represented himself. "Star and Star-Lover," he reflected, made a sad pair. He would have to inject some wit and satyr into what might otherwise become a mere tragedy.

He was twenty seven, unmarried and unemployed. The future which had looked so dazzling and assured in 1572 had lost momentum with the years and his mood, this autumn of 1581, was often one of frustrated bitterness. He had certainly dazzled Europe during his early progression from Heidelberg. He and his travelling companions, his cousin Thomas Coningsby and Lodowick Bryskett, had gone from Frankfurt, via the Imperial court in Vienna, to Bratislava, Venice, Padua and, finally, Cracow in time to see Henri, former Duc D'Anjou, crowned King of Poland. On the death of his brother, Charles IX, however, Henri bolted back to Paris, clearly delighted that the Polish exile imposed on him by Catherine de Medici was over and that he could wear the crown of France instead. He managed to break his journey home in Italy for some very unusual and questionable entertainments, nonetheless. Philip had no love for this decadent Valois Prince and considered him well served by a stretch in Poland. He then returned to England, summoned by his Queen in the early summer of 1575.

His two years of travel had taken him to many of the Renaissance Courts of Europe; he had seen the works of legendary artists (his own portrait had been painted by Veronese), perfected his horsemanship under masters of equestrian art and learned much of war and politics. He had met and mingled with kings, rulers, politicians, scholars and writers of the first order and the "young and raw" boy described by Leicester to Walsingham in his introductory letter had returned a young man of almost regal bearing and presence, with a thorough knowledge of Europe and its potentates. He was also recognised as a standard bearer for Protestantism and a possible "white hope" for uniting its many facets in Europe.

The reputation he had earned in Europe over the last ten years, however, was by no means reflected in his own country and his Queen, jealous of the high esteem in which he was held by other Courts and governments, seemed determined to keep him out of the limelight in England where he was equally popular. Her Majesty was never over fond of hearing the excellencies of others consistently extolled and Philip had never played the fawning courtier, unlike many. He even had the temerity to criticize Her Majesty's judgement over the everlasting question of a French marriage. Like Walsingham and Leicester, he was not in favour either of the Valois or of a union with France.

His relationship with the Monarch had begun well. He had performed before her many years ago at Oxford (a debate in unrehearsed Latin) and later at his uncle's great house at Kenilworth and wrote an amusing and highly topical entertainment, "The Lady of May" enacted for her at Leicester's house at Wanstead. He had written verses including some lyrical poetry and performed to the top of his exceptional bent in the Accession Day Jousts almost every November; he was acknowledged as one of the most brilliant of her courtiers, a diamond of the first water in the adornment of her Court, but still she would not accept him or give him any position of merit, either at home or abroad. Her one concession was to appoint him Royal Cup Bearer in November 1575 as his father had been before him.

On the family front things were no better. He returned to find that his uncle, Leicester, had become the father of an illegitimate son by his mistress, the lovely, bird-witted Douglas Sheffield. Lady Sheffield, who claimed that he had, in fact, married her, was persuaded, instead, to marry Sir Edward Stafford, now conveniently Ambassador in Paris, and Leicester had turned his attentions to Lettice Devereux, Countess of Essex. Lettice's husband, Walter Devereux, the first Earl of Essex, had been appointed Earl Marshal of Ireland, a life appointment, while Sir Henry Sidney's position as Lord Deputy of Ireland (an honour he found particularly irksome) was not, much to his relief. Philip accompanied Essex on 10th August 1576 to Ireland where he met his father in Dublin after which he spent an eventful month hunting down the rebellious sons of the Earl of Clanricarde and meeting the famed Grania O'Malley, a lady pirate and sea captain whose colourful career had included escape from hanging when the noose was almost round her neck.

He had been given charge of Clanricarde's grandson, Richard de Burgh, who was to be delivered to Essex as surety and brought up in his own household. This was the time honoured way of ensuring that doubtful allies remained on the right side and it was the practice to "anglicise" the sons of such nobility with an English upbringing, although it was not until 1582 that the Earl of Clanricarde agreed to serve the English crown. He carried the dark taciturn urchin before him in the saddle and when his tired horse stumbled on the atrocious road to Kilcullen, outside Dublin, and plunged forward, nearly unseating them both, he found the reins caught in dirty childish hands and the big beast pulled up before he could move. A brown face and blazing blue eyes were turned on him and Richard, in a ripe Irish brogue, told him exactly what he thought of his horsemanship. Knowing himself to be among the best, Philip chuckled and refrained from cuffing the little monster. Little did he imagine that he shared a saddle with the third husband of his future wife.

On 22nd September, the Earl of Essex died inexplicably and horribly in Dublin Castle of an agonising stomach complaint and before he departed he stated clearly that he would like Philip to marry his daughter, Penelope. Like so many, he had become fond of him and felt the touch of greatness that would prove him an exceptional man. Leicester's blossoming affair with Essex's wife was beginning to be known and there were to be some ugly stories circulated about the convenience and manner of Essex's death.

At last, in March 1577, Philip had been given a chance for serious diplomacy and was able to escape England for a while. The mission was to the Emperor, Rudolf II, in Prague to present credentials and to condole on the death of the late Emperor. Like most missions, it had other agendas which included the possibility of forming a Protestant league in which he would have been delighted to play a leading part, and visits to Don John of Austria, the hero of Lepanto, Johann Casimir and William of Orange. He also managed a meeting with his old friend and mentor, Hubert Languet. Marriage was talked of both with Casimir's sister and Marie von Nassau, William's daughter. As with Penelope Devereux, neither was pursued and a Protestant League still looked a long way off.

Now in September 1581, his life seemed to have ground to something of a halt. Not one of his great visions had materialised, he was not employed as either the diplomat or military commander he wished to be and Leicester's marriage to the widowed Countess of Essex in September 1578 and the birth of a son, Robert, Baron Denbigh, in May this year, had put paid to his chances of becoming his uncle's heir. He was short of money, his upkeep was expensive, particularly his horses, and he had already been obliged to borrow. The Sidney fortunes, never huge, were at a low ebb due to Sir Henry's expenses in Ireland and the upkeep of his estates in Wales. The Queen was not generous with allowances, or even basic expenses, to those she appointed to High Office.

Too late, he had fallen deeply in love with Penelope Devereux who no sooner showed her beautiful face at Court than she had been betrothed to the highest bidder her family and guardians could find, the uncouth and puritanical Lord Rich, whose huge wealth and estates in Essex were the proceeds of his late father's ruthless interests in the dissolution of the monastries under Henry VIII.

Penelope's father had promised her to Philip, her mother had married his uncle and her guardian, the Countess of Huntingdon, was Philip's aunt. There were many wheels within wheels, money not being the least of them, but Philip knew well that had he pushed his suit earlier, with Leicester's backing, he could have won her. "Too late" are truly the saddest words in the English language. Philip had met her five years before at the home of the Huntingdons as a precocious, flouncing thirteen year old and did not press his claim. Penelope, herself, would have greatly preferred him as a bridegroom. At eighteen, with her corn gold hair and dark eyes, she was striking enough. Add to that the impetuous charm of the Devereux and few could resist her. The Earl and Countess of Huntingdon had brought her up to London, together with her sister Dorothy, soon after New Year in 1581. She was accepted as a maid of honour to the Queen and, for a girl brought up very strictly in the wilds of Ashby-de-la-Zouche, Court life was all she had dreamt of and Philip had seemed the awesome epitome of the perfect knight. Inevitably, through family ties and events at Court, they were thrown together and, by May, a very bittersweet relationship had developed. Penelope was to be married in November and was making the most of her tragically short freedom. Her mother, Lettice, now aged forty one and the mother of Leicester's heir, could not help her. She had endorsed the guardianship of her daughters by the Huntingdons, thereby nominally washing her hands of them, and the choice of husbands was theirs. In any case, Lettice was, by nature, magnificently oblivious to the needs of anyone other than herself.

Philip knew that they would meet at Wilton, his sister Mary, Countess of Pembroke's home, for the October christening of her new daughter and that the pain of seeing Penelope so close to the time of her marriage would be compounded by his obligations at Court during a return visit of the Queen's now doubtful suitor, François Duc d'Anjou, who had succeeded to his brother's title once Henri became King of France. This pantomime of a courtship had been dragged out over a long period of time and everyone, including the Queen, would be delighted to see the end of it. She would never marry him but the protestations of love, the gifts and the performance went on. It was all very exhausting for those around them.

Philip's best loved sister, Mary, so like-minded and a gifted writer herself, had been his refuge when tides turned against him at Court and much of his earlier writing had been done at Wilton, particularly the "Old Arcadia", later dedicated to her. He resolved to leave Penshurst and travel down earlier than planned to see her.

She welcomed him with open arms, as always, and as they strolled down the length of the long herbaceous borders, still full of flower, he poured out his frustrations, his ill-timed love for Penelope, his anger at those who had betrothed her against her will to a rich, catechizing boor and asked her what, in the name of Heaven, was he to do now? Mary's fair face, so like his own, clouded and for some time she said nothing. She had only recently risen from childbed and was still feeling fragile, but she could clearly see beyond the turmoil in Philip's mind and she told him very firmly that he must marry, himself, and as soon as possible. It had long been in her mind, she said; his splendid isolation despite his many friends, his need for a wife and a family behind him. All simple things despite the grand designs in his life. The hurt of his infatuation with Penelope would fade and the anger at himself and others.

The choice, of course, was wide but he needed wise counsel and a father-in-law who was in a position to use influence on his behalf and was close to the Queen. Their own father, beset by the trials in Ireland and his mounting debts, had not been a great help. He was also keeping up two establishments, one for himself and one for his wife, Lady Mary, who had succumbed to smallpox while devotedly nursing the Queen through a near fatal attack of the disease in 1563 and whose beauty was so ravaged that he could not bear to look at her. Philip had caught the infection from her, aged nine, but with less devastating results.

Mary often entertained Walsingham and occasionally, Lady Ursula, at Wilton when he had business with her husband, Pembroke. She remembered that Philip had gone through much with them in Paris in 1572 and that Walsingham had made that first journey through Europe possible for him. She also remembered hearing that their small daughter had been confined with them in the Paris embassy after the massacre on St. Bartholomew's Eve that August. She would now be about fourteen; time to think of marriage. She was not the daughter of one of the great houses of England but her birth was unexceptional and her father was one of the triumverate ruling England under the Queen.

Philip's response was halting. There was Lady Dorothy Devereux, Penelope's younger sister, almost as pretty, whom Leicester strongly recommended him to consider, even laying aside £2,000 for the marriage, but that was far too close to home. Having passed a great many under mental review, he too remembered a small, dark child in Paris, riding happily beside him on a fat grey pony through the dappled light in the Bois de Boulogne and chatting to him in French so colloquial that he found it hard to follow. Her skirts had been soaked with blood that fearsome night and her large, light eyes had been wide with shock. She had not exactly occupied his mind over the last ten years though he remained much attached to the Walsinghams and visited both Barn Elms and Walsingham House in Seething Lane. He had seen Frances and Mary from time to time and stopped to talk to them and he had worked with Walsingham on several occasions.

He did remember, though, watching a girl from a window seat last year at

Barn Elms picking roses in the garden and dancing to an unheared melody while she did it. The girl, small and delicate, had moved over the grass with fairylike grace and he had wanted to lean from the window and applaud when she ended by sinking down in a curtsey like a windblown flower, the hand holding the roses extended in a gesture of donation. Someone then claimed his attention and drew him from the window or he would have called and asked if she was indeed, Frances, so rapidly grown up.

In his understated way, Walsingham had kept a watchful eye on Philip's progress and was well aware of his frustrations and ambitions. His opinion of him, over the years, was unchanged; he had watched him mature with interest and affection, also a certain amount of pride. He was not blessed with a son, but a son in law might prove very close to it. It was round his own dinner table that Philip had met some of the best and most influential minds in Europe and where firm friendships had been formed. Hubert Languet, the Camerarius brothers, Philippe du Plessis-Mornay, a friend of Henry of Navarre and later to be Ambassador to England, Anthony Bacon, up from Montauban, Jean Lobbet and many others.

After the recent shock of Frances's "contract" with John Wickerson, Walsingham was extremely anxious to get her safely and firmly betrothed, young as she was, as soon as possible. These contracts, as Walsingham knew and Frances had not, did carry some sort of validity if they were witnessed, and the scandal, should it become generally known, would have spoiled any chance of a good marriage for her. For that reason, he had not pressed the Queen to consider taking Frances into her household as a Maid of Honour. His best chance was to marry her to someone with a good position at Court himself and to do it quickly.

Since John had been taken from her, Frances relapsed into very much the state she had been in, as a child, on her return from Paris; quiet and withdrawn, pale and slimmer than ever. Walsingham had not heard her laugh since that dire morning and she spoke only enough for courtesy. The dancing girl, watched by Philip, was no longer dancing.

Walsingham was shocked and saddened and tried to divert her by taking her hawking and hunting as much as he had time for. Hawking was his particular passion and he had started teaching Frances as soon as she could ride without a leading rein. It was a skilled business, to control a horse and the accoutrements that went with the bird and there was much etiquette to learn as well. She had begun with a small kestrel and Walsingham now promised her a fully trained female merlin, in accordance with her status. (There were strict rules as to the type of bird used by every rank of society.) Barn Elms had an extensive mews and the falconer, Rob, had known Frances since childhood.

Lady Ursula, looking at her white face and shadowed eyes, could raise no enthusiasm in her for shopping expeditions, new dresses or even the string of perfect pearls given her for her fourteenth birthday. Something vital in her had disappeared but Lady Ursula was both brisk and optimistic and she assured Walsingham that, if presented with an attractive proposition as a husband and the chances of becoming a great lady, she would quickly revive.

For Frances, the loss of her first love had been so bitter and final that, for the present, nothing mattered very much. She had done her best to discover where they had taken John so that she could find a way to send him a message, but she was no match for Walsinghams's methods and she found that every path was barred. All she had was her father's assurance that he would not be hurt. The subject between them was now taboo. They both pretended that nothing had happened and that life must go on as before. Little did Walsingham guess that there was a strength in his daughter very like his own and a will that had hardened, unseen, beneath the dutiful exterior.

She did not want to go to Court, now, although she knew it had been her parents greatest hope for her and she had often imagined the delights in store. She had grown up knowing many of her father's fellow diplomats and courtiers, making her curtseys to them when small and bringing them wine and food while they talked or sitting at table with them when she was older. Not for an only daughter was the fateful dismissal to the nursery quarters. Her manners had been honed for society appearances and so had her remarkable memory; Walsingham often asked her to repeat a conversation that had taken place at dinner whether she had been a part of it or not and it still surprised him to hear the swift, verbatim response.

Sir Christopher Hatton she was particularly fond of; he always had a word for her or a gentle compliment. He was handsome, dark and kindly, and he genuinely adored the Queen. In the past, he had often fallen foul of Leicester on this count and Her Majesty was not above blatantly playing one off against the other although, unlike Leicester, Hatton had remained single for her sake.

They were all growing older now and the edge was off their rivalry. For Frances, Hatton's great virtue was that he was a superb dancer and, if he could, often spared time to teach her the latest dance steps, humming frantically to keep up with himself. It could be an energetic affair, especially when "La Volta" appeared on the Court scene which involved much leaping into the air and eventually a tossing of the lady skywards and catching her, farthingale and all. Despite his forty one years, he was still remarkably graceful and agile and he recognised his pupil's potential. Lady Ursula came upon them performing one morning in the big hall of Walsingham House. Hatton had thrown Frances, light as a feather, up so high that she could see into St.Olaves Church, opposite, through the top part of the windows.

Lord Burghley, too, had always been very kindly disposed to her, especially after the death of Mary, when he had gone out of his way to draw her close to him and give what comfort he could. He had so many children and foster children of his own that the loss of one would not have been a major tragedy for him, but he was able to sympathise with Walsingham to whom only one remained and that a daughter. Children and their marriages could be quite a catalyst in the fuelling of power and wealth.

Of the Earl of Leicester she had always been in considerable awe. He was a magnificent personage, the Queen's favourite since her accession, rumoured by many to have been her lover. His chances of ever becoming her husband had died at the foot of the stairs at Cumnor Hall with the unfortunate Amy Robsart, his wife, whose convenient demise was never proved to be either murder or suicide. The Queen was far too astute to contemplate marriage with him after that. He was a typical Dudley, ruthless and arrogant, born in the same month and year as the Queen and her equal in pride and force of character. His most endearing trait was his devotion to gardens and gardening which he shared with Walsingham and much of their lore had been passed on to Frances as she pottered along behind them at Barn Elms.

Walsingham resolved to approach Philip and tell him directly what he had in mind, before speaking to Sir Henry Sidney. He knew him quite well enough to do this and also to explain that he understood his circumstances and his present preoccupation with Penelope. Not much had escaped his analytical grey gaze and an understanding between the families, including the financial arrangements, could be reached long before a betrothal need be announced, giving Philip time for the blow of Penelope's marriage to soften. Walsingham had always had one eye on Philip for Frances, but it had seemed a forlorn hope and very unlikely that he would be single by the time she grew up. Circumstance had played his game and he was going to take the chance offered without wasting any further time. He did not propose, however, to press the matter until they had both ceased to eat their hearts out. Frances, certainly, would not welcome any matrimonial suggestions in her present state.

His opportunity came at Court a month or two later. Anjou was proving hard to dislodge and the Queen had greatly complicated the situation by behaving very uncharacteristically.

On 22nd November she provoked an absolute storm of diplomatic agitation by kissing Anjou heartily on the lips while walking down a gallery and in front of Walsingham, Leicester and the French Ambassador, and declaring: "you may write this to the King that the Duke Anjou shall be my husband." She backed this amazing statement up by exchanging rings with him, summoning the ladies and gentlemen in the presence chamber and repeating loudly what she had said to one and all. Meeting Leicester's eyes, Walsingham raised his own to heaven. Philip, recently returned, with Pembroke, from escorting Dom Antonio, the usurped King of Portugal, and his fleet of ships off English coasts with considerable difficulty, had come in also from the presence chamber in time to hear the announcement. He moved over to the tapestry against which Walsingham stood, struggling with his gravity but managing to keep his face straight despite his twinkling eyes. How much more difficult it would now be to get the Frog Prince over the Channel. The pantomime's plot had definitely thickened.

Walsingham tweaked Philip's velvet sleeve and drew him along the gallery and down the wide steps at the end of it into the gardens, leaving the stunned courtiers and the babel of voices around the Queen. There had been a sharp frost the night before and every twig and leaf winked and sparkled in the morning sunlight. The shadows thrown by the sculpted yews lay in orderly ranks of dark blue across their path. Having had their laugh over the Queen's intransigent behaviour, Walsingham pulled his cloak firmly round him and told Philip, without embellishment, what was in his mind. He said that there was no great urgency, but that he would like a firm understanding to be reached. Manipulative though he could be in the course of his work, with those close to

71

him, Walsingham was generally straightforward and he told Philip exactly what had happened at Barn Elms in September and he described the present state of Frances's mind. She was, he said, so young that she would soon forget her misery and be perfectly willing to accept him as a husband. Philip, suffering in exactly the same way, wondered if this was somewhat optimistic and explained his own state of mind, but freely admitted that he knew where his duty lay to his name and to his family. He would open the matter to his father and give him to understand that he was willing.

Penelope Devereux had been married to the tiresome Lord Rich at the beginning of November and Philip had since written many more sonnets for "Astrophil and Stella". It had been impossible to avoid Penelope whose marriage was far from happy and who made every excuse to leave hearth, home and husband in search of a more joyous existence and the love and admiration to which she had become used. To mitigate the anguish he felt, he told himself that the reason for such tormented longing was that too much was always imagined of the "might have been." However, this did not make Penelope any less of a magnet.

On this cold November morning, he realised that he was being offered Walsingham's hope for the future, his most treasured possession and his ultimate friendship. They shook hands and quietly walked on, their footsteps crunching on the frosty ground.

Sir Henry Sidney, when approached, gave the match his whole-hearted approval, but made it clear that his family was in dire financial straits and that, apart from inheriting Penshurst on his death, there was not much in the coffers for Philip. Walsingham already knew this and gave an assurance that he would shoulder some of Philip's debts and that the young couple would be very welcome to live at both Walsingham House and Barn Elms, equally convenient for Court and for other business in London. And there the matter rested.

Marriage, however, was always irresistible food for gossip and comment, particularly when it involved such a person as Philip Sidney, and among the family, rumour and conjecture moved apace. A month before this conversation even, Walsingham had received a letter from Edward Denny, a young cousin on his mother's side, and a fellow jouster of Philip's, who was clearly well informed. He wrote: "That I may be most humbly commended to my good lady, and to my cousin Frances, and I beseech you, good sir, make a great account of my matchless master Mr. Sidney. I speak it rather to your own good to hold now to you the most worthy young man in the world." Like so many letter writers of the time, Mr. Denny could not resist a pun and by "matchless" he meant both without a wife and without an equal.

Walsingham had taken fright at this letter and realised how fast news of the match was going to spread and that Frances herself was very likely to get wind of it before long. He would have to tell her soon what was in store for her.

Philip was spending Christmas at Wilton with the Pembrokes. On 17th December he wrote from there: "The country affords no other stuff for letters but humble salutations which humbly and heartily I send to yourself, my good lady and my exceeding like to be good friend." This reference to Frances was a clear indication that the time had indeed arrived.

Calling his daughter into his library at Barn Elms, Walsingham drew her to the blazing fire and sat her in a padded high backed chair near it. Her small hands felt frozen and he asked her if she had been out that morning with her merlin. Since September, this room was not welcome to Frances and the fire reminded her of watching her pathetic effort to keep her love, her "contract," reduced to ashes. What was coming now? She could feel herself stiffening against the chair back and her heart beginning to pound.

Looking hard at her, Walsingham thought she seemed much recovered. Her face was delicately coloured from the cold air, her strange eyes, which today looked grey, like his own, had regained their intensity and, if she would only smile, he could believe this much loved child was returning to life.

He put a glass of warmed wine into her hand and bade her drink it, then asked her if she remembered Philip Sidney who had ridden with her in Paris and stayed with them at the Embassy. He very seldom reminded her of those days, there were too many bad memories for them both, but some had been happy. She was quiet for a little for she did indeed remember him and that he had seemed, to a child, so grand and wonderful, that he had a sweet smile and that he had gathered her into his arms when everything else was night and there was no other comfort. She remembered his laughter when they rode out together and his refusal to remove the lead rein. She also remembered that he sometimes stopped to speak to her on his visits to her parents, always knowing who she was, despite long absences, and treating her as a friend.

She smiled slightly and replied that she did remember him well.

Walsingham handed her Philip's letter and watched her while she read it. Her eyes flew to his face and she rose quickly from the chair, almost throwing the letter back at him as the truth of what it meant struck at her like a blow. She had known that this would come, but had lived in the twilit world of the present, hoping that her father's plans for her, unfolded in this very room, were part of a distant future and that intervention, heavenly or otherwise, would prevent her having to face marriage with a man other than John.

She cried out that he was too old for her, that she did not love him or ever would, that the only man she ever wanted was John; all the arguments launched by daughters against forced marriage since time immemorial came pouring out as she slammed her glass on the table and ran from the room. Walsingham knew he could not expect gratitude for arranging such a splendid marriage for her but he had not expected an undutiful tirade and he felt slightly aggrieved after all his careful planning. He was, despite himself, very impressed with the cogency and reasoning that had gone with the arguments. Lady Ursula was considerably more downright and said the silly little wench would change her mind given time and a gentle hand from Mr.Sidney. She had, as yet, no idea how lucky she was, so many girls at Court and elsewhere had set their caps at him; what a perfect gentleman he was and from one of the best families in England; again, the arguments of mothers down the ages.

Between them, they agreed that Frances should not be forced to meet Philip immediately, but that they would take her to Court where they would meet against a background of many people and events and she could be brought to realise, through other people's opinions of him, that she was indeed fortunate. Philip, himself, had all the skills, tact and kindness to win her over. They proposed, for the moment, to skate over the subject of Penelope although it would have to be faced before the gossips reached Frances. And there, at that Christmastide of 1581, the matter really did rest.

1582-1583 – Englefield – Court

Christopher Carleill, still serving with Prince William of Orange, managed to return briefly to England in the summer of 1582, having handed over the command of the English military camp at Antwerp to Sir John Norris, the Queen's old and trusted friend.

His activities over the past ten years had been fast and furious. In 1572, while Walsingham was in Paris, he went to Flushing in time for the siege of Middelburg under the Dutch admiral Lodewijk van Boisot who, apparently, formed a high opinion of him. From there, he sailed with two ships to La Rochelle to assist the Prince de Condé, now released from Paris and re-united with the Huguenots, who gave him the command of an attack on the Royalist forces. Having completed this successfully, he rushed back to the Low Countries where he took charge of the English troops at the fort of Zwarte Sluis and beat back a Spanish offensive of very superior force. There had been several other missions in the Netherlands, some clandestine and extremely dangerous. This was all meat and drink to Christopher. He was extremely able, he adored fighting and he was assisted, whenever possible, by Walsingham, in the wings either in Paris or London. Walsingham's lines of communication were long, often operating through what was, by now, a very comprehensive intelligence service.

The Prince of Orange had failed to pay Christopher for almost five years and his pockets were to let. Walsingham held funds for him in the Muscovy Company and some of these he now proposed to collect, his father, Alexander Carleill, having been a founder member. He was almost thirty years old but still athirst for adventure of any kind, preferably violent.

He burst upon the family in Walsingham House in May, laden with gifts and full of news, having obviously enjoyed his military and naval engagements enormously. He looked a little older and more weatherbeaten, his skin a deep mahogany brown but his spirits undimmed. He caught Frances up in his arms, hugging and kissing her and exclaiming at her beauty. He then dived into the mountain of baggage in the hall and came up with a small, scared-looking green parrot in a cage who could, purportedly, sing "Greensleeves" in English and Portuguese. It shut its beak with a snap and was clearly unprepared to demonstrate. He also brought a quantity of beautiful cloth for mother, daughter and sister, Alice Hoddeson. Silks, brocades, figured velvets and damasks, all of subtle and unusual colours not often seen in London came tumbling out of boxes and trunks. The dyers in Antwerp, Amsterdam and Bruges, he said, were far in advance of the English. He had managed to "confiscate" this load.

He had much news for Walsingham's ear only and when he had unburdened this, he sought out Frances again and demanded to know how life was with her and what were her hopes and fears. He was an easy person to talk to, very much a part of her life and genuinely concerned for her. Before long she had poured out the whole story of her "contract" with John and her impending betrothal to Philip. He was a good listener and, although he had been primed by Walsingham, he did not interrupt but kept his eyes on the vivid little face before him, for once both animated and frank. She had, he thought, grown into something so lovely and unusual that she was going to be a danger to any man. She was not exactly precocious, but she did not talk like a girl of fourteen. She occasionally broke into French when unable to find the right word in English, her hands expressively fluttering as she did so. Christopher thought, too, that young as she was, she should certainly interest Philip Sidney, whom he had met in Flushing with the Prince of Orange on the diplomatic mission in 1577.

His advice to this beleaguered little "sister," given with understanding, was to make the most of the last year of her girlhood, go to Court and enjoy herself, and then to wed, with a good grace, a man whose reputation was well-known and respected throughout Europe. She would be happy and safe with him and who knew to what exciting places she might not travel. Like Christopher, Philip had colonial ambitions. He himself had found no time for marriage; it would interfere with his life and it was easier, by far, to have mistresses wherever he happened to be.

Within two weeks he had gone, money in his pockets and due to convoy English merchants to Russia, partly on behalf of the Muscovy Company. He expected trouble from the Danish fleet, but he was taking an intimidating squadron of eleven ships which he thought was deterrent enough. If this mission was successful, he would try to raise further money from the Russian merchants for an exploratory expedition to the American coast south of Cape Breton.

What time, indeed, did he have for marriage, confided Frances to the green parrot, wishing she had been born a boy. The little bird was beginning to unbend and it shuffled along its perch to her with its head on one side. She had named it "Greville" and hoped for virtuoso performances in due course.

She still longed for John; the thought of him had the power to make her twist with anguish and mentally to blank out the future.

The year passed rapidly enough. Like all their contemporaries, the Walsinghams were constantly on the move. Houses needed to be thoroughly cleaned and fumigated at least once a year and it was always wise to remove from London, if possible, during the summer months. Plague, sweating sickness and agues lurked when the river sank in the heat and the banks became a stinking mass.

The Queen, in a mellow mood, had lately given Walsingham the use of Englefield House in Berkshire. Its present form had been built in 1558 by the Englefield family, Catholics devoted to her sister Queen Mary; they had been obliged to depart the scene to Spain for religious reasons, astutely leaving a nephew in charge of the estate. He continued to manage the land in exchange for keeping a certain amount of acres on behalf of the family. This arrangement suited Walsingham very well, particularly as the estate had an excellent deer park and he could take hunting parties down without much upheaval for himself or Lady Ursula. It was an impressively beautiful house, very much in the grand manner, with large gardens. Frances loved it, though Barn Elms remained her favourite, and the hunting, now that she was allowed to join her elders was an excitement that made her forget her troubles in a whole day of furious, scrambling activity and rushing adrenalin. A beautiful new riding habit had been constructed for her of dark forest green and a matching hat with curling feathers brushing her face. She knew it became her and it was vital, from all points of view, not to take a tumble in such a creation.

The Queen hunted almost daily and it would be well if Frances became familiar with the hunting terms used at Court, the different breeds of hound and their functions, the procedures at various types of hunt and who took

77

precedence over whom. It was all quite structured, a formal hunt having eight distinct stages and it was important to be in the right place at the right time and, above all, in control of one's mount.

It was here, at Englefield, that Frances first met Robert Devereux, the young Earl of Essex and the brother of Penelope and Dorothy. He had come over with his stepfather, Leicester and his mother Lettice from Wanstead, their home in Essex; Leicester to see Walsingham privately and for a days hunting.

Leicester's presence was still magnificent but there was now a distinct mellowness about him, a widening of girth, and a reddening of the face. Lettice undoubtedly had him where she wanted him. The birth of the longed for son, the small Lord Denbigh, had more than confirmed her position. She was under full sail; making her presence felt in every way. She was no favourite with Lady Ursula who bristled with anger when the Countess dismounted and peremptorily began to give her orders to the Walsingham servants before so much as greeting her hosts. Her opinion of herself had always been high, but now that she had cornered the Queen's favourite in marriage and produced an heir in quick time, it knew no bounds. At forty two, she was still a very beautiful woman, with red-gold hair, pale skin, an aura of self-satisfaction and an iron will. She was a cousin of the Queen and very like her, the daughter of Sir Francis Knollys and Catherine Carey, (Mary Boleyn's Royal bastard.) She had been banished from Court by the Queen for her arrogance and her marriage, the shock of which had seriously upset her Majesty, the news delivered, as it had been, by Simier, the French marriage broker for the Duc D'Anjou of all people. No one else had dared.

The Countess looked Frances over from her head to her heels with a gimlet eye, remarked how small she was and turned away to dazzle Sir Christopher Hatton.

Her son, Robert, now sixteen years old, was a quieter, more studious character than Penelope but with all the Devereux magnetism and beauty. At this age, he had no idea of the power he could wield, or that he possessed it. He was charming, deferential to his elders and a model son and stepson. When he greeted Frances, on the steps of Englefield, however, there was more than a hint of mischief in his smile. He was so tall she barely reached the height of his shoulder. He asked, with a distinct Welsh lilt in his voice, whether she would be hunting with them. Yes, indeed she would.

The Leicesters were not the only guests. With Sir Christopher Hatton was his nephew and heir, Sir William Newport. From nearby Bisham Abbey had come Lord John Russell, son of the Earl of Bedford and his wife, Lady Elizabeth with her two sons, Edward and Thomas Hoby. These were joined by William Davison, Walsingham's colleague and protege, now a member of the diplomatic service and a collection of near neighbours, some with their offspring. It was a distinguished gathering which Lady Ursula could view with satisfaction if not complacency. There were two very formidable women to be kept content. Every bit as domineering as Lady Leicester was Lady Elizabeth Russell. She was one of the four notably erudite Cooke sisters, Mildred, married to Lord Burghley, Anne, a former governess to the young King Edward VI and married to Sir Nicholas Bacon, and Catherine. Elizabeth, formerly Hoby, had remarried at forty six and produced three more children. She was reputed to have beaten one of her sons for blotting his copybook, shut him in a cupboard and rushed off to Court forgetting his existence. The poor child was found dead on her return. Her surviving sons would hardly have been taken for brothers. One was a thin, angular poseur and a perfect nuisance, and the other was a recognizable product of Eton and Cambridge who never put a foot wrong. Both viewed Frances with admiration, the dreadful Thomas Posthumous leaning all over her telling bad jokes and breathing unpleasantly into her face. She decided to give him the widest berth.

The day after, the whole party foregathered for the hunt breakfast, or "assembly" held in a rustic construction in the woods, accompanied by grooms leading spare horses, rows of dog handlers with their charges, servants unloading food and drink on to long tables within the pavilion (Englefield was fully staffed) and the huntsmen standing by for orders once the "fewmets", or droppings, collected that morning had been examined and the course of the hunt decided. The quarry this day were fallow buck, only those with a good head, and a worthy specimen had already been "harboured", that is tracked, spotted and marked without disturbing it. This task had been done by the "lymers", the specially trained scent hounds early that morning. When Walsingham had given orders as to the direction of the hunt, the relays of hounds were sent off and positioned along the way as relief if the leaders tired. Once they had been given time to do this, a horn was blown by the huntsman and the shout rang out, "The hunt is up."

Frances was still enthralled by the sound and the thrill of that first surge when riders, in order of precedence, took off in the appointed direction. She was riding a pretty roan mare, carefully chosen by her father as being an experienced jumper, with plenty of dash, but not over-excitable in a hunting field. Following her was a groom to see that she came to no harm. The pace was fast, but there was a clear path through the wood with not much to jump to begin with. When the buck was roused from cover, "unharboured," and hounds had a good scent, however, things became more exciting and the pace quickened. There was a gate to clear, from the wood to an open field and the horsemen could then spread out and let their mounts go. The mare lengthened her stride, but not recklessly enough to stop Frances holding her in order to prevent her overtaking any guest to whom she should give way, particularly the Ladies Leicester and Russell. The latter, though over fifty like the Queen, still rode to hounds with the vigour she brought to everything else in life.

Frances could see three buck charging up a grassy hillside beyond, one considerably larger than the others, with hounds and horsemen strung out fairly close behind. Not far from the leaders, a tall grey horse with a raking stride was battling with its rider and covering the ground in a plunging gallop, tossing its head and demanding to be allowed to lead. She recognised the red hair of the young Earl of Essex and wondered, smiling, how much encouragement it was getting. Her own mount was taking all her attention however and she knew a moment's panic when she realised there was a large bank and a ditch to be cleared before she could follow up the grassy hill. The mare was clever and knew her work well. She leapt on to the bank, changed feet and cleared the wide ditch with ease, landing lightly and immediately picking up speed. Reckless exhilaration rushed through Frances and she let her have her head. She would catch my Lord of Essex and show him the way, even though she had not seen which route he took. Also, she had seen the Hoby boys riding up the steeper way and wanted no further contact with Thomas.

She galloped round the shoulder of the hill, having seen most of those ahead of her following the bucks' line higher up and knowing she could keep a better pace at a lower level. She also knew the buck would descend as soon as possible and make for cover and hoped she was taking a short cut. So far, so good, but her vision was limited. Round a particularly sharp bend of the slope she ran headlong up to the bank of a torrent pouring off the hill. One or two riders had halted trying to find a crossing, among them a tall grey horse. Frances charged straight at them, quite unable to stop. The mare thought she would clear the water and hardly slowed. As she gathered herself for the leap, a hand shot out and grabbed the rein just above the bit, wrenching the mare round and forcing her back on her haunches as the grey horse moved to block her path. It all happened too fast for fear and all Frances could do was struggle to keep her seat and her dignity. She was thrown first forward then sharply back as the mare reared up. She could feel herself slipping, but a long arm went round her and manoeuvred her back into the saddle. The mare stopped plunging and she looked up into the laughing face of Essex. It was neatly done and very neatly had the tables been turned. She was mortified and furious, particularly as there was laughter all round her, albeit some of it admiring. Did they really imagine she was fool enough to have willingly attempted that torrent? She could hardly bring herself to thank Essex, or meekly follow him downstream where they could cross. She dropped back and rode sedately with some of the other ladies who had now come up and were content with a less punishing pace. Her groom, sweating profusely, caught up with her. Thinking about it dispassionately, she was forced to admit that Essex had probably saved her from a fall or a wetting, or both, even if he had almost unseated her in so doing; she had been going far too fast for the terrain, and she would apologise to him and to the others she had startled that evening. At least, the treasured green habit was unspoiled and she could enjoy the rest of the day. She was also forced to admit that his action had combined great speed with great horsemanship.

Much later, as she waited with her parents for Leander to announce that supper was ready, she apologised very sweetly to all those who had been obliged to pull aside for her that morning and, lastly, forced herself again to thank Essex. He took her hand, turned it over and kissed the palm so that she looked sharply up into his eyes and received a grin of such guileless charm that she could not help but return it. They were seated next to each other at supper and learned that they would both be at Court for New Year. By the end of the meal the ice was broken and they were friends. He would look for her at Whitehall and, perhaps, she would teach him to dance. Rolling his eyes, he confessed to being quite useless on the floor, he was far too tall, his feet were too big, but he did enjoy jousting.

Philip Sidney had been among the party which finally escorted the Frog

Prince across the Channel in February. The Royal charade of impending matrimony had been played out to the bitter end, becoming increasingly lachrymose, particularly as Elizabeth had eventually been obliged to buy her suitor off with a far larger sum than she cared to part with. (The appalling sum of £60,000 had changed hands.) Farewell gifts, jewelled frogs and memorabilia of all kinds had been exchanged and, declaring undying love to the last, Anjou sailed on 7th February with an enormous face-saving retinue which would escort him to Antwerp where he was to be installed as Duke of Brabant. Besides Philip, this included Leicester, Vice Admiral Lord Howard, Lord Hunsdon, and Walter Raleigh. They were welcomed in Flushing by William of Orange and proceeded in great splendour to Antwerp. There were reunions with many of Philip's old friends and heart warming recognition of the esteem in which he was held. There was, however, one sad gap in the ranks. Hubert Languet had died of a fever in Antwerp in 1581, nursed by Charlotte, the wife of Philippe du Plessis Mornay who lived in the same street. Languet, like a fond and fussy nanny, had corresponded faithfully, sometimes dictatorially but always with affection over the last ten years and had done much to guide Philip's footsteps through the maze of European politics.

Returning, Philip had retired from Court in the Spring to spend time with his father in Herefordshire and in the Welsh marches. It was hoped he would eventually succeed him as Lord President there. This rustication gave him respite on two fronts. He was able to curb his expenditure and he was able to continue writing. He had begun work transforming "The Old Arcadia" into something much larger and more serious and there was still enough heartache involved to make "Astrophil and Stella" flow with ease. He found Penelope more beguiling than ever and despite her marriage, it was hard to resist her. She was not at all delighted with her husband, whom she found a great bore and was in sore need of comfort, admiration and diversion. She was obliged to spend much of her time with Rich in Essex, but seized every opportunity to come back to Court where she provided a distinct trial to Philip's peace of mind and body.

Philip himself was sick to death of the fierce intrigue and barefaced jockeying for favour, power and position which was an ongoing part of the stilted life led at Court. It seemed power was ambition's end and he would not stoop to the grovelling and back-stabbing involved, neither would he indulge in the languishing sighs and obligatory declarations of love for a woman well old enough to be his mother. He was quite happy to write poetry and prose in her honour as his Queen and the ruler of his country, but honesty kept him from the fulsome nonsense uttered by many of those with an eye on the main chance. She had sensed his withdrawal and it was one of the reasons she would not give him position or preferral. He was becoming increasingly bored and frustrated and had even bought the rights to approximately three million acres in America which he hoped Sir Humphrey Gilbert would discover on his next expedition. Philip would give much to accompany him; anything to get out of England.

He had agreed with Walsingham that he would meet Frances at Whitehall over Christmas and New Year and that the marriage would be arranged for the early Spring. He realised the necessity but did not think it need change his way of life very much or his ambitions.

The Queen kept New Year of 1583 at Whitehall. It was a particularly cold winter; the Thames, sometimes a doubtful pleasure during the summer, was frozen hard and sparkled with diamond brilliance. The swans, dispossessed, beat their way upriver, looking for somewhere to land. They were nearly all owned by the Queen and the London Guilds, their beaks marked with so many notches for each owner. This was done on "Swan-Upping Day", later in the year, and some of the down on their breasts was plucked from the live birds "with no harm done to the bird" for the stuffing of Her Majesty's, and others, pillows and mattresses.

This New Year there were no boats or barges afloat, but a fair was held on the ice-bound river with booths, games, dancing and whole beasts roasting on spits. The Court rubbed shoulders with the Londoners for the spectacle and there was much rough banter, snowball throwing and very lewd jesting, some of it on the sour side since all the boatmen and river folk, except those permanently employed by various nobles, were unable to ply their trade and were having to find employment elsewhere. They suffered, with the country people, as they always did in a hard winter, and seldom in silence.

Frances Walsingham was going to Court with her parents for the festivities; apprehensive but reassured by the knowledge that she need not blush in any way for her appearance. Christopher Carleill's offerings had been put to good use and a series of beautiful day and evening dresses had been made up from the fabrics he had given her. As a Knight's daughter, Frances was allowed to wear silk, grosgrain and taffeta gowns, satin or damask kirtles (decorated underskirt) and damask or taffeta cloaks. Her furs could be genet, bodge (badger) and wolf, or the faithful rabbit. This was all laid down in the Sumptuary Laws which covered many other aspects of life as well. Their purposes were to maintain the social structure and to control excessive expenditure. The rise of wealth in the merchant and middle classes and a natural desire on their part to dress and behave above their station was controlled by the Laws thereby enabling Royalty and the nobility to ensure that there was no unseemly encroachment from below and that there was no confusion between wealth and birth. People were obliged to dress according to their rank and class and so were quickly recognised for what they were. No amount of money could prevent their being instantly pigeon-holed. The penalties for breaking these laws were harsh, ranging from fines to loss of title and property; not worth the smallest risk.

No monarch was better equipped than Elizabeth to spot excess, to know how her subjects might manoeuvre the rules to outshine each other and no one had a more piercing eye for competition, not to mention the power to enforce restraint.

Frances made her curtsey to the Queen on the thirty first day of December in the Presence Chamber at Whitehall. There was an enormous throng of people, warmed by vast log fires, waiting their turn to present New Year gifts to Her Majesty. As Lady Ursula, who had been doing it for years, knew well, it was a good moment to choose for an introduction. Presents at any time, particularly lavish or clever ones, always pleased the Queen unless she suspected some innuendo attached to them. The Walsingham gift was perfectly straightforward. A bolt of heavy, unusually beautiful blue silk satin, a shade not seen in England, from the collection brought over by Christopher Carleill.

As a Secretary of State, Walsingham did not wait his turn for long and a Chamberlain called him forward, clearing a way to the dais and the enormous carved chair in which the Queen was sitting, surrounded by her ladies and a few of her courtiers. He led Lady Ursula forward beside him and Frances followed between and slightly behind them. She was dressed, for this first presentation, in the palest lavender silk, the kirtle and the sleeves embroidered with pearls and with a small ruff of lace decorated with threadwork in lavender silk. Her hair, brushed and polished until it shone was very loosely confined as befitted her age and maiden state. She walked behind her parents with her own peculiar grace and her head held high until she sank into a deep curtsey when her mother did, lowering her eyes as she had been taught. Walsingham handed the tissue wrapped parcel to the Queen who immediately opened it, exclaiming, unusually, at the beauty of the colour. (She very often took the gift, handed it to a chamberlain and nodded dismissal). She thanked "Her Moor" and his lady for the gift. Walsingham had been elevated to familiarity by the nickname, prompted perhaps by his dark looks and habitual black clothes. Nearly all her favourites had nicknames bestowed on them and it was a sign of admittance to the ranks.

The Queen then looked beyond him to Frances who moved forward a little and curtseyed once more as Walsingham presented her as his only daughter. As she rose, she raised her eyes and looked fully at this being who was, in many ways, to ordain her life as she had ordained her father's.

Elizabeth I was now fifty years old and it did not always please her to look at a girl of fifteen for the first time. She had an extremely jealous nature although her ladies were chosen for their looks and their birth. Her eyes narrowed as she inspected Frances; she saw no regular beauty, the hair was too dark and the skin not white enough, but beyond the graceful carriage and the arresting eyes with their sweeping lashes she could glimpse something that men might find hard to resist. There was no arrogance or challenge in the girl, but a presence and a promise of which she was clearly unaware. It was an ingredient she herself had once possessed and she did not care to see it in another, especially a small piece of perfection such as this. She also sensed a mind at work.

She, therefore, spoke the conventional words of greeting and congratulation to Lady Ursula; she had not known they had a daughter, she must see more of her at Court, they must bring her to the New Year joust, to the dancing and the play, but, unspoken, her mind had registered a threat.

Frances saw before her a rigidly upright woman, utterly resplendent in a gown so covered with jewelled embroidery, gold lace and knots of ribbon that she must surely have trouble moving at all. Her face was whitened and the wrinkles covered by the aid of "ceruse" a concoction containing white lead and vinegar, her lips and cheeks reddened with cochineal and when she smiled, which was not often, it could be seen that her teeth were badly discoloured.

What was visible of her hair appeared as an elaborately curled ginger fuzz, adorned with jewels, a huge pearl resting on her forehead. She dripped with jewelry of every kind and the aura of majesty around her person was overwhelming. Not for nothing had she gradually changed her image from Virgin Queen to Gloriana, the unattainable legend and ultimate Ruler. There was nothing passive about this Queen, either, even when accepting gifts from a chair. Energy flowed from her, her dark eyes snapped and nothing much would be missed. There was a razor sharp mind too behind the intricate façade and a powerful intellect waiting to pounce. Well to watch one's every word. Thus, to Frances's startled gaze she appeared a magnificently arrayed and fearsome old witch with whom she must be very careful.

Watching her presentation from behind the Queen, Philip drew in his breath and realised that the years had indeed passed. The frightened child had certainly emerged as an extremely poised young woman whose every move was a joy to watch. This arranged marriage was not going to be a difficult proposition at all. He saw a dazzling smile directed at Her Majesty and realised that although she was not a beauty like Penelope Devereux, she was lovely in a very different way. He resolved not to make any more comparisons. Beside him, Edward Dyer, a great friend and fellow poet, whistled softly. Fulke Greville, his oldest friend, had also drawn in his breath. He knew that Philip was intending to marry this girl and his first reaction was that she was far too young. There were some thirteen years between them and there was still something very childlike about her. She was easy to look at but she would surely bore him to death, a chit barely out of the schoolroom.

But there he was wrong. Carefully arranged by Walsingham, they met the following evening in the Great Hall, after the New Year Tilt, surrounded by firelight and the soft glow of hundreds of candles in their branched sconces and in the company of a glittering Court. Philip had changed his jousting costume for a dark suit of brocade which well became his tawny hair and still glowing face. There were many languishing or hopeful eyes following him. As so often, he had been more than successful and had not lost a bout. Carrying his pennant with the Sidney arms had been brother Robert. Flanking him was the Earl of Essex, wild with excitement at this his first appearance, bearing Philip's shield on which was inscribed and painted an "imprese", a device suggesting the owners mood or state, in today's case a sheep adorned with the planet Saturn underwritten by the motto "Macular modo noscar" (I am marked so I may be known.)

This was the second time that Frances had watched Philip joust. She had not forgotten the spectacle in the Louvre before the Navarre wedding. This time she was more detached but, nonetheless, she was impressed by what she heard amongst the chatterers around her. Philip was clearly a favourite in all ways. He and Sir Henry Lee, the Queen's Champion, were considered the best of the combatants. Wrapped in a fur cloak, she drank in the compliments and the gossip and could not help wondering what these grand people would say if they knew she was soon to be his wife.

He was a splendid sight. Mounted on an Andalucian stallion which Don John of Austria had managed to obtain for him from Vienna, he delighted the crowd by putting the big horse through its paces before running his first course. It had been schooled by Philip as he had been taught in the Austrian Riding Academy, its every muscle used to demonstrate skill and strength and discipline. Very few in England rode as well as Philip. Man and horse seemed to float, the hoof beats muffled by the sawdust covering the tiltyard floor, the stallion's long, creamy mane and tail whisking and tossing as it passaged and waltzed across the ground. There were not many of the breed in England, or anywhere else for that matter, and they were greatly prized and hard to obtain. There was cheering and shouting and a gracious wave from the Queen's window.

Meeting him now in the Great Hall, relaxed and happy, brought back the best of her childhood Paris memories. The rides in the Bois du Boulogne, the laughter and, for her, a suggestion of hero-worship. Nonetheless, Frances was frightened, and hoped when he bowed over her hand that it would not shake. He was still a stranger and in a few weeks she would be married to him. Philip did feel a slight tremble in the small hand extended to him and he instinctively closed his own over it reassuringly. Some good angel prompted her to ask about the horse she had watched that afternoon and, sensing genuine interest, Philip told her how he had managed to get him sent over from Vienna, describing the breeding lines originating in Spain and the wonderful temperament and brave hearts of these horses. He talked to her as an old friend about many things, but also as an equal and he soon realised that he was not speaking to a child at all but to a girl who was not only very well read and educated beyond her years, but who also had an enquiring mind and an exceptional memory. When he heard that she had the use of John Dee's great library and had listened to many of his arguments and theories, not only understanding them but remembering minutely what the arguments had been, he began to listen with interest. He, himself, had many dealings with John Dee from time to time. They both had interests in the New World and John Dee was something of a cartographer among his many other talents. Walsingham and Lady Ursula quietly melted into the background, well satisfied.

They were standing near a blazing fire stoked by great logs of ash; Frances's face was glowing and her eyes sparkling, when suddenly, like a wind in the trees, the Devereux clan emerged from the crowd with a rush and surrounded them. Penelope, her figure thickened by her first pregnancy but her beauty enhanced by it, Dorothy, so like her, and Essex, with an arm round each of them, made a trio it was hard to mistake. Behind them slouched Lord Rich, a thoroughly dreary young man who plainly disapproved of what he considered an extravagant and potentially sinful gathering. Leicester, Philip's brother Robert, and Fulke Greville followed them. (Lettice was still excluded from Court.) It was Leicester who slid an arm round Frances, kissed her cheek and wished her a Happy New Year. When he noticed her, he had always been avuncular and kindly though it was not in his nature to be either. Now, he whispered in her ear that he wished her happy in her marriage too. She blushed vividly and could see the beautiful face of Lady Rich harden and her black stare become very focused. What Penelope had just seen was Philip, her erstwhile lover, talking with animation and laughter to a small, exquisitely dressed girl who, when she turned, with a slow, deliberate movement to face them, revealed a countenance that made her revise altogether the mental picture she had ascribed to Frances. She, too, knew of Philip's intended marriage but, secure in his known love for her, her own beauty and her new wealth, she had imagined that he married, as she had been obliged to, to please his family and for the sake of an heir. His wife would stay at home and breed and he would continue to write beautiful verse to her and remain her slave. At a glance, she knew that this comfortable state of affairs, concocted for herself, was unlikely to materialise.

The girl looking at her showed no emotion, no embarrassment and no recognition. Penelope, by now, was accustomed to all these things and to deference and admiration as well, from both men and women. She considered the centre of attention her rightful place.

To her added indignation, her brother Essex stepped forward, picked Frances up with his hands under her elbows and kissed her also, demanding to know where she had been and when she was going to dance with him; he had been taking lessons from Fabritio Caroso, the Italian Master of Dance, and would promise not to tread on her. He then made her known to his sisters and to Rich while Philip introduced his younger brother, Robert and Fulke Greville. She greeted them all with perfect composure, curtseying gracefully and at the right depth to each, then suddenly, as Fulke bowed to her, she laughed delightedly. He kept her hand in his demanding to know the cause of the merriment. Her other hand went up to her cheek and her eyes, so enigmatic till now, began to dance as she confessed to owning a small, green parrot named "Greville". There was a general shout of laughter and, Philip, not for the last time, felt an easing of the tension as he looked from the face of his mistress to that of his future wife. He had known Penelope would not take kindly to Frances when once they met. She was pregnant and Frances was five years younger and sylph-like. She did not like competition and her impulsive nature made it hard for her to control her temper. Frances had come as a shock to her, as he had known at the back of his mind, she would. My Lady Rich was not going to be easy, but, for the moment she had been distracted.

Robert Sidney, now nineteen, was nearly as good looking as Philip, though darker. He favoured the Dudley side of the family but without their temper. He viewed his brother's prospective bride with interest and smiled encouragingly upon her. Anything Philip did was "sans reproche" and at this stage of his life, where Philip led he would follow.

Fulke Greville was another matter. He had been Philip's greatest friend since the day they entered Shrewsbury School together and their lives were very closely linked. His admiration for Philip knew no bounds, he would cheerfully die for him and anything he wrote to him or about him was positively eulogistic. Walsingham, observing and fearing this admiration might have hidden depths, had gently suggested to Frances before their meeting that she made it her business to enlist his friendship. Jealousy could be a corrosive business. Fulke, who came from Alcester in Warwickshire, had been given a position within the Court of the Welsh Marches by Sir Henry Sidney but had resigned it in order to join Philip at Court in 1577. With Philip, he wrote good but somewhat melancholic poetry, his religious views veered towards Calvinism and Frances thought he looked like a mole with his small expressionless eyes and prim mouth. He was capable, loyal and incredibly neat but when seen among the flamboyant Devereux, Sidneys and Leicesters, he tended to be overlooked.

The evening was one of great excitement for Frances. Dressed in pale primrose taffeta, she knew she looked her best, she was losing the shyness that drained her face of expression and she loved dancing.

Essex led her gingerly on to the floor first to dance the Galliard, a sprightly, fast-moving affair. Concentration held them both silent to begin with but as their feet and the music took over, their confidence grew and although a couple of wrong turns made them giggle, they decided they had done passably well. Philip then shooed Essex laughingly away and took Frances back into the set for a stately Pavane. She stood very straight and solemn, determined not to disgrace him, and performed with such unerring rhythm and controlled grace that he bowed to her deeply and clapped in applause.

Sir Christopher Hatton claimed her for "La Volta", tossing her around like a wind-blown leaf with a precision born of practice. (There were small pads attached to the hands of the gentlemen so that their fingers did not mark the delicate silks of the women's dresses as they caught them.) They were, of course, old partners and so relaxed that they could chat despite the vigour and speed of the dance. They cavorted through the difficult steps with such ease and enjoyment that they did not notice the many eyes following them. A particularly beady pair was, unfortunately, Royal. This was, indeed, cause for annoyance. The Queen had always prided herself on her dancing prowess and "La Volta" was her prerogative. There was, even now, a picture being painted of her performing with Leicester; Majesty aloft and in absolute control. To her jaundiced eye, this slip of a girl was not only dancing it with practised perfection, but doing it with her own most devoted swain, Sir Christopher Hatton, known for his expertise. It was also the only dance in which the partners came into physical contact.

She slammed down her fan, gestured to Hatton to stop the dance and to clear the floor and then to hand her down from her chair and to perform with her alone. They were good and the applause was loud and prolonged, but Her Majesty knew well that she had just seen a better interpretation. Once more, she sensed some kind of threat from Walsingham's daughter.

Thoroughly alarmed, Frances faded backwards into the crowd of watchful courtiers, looking for her parents. She retreated as far as she could and found herself standing next to a very small fair girl, no more than a child, who was making herself even smaller among the folds of a hanging tapestry. She looked nervous and unhappy and her rich clothes seemed incongruous below the frightened little face. Frances asked her what had happened to make the Queen so angry and aggressive and received the quick answer that Her Majesty did not like anyone to dance "La Volta" better than she and that it was advisable not to dance at all with Sir Christopher Hatton in her sight. The quaint wisdom and informed reply prompted Frances to ask the girl's name. It was Lady Bridget Manners, the eldest daughter of the Fourth Earl of Rutland, recently come to Court under the auspices of her grandmother, the Countess of Bedford, from Woburn Abbey. She was eleven years old and had never been away from home before. It was all so huge and strange and she longed for Rutland and her brothers and sisters, her ponies and her dogs. Fat tears began to pour down her round face and Frances, putting both arms round her in the same way she used to do with Mary, drew her to a wall bench, holding her close as they both sank down on to it and begged her to tell all her troubles.

Bridget's father had died, leaving debts and a badly executed will and her mother, in great distress, had relinquished her eldest daughter and all power over her to her grandmother, Lady Bedford, herself a widow of the Second Earl of Rutland. She had come up for Christmas and New Year in Lady Bedford's train and now her great-uncle, Roger Manners, was arranging a place for her as a Maid of Honour to the Queen. The prospect terrified her. The only person who had come with her from Rutland was Mary Harding, her maid and factotum. She was doing her best to be helpful and cheerful, but she longed to go home. She was not well educated and all she could do was play the lute a little. Her only other acquaintance in this frightening milieu was a distant cousin from Rutland, Robert Tyrwhitt, employed as a page to the Queen, who had sought her out and been kind to her. Her round face grew quite pink as she described how good and helpful he had been.

Frances knew a certain amount about loneliness and her heart was wrung. She briskly dried the tears, told Bridget that she would arrange for her to visit Walsingham House with her grandmother's permission and took her to find Lady Bedford. She did this by enlisting Lady Ursula's help who found the redoubtable dame playing cards with her cronies in an ante-chamber. A visit to

Seething Lane was arranged and Lady Bridget, or "Brie" as she was known, began to look more cheerful.

During the next two weeks, Frances's feet hardly touched the ground. There was constant entertainment, music, masques, plays and dancing. She seemed to spend much time struggling in and out of one costume after another, having her hair arranged, her nails polished and oils and unguents rubbed into her skin.

Then there was the almost daily hunting or riding. Whitehall was like a very grand village and the stables were vast. Only a certain number were ascribed to each member of the Court and the Walsingham horses were rotated with those housed in Seething Lane. The organisation was meticulous but disagreements between ostlers and grooms were inevitable and there was constant fighting over precedence.

The merry-go-round of events had the Queen at its centre. During the morning hours, she danced at least seven Galliards before hunting or hawking. She lunched in her own apartments, usually very frugally, then devoted herself to matters of State and Parliament during the afternoon, including the reception of foreign ambassadors and suppliants. She dined publicly at six o'clock and the rest of the evening was spent in entertainment and further presentations. She was, for her age, amazingly vigorous in body and mind. She seldom forgot a face and she never forgot a grudge. Considerable erudition was essential for a courtier in order to keep up with her at all; she spoke Greek, Latin, German, and French fluently, but confessed her Spanish was not perfect.

One freezing afternoon, Philip, together with Robert and Fulke Greville, took Frances and Brie to the fair on the frozen Thames beyond the Palace. The sky was a mutinous violet and the buildings stood black against a fresh fall of snow. The girls, their cheeks scarlet with cold and excitement, wore fur cloaks and fur-lined hoods and there were fur soles in their boots.

They ate roast capons from the spit, with fresh-baked bread and drank warm, spiced wine. In one booth, they threw leather balls at moving targets, tokens and toys which were claimed by a winning shot. In another they gaped at a man with three legs and further on there was cock-fighting, bare-knuckle boxing and a form of tenpins marked out on the ice. There was much music and dancing; it was wise to keep moving in the bitter cold. After the rigidity of the life at court it came as a relief to be able the laugh, shout, throw snowballs and kick up their heels.

They heard, nearby, a terrible animal roaring mixed with growling, snarling and a lot of shouting. A bear was being baited, not only by trained mastiffs, but by many other dogs infected, pack-like, by the noise and the blood. The bear was old and weak, blood poured from new wounds, one eye was almost gone. It was plainly about to be torn to pieces by sheer weight of numbers. Its chains, fastened to a ring through its nose, clanged and the roars turned to a horrible agonised keening. Frances could not bear it. She burst into tears and fled blindly in the opposite direction. She had not gone far when her way was barred by a tall, very dark man, his dress and bearing that of a courtier from the Palace. He held her at arms length while a slow, derisive smile spread across his face. Philip, hard on her heels, snatched Frances from his hold and requested him in icy accents, to leave the daughter of Sir Francis Walsingham alone. His hand was on his sword. The smile grew wider and more derisive. Philip turned on his heel, one arm round Frances and nearly collided with Fulke who slid to a halt beside them.

Philip was in a towering rage, his mouth a hard line and his eyes blazing. Frances tried to explain about the bear, that she could not stand to see an animal suffer, but he was still a stranger, a world away from her and, in truth, she was very much in awe of him. Her words drifted away into the snowflakes. She wondered what could have made him so angry.

It was Brie, surprisingly, who supplied the pieces in the jigsaw. Like Frances, she had an excellent memory and was very good at putting together bits of information. Her grandmother was an insatiable gossip and had no hesitation in sharing her knowledge with the world, young and old alike. Brie knew the story, chapter and verse.

In 1579, shortly after Anjou's first arrival in England, Philip had sent to the Queen "A Letter to Queen Elizabeth Touching her Marriage with Monsieur". This was quite widely circulated and it argued against the marriage with Anjou, mainly on the grounds that any change in the Queen's state would be highly detrimental and unpopular with her people, which, in turn, would upset the safety of the realm. Philip had a deep-seated dislike of the Valois princes as a result of his presence in Paris on the night of St.Bartholomew's Eve. He was strongly Protestant and still dreamed of forming a Protestant League in Europe. This letter may have been the basis for a fierce quarrel over the use of a tennis court with the Earl of Oxford who was a Catholic and in favour of the French marriage. He was also an old enemy of Philip's. Oxford ordered him and his friends off the court on the grounds of rank and Philip refused on the grounds of his bad manners. Oxford called Philip a "puppy" to which he replied "all the world knows that puppies are gotten by dogs and children by men." Things went from bad to worse and Oxford issued a challenge to a duel via Sir Walter Raleigh whereupon the Queen intervened reminding Philip that Oxford was of senior rank and there was to be no duel. Since then, they rarely spoke.

The man who had accosted Frances was Edward de Vere, Earl of Oxford. Small, worldly-wise Brie, had heard that he was vicious and a menace to women. She also reported that Philip and Fulke had put a stop to the baiting of the bear.

On 13th January, Philip Sidney was knighted by the Queen. He was received in Europe as a powerful figure already, and this knighthood came about because Johann Casimir, his old friend from Heidelberg, now ruler of part of the Electoral Palatinate, had asked him to stand proxy for his own appointment as a Knight of the Garter and it was necessary for the proxy to be a Knight of the Realm. Not before time, it was generally felt and Frances, on her marriage, would be My Lady Sidney.

On this happy note the Walsinghams left Court at the end of January and went down to Barn Elms, taking with them Alice and Christopher Hoddeson and their daughter, Ursula.

1583 – Barn Elms, London

Walsingham sat at his table in the library at Barn Elms, a grubby piece of paper in his hand and a thunderous frown on his face. As always, he was dressed in meticulous black and it suited his mood as did the leaden sky and deep snow outside.

Through a roundabout route he had received a letter from John Wickerson, still in the fastnesses of the Marshalsea prison. John had survived nearly eighteen months in this unholy place and his words struck a raw note for Walsingham. Pointing out how long he had been incarcerated, he had written:

"For his rash contract of matrimony with Mistress Frances, which to relinquish would be a perpetual scruple and worm in conscience, and hazard of body and soul," and imploring Walsingham "to weigh and have remorse unto his perilous state and vouchsafe the word at the length to grant your consent and goodwill for performance of the said contract in the Holy state of matrimony."

Briefly, he still considered himself contracted to Frances and very much wanted to marry her, despite the treatment he had been subjected to and the fact that the "contract" did not exist. Walsingham, in spite of his annoyance, was obliged to concede that he had tenacity and courage. To refer to his "perilous state" was a massive understatement of the horrors of the Marshalsea and to appeal to the one who had put him there to reverse the decision on his supposed crime rather than to beg for his release, was an act of selfless valour. Walsingham's own two marriages had been comfortable and well arranged but he had never been through the blast furnace of love.

Whatever action was decided, Frances must never see or hear of this letter. She was just becoming herself again and there had been no more tirades against marriage with Sidney. The glimpse of Court life had fascinated her and her remarkable memory had made it easy for her to sort out the ramifications, both of precedence and of who did what, with whom and why. Above all, in what degree people were related to each other. Very early on, she realised it could be fatal to disparage anybody; one would almost certainly be speaking to a kinsman.

Walsingham felt strongly that the sooner she was wedded to Philip, the better. He would then be prepared to release John Wickerson on the condition that he never, on pain of an immediate return to the Marshalsea prison, made any attempt to contact Frances again. It was a miracle that he had survived for almost two years. He might even send him money to return to Staffordshire and stay there.

He could see Frances through the window, playing with Alice's daughter, Ursula. They had a pony harnessed to a sledge and were driving it down towards the river. This little girl had something of Christopher's restless spirit and was afraid of nothing, unlike her gentle, quiet mother who rarely left home and considered a visit to Barn Elms a high treat.

Walsingham's load of work was enormous, increasingly so since the death, in 1581, of Sir Thomas Wilson, his fellow and unreplaced Secretary of State, and his health was intermittently bad. He was plagued with kidney stones which made his life a misery and which often obliged him to take to his bed for days on end. The trouble had started as long ago as 1571 and attacked him regularly over the years until his death. Described by Motte Fénelon as a "certaine difficulté de uryne qui le travaille fort", he mainly struggled on, writing doggedly from his bed until it became so acute in 1576 that he informed Burghley that he wished to resign. Eight years on, he was still in harness, relying heavily on Robert Beale, his now distinguished brother-in-law, but he was paying a high price for his loyalty. His intelligence work was only a part of the whole that made up the function of a Secretary of State, although his own development of it and the part it played in the defence of the Realm and the Queen's person, was immensely valuable. Since the Papal Bull, published by Pope Pius V in 1570, in which he had excommunicated the English Queen, one plot after another had been unearthed and scotched. Most of these were centred upon Mary Queen of Scots, Elizabeth's unwelcome guest, and their aim was to restore England to Catholicism and dispossess the bastard, heretic Queen. The Bull was a call to arms for English Catholics and a constant encouragement to rebellion or assassination attempts.

Walsingham's methods were devious and very often ruthless when it came to intelligence work. Well-rooted in this service now were Francis Milles, a certain Laurence Thomson, Thomas Walsingham, his nephew, his old friend Walter Williams and Nicholas Faunt; these last his two memorable messengers from Paris. They had all been, or were, his personal secretaries. There were other far more shadowy figures weaving their way in and out of the tapestry of agents, de-coding experts and counterfeiters, plants in the major prisons and extractors of information. Walsingham "waited on men's souls with his eye, discerning their secret thoughts through their transparent faces." His own face was less transparent and his thoughts not at all discernible.

By early February, the news of the Sidney marriage was out and the Court was humming. Too many people already knew for it to have remained a secret any longer. Philip was obliged to endure the usual congratulations, exclamations, and jocularities. Frances was considered to be, overwhelmingly, the more fortunate of the two and speculation ran like bushfire about the political implications. Would this create a block of power under the Queen consisting of Walsingham, Leicester, his brother Warwick and the Sidney-Pembroke family?

Whatever the real reason, Her Majesty made it clear that she was not pleased about the marriage on the grounds that she had not been consulted. She may well have had misgivings about this closer alliance of some of her more powerful servants, but she may also have been picqued for another reason. Whatever her personal feeling about Philip, she would, and always did, strongly resent the marriage of any of the leading lights of her Court. He was an adornment of the first order, a poet, playwright, champion jouster and a powerful tool in dealing with European courts and personalities. He would remain all these things but somehow the edge went off the magic if it was known that he was married. Also, almost unacknowledged, there was the threat she had felt in Frances herself, undefinable but present. The girl was too poised, too attractive to men, too eye-catching. Quite apart from anything else, she danced too well.

So Her Majesty sulked and Walsingham was furious. It would be a mistake to proceed with the marriage without her approval, but he was hurt and deeply incensed.

Burghley wrote on 10th February congratulating both Walsingham and Lady Ursula on "the comfortable purpose" concerning their daughter. "God Bless it," said the Lord Treasurer.

He then received a rambling and somewhat ambiguous letter from Sir Henry Sidney, who, having previously agreed to all the marriage terms, including the settlement by Walsingham of £1,500 of Philip's debts and the housing of the young couple and their household at both Walsingham House and Barn Elms, now appeared to be having various afterthoughts. The letter was dated 1st March and read:

"I have understood of late that coldness is thought in me in proceeding to the matter of the marriage of our children. In truth, sir, it is not so, nor shall it ever be found. I most willingly agree, and protest I joy in the alliance with all my heart." He then explained his embarrassment at being unable to provide Philip with a suitable income to cover all his expenditure now, and as a husband. The next part of the letter was quite abstruse. "As I know that it is for the virtue which is, or which you suppose is, in my son, that you made choice of him for your daughter, refusing haply far greater and far richer matches than he, so was my confidence great that by your good means I might have obtained some reasonable suit of Her Majesty, and therefore I nothing regarded any present gain, for, if I had, I might have received a great sum of money for my good will of my son's marriage, greatly to the relief of my present biting necessity." The first part of this almost grovelling statement suggested that Walsingham could have had the pick of any husband for his daughter. Both knew this to be untrue; they were very fortunate indeed to have secured Philip. The second part suggested that he might have received a large sum of money for Philip as a husband elsewhere to alleviate the "biting necessity". Walsingham was left wondering whether Sir Henry was now hinting that he should receive renumeration for his own use over and above the generous offers made to Philip and Frances. (Walsingham was also proposing, indirectly, to settle land on them in Wiltshire and this he did in 1584.) Sir Henry ended his letter on a more uplifting note, speaking of "the joyful love and great liking between our most dear and sweet children, whom God bless. Commend me most heartily to my good lady cousin and sister, your wife, and bless and buss our sweet daughter."

Walsingham was not particularly plump in the pocket either. The Queen tended to expect public services to be their own reward and he was largely obliged to maintain his intelligence services and their agents at his own expense.

Once again at Barn Elms by 10th March he wrote to thank Sir Christopher

Hatton for his: "honourable and friendly defence of the intended match. I find it strange that Her Majesty should be offended withal, it being only a private marriage between a free gentleman of equal calling with my daughter. I hope that when Her Majesty shall weigh the due circumstances of place, person and quality there can grow no just cause of offence. I pray you, sir, if she enter into any further speech of the matter, let her understand you learn the match is held for concluded, and withal let her know how just cause I shall have to find myself aggrieved if Her Majesty still show her mislike thereof." He was not having any more nonsense to spoil his careful and lengthy planning for Frances's future.

The Queen, however, continued to sulk.

In the meantime, Philip was visiting Barn Elms more and more frequently. One brilliant sunlit morning, he rode the Andalucian down from London, starting early as the sky, still dark blue and studded with stars above his head, was beginning to turn a magical acquamarine and green in the east. The glow grew until streaks of rose gave way to gold and the sun, round and red as a cherry, rose through the river mists to light his road. There was a faint promise of spring in the blurred outlines of some of the trees and an occasional fuzz of white blossom in the blackthorn bushes. Quantities of geese were shouting up and down the river; mainly Greylag and the small black Brent, the beat of pinions and their overhead chatter deafening the songbirds. It was going to be a late spring and the wind was sharp.

Frances, watching for him, saw the small company through the still bare trees in the park, flung a fur-lined cloak around her and rushed headlong down to the stables. She knew well this was somewhat disorderly behaviour, but she had spotted the horse and wanted to have a few words alone with Philip before the pleasantries which her parents' presence made obligatory. She had never done this before and by the time they rode through the arch she was standing on the mounting block feeling rather shy. As always when this happened her face gave nothing away, and she made a delightful picture in the morning sun, swaying down in a curtsey on her perch. Philip rode straight up, scooped her into the saddle before him and rode off into the park at a canter, the stallion's waving mane blowing in her face. This was an adventure and she leant back against his warm padded doublet, her hands on the reins above his and her face slightly tilted to look up at him. Glancing down, he could see the long lashes fanned against her cheeks and impulsively tightened his hold and kissed her.

He was always startled by how small and light she was, but this was no child and she returned the kiss with interest.

They came into the house together, flushed and windblown, Frances talking excitedly about the stallion's paces and how Philip had made him dance for her. Lady Ursula exchanged glances with her husband.

Philip's intention that day was to tell Frances, in his own words, the truth about his liaison with Penelope Devereux and he hoped that she would, in turn, be honest with him. It was going to be difficult to explain that he had been unable to resist Lady Rich even after her marriage, that her misery and the fact that she had turned to him for comfort had softened his resolve. Since agreeing to marriage with Frances, however, he had managed to stay away from her. It would have been, in his eyes, dishonourable, whatever the temptation, and Penelope had made sure there was no lack of that. Far more dishonourable would have been a child through Lord Rich's back door.

His opportunity came when Walsingham was called away by Phelippes to give his opinion on a cypher. Lady Ursula tactfully slid out of the room after him, leaving them alone in the big library.

Choosing his words carefully, Philip told his story with no embellishment and with scrupulous truth. He would not start a marriage with this girl without honesty and found that it was much easier than he had imagined. She hardly took her eyes from his face even when he had finished speaking and he had the strange feeling that he was looking through their changing colour into her soul. He was being studied.

Slowly, she turned, sat down on the window seat like a cat softly settling herself and began to tell him about John, from the moment she saw him getting out of her father's barge to the moment he was shoved back on to it in the pouring rain; her final sight of him. She told him the facts without any sentiment or self-pity and he realised she was paying in coin; he was getting the whole truth and he was sure of it when tears began to well up and trickle down her face. John had been receding from her mind without her knowing it and now he came back with a rush and with the memory came the pain. Frances was not accustomed to baring her soul to anyone; her thoughts were her own but, perhaps, she had now found someone to share them with. She had never suspected what a relief it would be to trust someone enough to pour out the story of that autumn idyll and to know that they had trusted her enough to do the same. Philip made no attempt to interrupt her or to offer physical comfort. He knew no more than she did where John Wickerson was and Walsingham had made it clear that he never would. Listening to her, he also realised that what was so easily discounted as infatuation or the throes of calf love was perhaps more intense and devastating than anything that came later when reason could argue some of the pain away. He told her that they had both loved and lost and been bruised in the same way and that he, for one, would put it behind him; Penelope was a married woman and there could be no going back. For her, it was a little different. John had been forcibly removed from her and, if her father were to be believed, was alive though inaccessible. Could she accept that it was finished for her and start another life with him? After a long pause, she slipped her hand into his and sat looking out into the early dusk.

Next month, on 20th April, Roger Manners, the great-uncle of Brie and an over-busy courtier, wrote to Brie's brother, the young Earl of Rutland, saying "I have been with Mr. Secretary, who is somewhat troubled that Her Majesty conceives no better of the marriage of his daughter with Sir Philip Sidney; but I hope shortly all will be well."

Roger Manners was an unbearably silly man, though an effective intriguer where his family was concerned. He had been in and out of the Court like a rabbit for years. He regularly wrote reams of good advice to Brie and it had been he who had originally suggested and arranged for his niece to go to her Grandmother at Woburn Abbey and he was still busy on her behalf, manoeuvring for a post as a Maid of Honour. He knew full well that Brie had become a friend of Walsingham's daughter and used the connection for all it was worth. Her brother, the boy Earl, was known to Essex, who, in turn, was a great admirer and follower of Sir Philip Sidney, so it was all very interesting for him and gave him a good excuse to edge up to Walsingham himself. Brie's chances of returning home were receding as he was now sure that a post would be available for her next year when she would be thirteen. The two girls had managed to spend quite a lot of time together in the past two months and Brie had slipped effortlessly into the role of younger sister, Frances trusting her as she would have done Mary had she lived. Now that the Countess of Bedford had removed to Woburn, meeting was going to be more difficult.

Two weeks later, Roger Manners wrote again to his kinsman, the Earl of Rutland, concerning Sidney's marriage, reporting that the Queen had "passed over the offence" and so it proved. The storm, it seemed, was no more than her usual reaction to her most valued courtiers showing allegiance to any other than herself. He was, after all, the eldest son and should be thinking of an heir to his name.

Walsingham gave orders that John Wickerson was to be released from the Marshalsea and sent home to Staffordshire with enough money to enable him to start life again there. Strangely, in view of the possible scandal it might have caused, this order was endorsed by Walsingham himself and later appeared in State Papers.

Walsingham and Philip now began to busy themselves about the advancement of his career. Two posts seemed possibilities. The Governorship of the Isle of Wight, previously held by Walsingham, and the Ordnance Office over which Philip's uncle, the Earl of Warwick, had control. Despite their efforts, the Isle of Wight did not succeed. His old friend Edward Dyer was also after it and also failed. Philip turned his attentions to the Ordnance and in January this year of 1583 Warwick approached the Queen asking that his nephew be made joint master. This was endorsed by Walsingham who asked the Solicitor General to draw up a joint patency to this effect. Disappointingly, he was finally given a junior appointment under Warwick. However, this did put him in close touch with any type of military or naval planning and with some noted scientists, mathematicians and engineers. He was to oversee the repairs to Dover Harbour, vitally important for England's defence. The Ordnance was based in the White Tower in the Tower of London and it would serve several of Philip's interests. It was a start.

Philip had given Frances his "Arcadia" to read. It was a huge work of five books and eclogues, begun in March 1580 at Wilton when Philip had been with his beloved sister, Mary Pembroke, for the birth and baptism of her first child, William, for whom he stood as godfather alongside the Queen and the Earl of Warwick. He always found Wilton the perfect place to write and Mary the gentlest and most encouraging of critics, being herself a lover of poetry and literature. "Arcadia" was an epic based on English chivalry, as full as it could hold of distressed maidens, gallant knights, magicians and their prophecies and ravening beasts; Arthurian in flavour and full of innuendo and romantic double meaning. Less amusing, it contained a grim and graphic description of a rebellion which Frances, looking down the vista of the years, recognised as a description of St.Batholomew's Eve whose memories still had the power to haunt her.

She lay on her stomach reading it to Greville, the green parrot, who was greatly entertained and occasionally repeated a word or two. She felt she was enlarging his vocabulary which was proved when he suddenly looked intently at her, put his little beaked face close to hers and said clearly, "Philip," the last syllable going up in interrogation. She was delighted and they spent many more hours reading together. In a little while, he was able to pick out some of the names of characters who appeared frequently but the word he caught on to was "help" which came out as "Elp! Elp! Oh, Elp!Elp!" uttered in an excited squawk. He was very fond of Frances and would sit listening to her and gently nibbling her ear or available strands of hair. Alice Poole had not a good word to say about him and deplored Frances allowing him to march, pigeon-toed, about the room and to fly from shutter to shutter when the door was closed.

In May, Philip was called upon to entertain the intellectual Polish Prince, Albert Laski, whom he had met in Venice nearly ten years ago. Together with Leicester and the current French ambassador, Castelnau, they travelled to Oxford where they joined the Italian astrologer and one-time Dominican friar, Giordano Bruno and witnessed his awesome disputation on the theories of Copernicus. The Italian "got up into the highest place of our best and most renowned school (Balliol) stripping up his sleeves like some juggler" and proceeded to go to work on the subject of the earth revolving round the sun, (which was, he said, a star) and his theory that the universe was full of other inhabited worlds. Philip was both amused and intrigued and, on 15th June, took them both down to visit John Dee at Mortlake, conveyed in the Queen's barge in great state. By this time they were all firm friends, Laski respecting the younger man's intellect and understanding and Bruno keeping the whole company in gales of laughter. Philip brought them over to dine at nearby Barn Elms where they had a riotous evening putting this world, and others, to rights. Frances, unlike herself, laughed until she cried at Bruno's antics and his flamboyant English. He had already had dealings with Walsingham and knew his Italian to be faultless and he really began to enjoy himself. Frances spoke enough of the language for dinner conversation, but could not follow Bruno into the realms of Petrarch and his poetry. Suddenly whisking round at her, he grabbed her hand, kissing it hysterically from finger-tips to elbow and apologising for his rudeness in criticising those who gazed at women when he had so lovely a girl sitting next to him. He promised to dedicate his book on the Petrarchian poetry to Philip, which he did. Who could have foreseen that his beliefs would end, after a seven year trial, in fire, smoke and a hideous death at the stake?

There was a darker side to that evening about which Frances knew nothing. It was no chance that Philip had brought Bruno to dine at Barn Elms. He was well known to Walsingham and was proving very useful as the extrovert guest of the French Ambassador, stirring up the bibulous after dinner talk with his witticisms and passing on what he heard. It was all extremely interesting to Walsingham who was so convinced that the French Embassy was the centre of operations for information passing to and fro between the French, the Spanish and the Queen of Scots that he introduced his own agent into Castelnau's household and good graces. Added to that he had persuaded the Ambassador's secretary, Nicholas Leclerc, to collaborate with Bruno. Thanks to Bruno's information from the French Embassy, he was having one Francis Throckmorton, a nephew of his old friend Nicholas Throckmorton, closely watched after he had passed 1,500 gold crowns to the Queen of Scots, through Castelnau. Bruno had also passed on the sinister information that the Duke of Guise was encouraging the French Ambassador to increase his clandestine activities on behalf of the Scots Queen. This was subsequently proved when the young Throckmorton was arrested and racked. Despite his gallant assertion that "he would rather endure a thousand deaths than accuse anyone", the second introduction to the rack was too much for him and, in a blur of the most exquisite agony, his bones springing out of their joints and his muscles cracking, he screamed out that the Duke of Guise, intending to lead the invasion, was planning to come ashore at Arundel. Utterly dispassionate, Walsingham stood by the rack, his face a mask. Lord Henry Howard, younger brother of the executed Duke of Norfolk, was implicated, as was Henry Percy, Eighth Earl of Northumberland, brother of the leader of the Northern Rising of 1569. This was serious; history could repeat itself. Throckmorton was to suffer a traitor's death at Tyburn, Henry Howard was imprisoned, none too comfortably, and the Earl of Northumberland was to shoot himself in the Tower. It was not a pretty story but one that was all too familiar to Walsingham.

His life's work and duty was to protect the stability of the realm and the safety of the Queen. Elizabeth's reign, though viewed in retrospect as a golden age of success, prosperity and national unity was, in fact, riven by internal division which threatened very real danger to her and to the established religion. For Walsingham, there was little room for finer feelings.

In early July when London began to fester and the river to show its bones, Philip escorted Lady Ursula and Frances on a visit to the Pembrokes at Wilton. He had already taken them to Baynard's Castle, the Pembroke's great house in London, where they were warmly welcomed. Mary, determined to embrace her brother's intended bride, was very pleasantly surprised to find that she was nearly as erudite as herself, with a quick understanding despite her youth. Mary had also been married at fifteen and to a much older man. Frances's quiet assurance impressed her and she later told Philip he could not have made a better choice. She perceived that Walsingham was already inclined to treat him as a son and would be determined that he should realise his ambitions.

The visit to Wilton was an unqualified success, as was a subsequent visit to Penshurst where Sir Henry Sidney made them very welcome and conducted Frances all over the house and gardens of which she would one day be mistress. Present also was Philip's mother, the disfigured but extremely imposing Lady Mary Sidney. Once a close confidante of the Queen, her life blighted by the small pox caught from her, she had continued to make her presence felt in the family. Out of her own chamber, she always wore a veil over her face. She told Frances that she had tirelessly worked to further her husband's career, that she had always accompanied him, if possible, on his missions, and that she hoped Frances would do the same for Philip. As she remarked, there would always be someone to look after the children, but only one person could look after the husband. She was, unmistakeably, a Dudley and a powerful woman but she approved her eldest son's choice of a wife and she could see, as had the Queen, that she was not in the ordinary mould.

Looking round the Great Hall at Penshurst, Frances felt a sense of awe. Generations of Sidneys had stood gazing, as she did now, at the medieval stone tracery and the huge timbered span of the roof with the strange stone figures supporting it, each different but telling its own story. Who had carved them nearly three hundred years ago and why? Despite its size and grandeur, Penshurst had remained a home and it had shaped and formed the man she was to marry.

Walsingham found that Scottish affairs had become so out of hand and the relationship between Mary and her son James VI so tangled and fractious, that he was obliged to lead an embassy there in August. The marriage of Frances and Philip had been arranged for 21st September and he hoped to be back but his health dictated the speed at which he could travel and he left in late July. He was not to return until the beginning of November.

He was, therefore, unable to see his daughter, on a bright autumn afternoon at Barn Elms, repeat her vows and become Lady Philip Sidney.

1584-1585 – London, Plymouth

The candles in the small wainscotted parlour burnt clear and tall; no wax dripped unevenly down the brass candlesticks, which was surprising because there was a savage and unseasonal storm blowing outside. The hail and wind beat on the panes and round the house but only served to draw the log fire and its smoke up the chimney leaving the room bright and warm and still.

Frances Sidney sat in the glow, listening to the rampaging of the wind, her needlework on her knee and her hands idle. She loved this little room on the second floor of Walsingham House. It had only one door, hung with a tapestry depicting a rather peculiar hunting scene. Frances, looking at it with her head on one side, decided it was mad. The quarry ran in one direction, hounds in another and the horsemen in quite another. Whatever had the needlewomen been thinking of? Perhaps they had all been in the same state as she was herself; lazy, stupid, sleepy and definitely not hungry. All she wanted was hot beef tea. Lady Ursula, counting on her fingers and eyeing her daughter narrowly, had decided the baby would be born in November.

There had been great rejoicing both in London and at Penshurst and Wilton, though Frances had been careful to keep her counsel until she was perfectly certain of her pregnancy. So much depended on this child.

At the end of July last year, Leicester's baby son, Robert, Earl of Denbigh had died suddenly at Wanstead. The likelihood of Lettice having another child was remote. She was now forty-six and nature was not on her side. Philip was once again heir to the earldoms of both Leicester and Warwick with all the vast estates that went with them.

Leicester had been heartbroken. His adored "noble imp" had been his only hope for the future of his line. His bastard son, by Douglas Sheffield, born in September 1574 and now ten, (another Robert Dudley), could not inherit, though thereby would hang another tale.

Frances leant her head comfortably against the chair back and reflected on a year and a half of marriage.

In September last year, engineered by brother-in-law Pembroke, Robert Sidney had married an heiress from Glamorgan, Barbara Gamage, amid much good will. Barbara's father had died and her guardians were delighted with Pembroke's proposal. It put paid to the encroachments of many kinsfolk and other suitors falling over themselves to get at her large fortune and it gave her entrée to a very significant English family. It would alleviate Sir Henry's "biting necessity" and greatly assist the Sidney fortunes. Plain, red-headed Barbara, a few years older than Robert, was proving a gem of domestic and financial dependability and they were already devoted to each other.

Having been in Wales for their marriage, Frances and Philip then travelled on down to Wilton with them for the christening of another Pembroke son, the occasion spoiled by the sudden death, the day after her birthday, of their little daughter, Catherine, born just before Philip discussed his own marriage with Mary. She was only two years old and a most delightful child. The christening party ended in a flood of tears, her grandmother, Lady Mary, writing in her psalter "a child of much promised excellency if she might have lived."

Barbara found herself pregnant very soon after her marriage, the first of twelve children, and Frances felt acutely that many expectant family eyes were swivelled upon her also. Barbara could not have been further removed from Frances in looks, nature or learning but she was downright and deeply kind and she sensed Frances's distress, stepping in swiftly to silence pointed remarks about her year long marriage with no sign of an heir. Philip, when tackled on the subject, replied that it "ought to be accepted as in accord with the divine will which alone brings anything to pass"; quite quelling and with no invitation to further comment. Never once did he reproach Frances or show any impatience.

He was now wholly delighted, not assuming the baby would be a boy and treating Frances as if she was the first woman in the world to conceive a child.

Eighteen months as Philip's wife had taught Frances a great deal. She was still slightly in awe of him, partly because she was quick to realise that many of the great and good regarded him in the same way. She knew he did not suffer fools gladly; she had seen his quick Dudley temper flare if faced with stupidity or sycophancy. Comparing him with most men of her acquaintance, both great and humble, he was in a league of his own; he had a sense of honour in his dealings with his fellow men which gave him the rare ability to embrace all ranks and to make him at ease with every walk of life. Frances, watching and listening, unconsciously took her tone from him and found it very rewarding. She, too, could feel the hint of greatness and sometimes found it daunting.

He had taken time and trouble with her horsemanship which was good but not up his own standards and Frances put heart and soul into this because it plainly pleased him. Shades of their rides in Paris, perhaps, though now there was no leading rein and a much sterner critic. He would make her go through an exercise time and again until she, and the grey mare he had given her, got it right. This wedding present from Philip meant more to Frances than any jewel and, at first sight, had taken her breath away. She was small but compact, bred from a Turkish mare with the dish face and the high, flowing tail of her race and her stamina was phenomenal; she was an endless source of delight to Frances.

Occasionally, Philip would withdraw into himself, either from anger or frustration, refusing to share his thoughts with her and usually removing himself from the family circle altogether and going off with Fulke, Edward Dyer, Edmund Spenser or other friends. This was rare, however, and she took care not to intrude but to welcome him back in small ways and stick to neutral matters. She loved his company, his wit, his laughter and, solitary as she had always been, his friendship. He was unfailingly kind and courteous, even when it came to Greville the parrot, but did he love her? She knew it was no necessity in a marriage such as theirs but she longed for it and, unbidden, she remembered what she had felt with John, both loving and loved. She had also discovered in herself a distinct liking for the physical side of marriage.

Her parents had given them their own apartments in Seething Lane and at Barn Elms and accomodation for their servants, grooms and horses. They could be quite private when they wished though generally they ate with the family and the usual guests. Her cousin, Thomas Walsingham, was now working actively for her father, as was Nicholas Faunt, his Paris messenger, and they were part of the household when not on missions.

To Walsingham, Philip was the son he never had who could be trusted implicitly and there was a strong bond between them which in no way excluded Frances. Very soon after the marriage, Philip began deputizing for him in a variety of situations, especially when his health let him down. He had, for instance, been closely connected with Walsingham's Scottish Embassy and had often entertained their representatives in London.

Fulke Greville was to write later of their relationship: "That wise and active Secretary has often confessed to myself that "his" Philip doth so far outshoot him in his own bow, as now those friends which at first were Sir Philip's for this Secretary's sake, within a short while became so fully owned and possessed by Sir Philip as now he held them at the second hand by his son-in-law's courtesy."

The Frog Prince, François Duc D'Anjou had died on 10th June 1584 and Philip had been sent to France leading a diplomatic mission of condolence to Catherine de Medici and his brother, Henri III. The Queen's outward grief had been intense but brief.

Occasionally, Frances and Philip went down to Englefield, taking a party of friends and hunting for a couple of days. Frances found this quite intimidating at first. She was the hostess in this great house now and in charge of the domestic side of the visits and she was very much younger than many of her guests. Philip was a polished host, however, and made it easy for her, never allowing her to feel small and keeping everyone in the highest of spirits. She soon began to enjoy herself and his friends became hers. They treated her like a younger sister and formality rapidly went by the board. Robert and Barbara had been among their first guests, Barbara quickly coming to her aid in arranging the household and giving orders to the senior member of the resident staff, the steward. The actual control of the vast kitchens, provisions and kitchen staff was then delegated to the clerk in the kitchen. Both girls had been brought up to large house parties and the entertainment of numbers and they soon found their feet, shared their known recipes and giggled together over the pomposity of the upper servants. Philip managed the hunting and shooting and in the evenings there was music and dancing and the reading of poetry. Philip's circle of friends was alarmingly large, the literary mixing with the grand and the scholarly.

Sir Henry Lee came several times to Englefield and informal jousts were set up for the guests' entertainment. Sir Henry was considerably older than most of these, being now fifty and as straight and lean as the lances he bore. Not for nothing had he been the Queen's Champion for so many years; he was the instigator of the Accession Day Tilts held to celebrate the Queen's succeeding her sister, Mary, on 17th November. He had seen her favourites come and go and had wisely followed the counsel and course of Sir William Cecil, now Lord Burghley, whose intuition in the matter of coat-turning was an excellent model for anyone. Sir Henry was, first and last, a soldier but his talent for inventive entertainment had made him popular with any lucky, or unlucky, host singled out for one of the Queen's annual Summer Progresses. His own estate at Woodstock was well known for its standard of elaborate performances, cleverly combining allegorical and romantic stories with much dashing around on horses and mock fighting. Philip had been brought up on these since attending Leicester's unforgettable hospitality to the Queen at Kenilworth in 1575 when day after day the festivities flowed, along with 112 ton of ale and beer. He had learned much from Sir Henry. December 6th 1584, the first joust after his marriage, saw Philip pitted against his erstwhile comrades in arms, Fulke Greville, Frances's cousin Edward Denny and Henry Brouncker, in a sword fight with married men on one side and bachelors on the other. There was much hilarity and a good time was enjoyed by all.

Edward Dyer was also a frequent visitor to Barn Elms, Walsingham House and Englefield. He had been in Leicester's household since the 1560s and although eleven years older than Philip, had become a close friend. Together they were acknowledged as arbiters of poetic and courtly writing. Edward Dyer was well known to the Sidney family and a favourite of Lady Mary. He frankly adored Frances and took pains to include her in literary discussions, ask her opinion on poetry and music and gradually set her feet on the rungs of sponsorship. Like Philip, he deplored the sycophancy practised at Court.

Frances was well able, even at this early stage, to hold her own although reluctant to put herself forward amongst such erudite company. Philip clearly wanted her to be more than a decorative ruler of his household and Englefield was a good training ground for what was expected at Court. As Lady Sidney, she had to do more than dance and they were spending much of their time there. She was, in fact, beginning to acquire a standing as a patron in her own right.

All Walsingham's careful grounding was taking shape, fired up by her own interest in the arts, cultivated since childhood and now beginning to flower. A pictorial work "La Clef des Champs" by Jacques Le Moyne was in the making and dedicated to her. The poet, Thomas Watson, was writing eclogues in her name and a young and brilliant playwright, William Shakespeare, was to base his heroine in a play called "Much Ado About Nothing" upon her. This was heady stuff for a seventeen year old. The play was based on "Orlando Furioso" by Ariosto which had been translated by the Queen's godson, Sir John Harington, into a very bawdy affair indeed and which had the Ladies in Waiting in stitches for days. There was paralytic laughter behind many doors and in hidden wall niches. It had been performed by "Pembroke's Men," the Earl's own theatre company, initially at Baynard's Castle, and the cast, as so often, was based on Court characters, mirroring what was happening in the here and now, or what had already happened. Thus, Frances was depicted as Hero, the young bride to be, Philip as her suitor, Claudio, The Queen as the authoritarian Don Pedro, the Earl of Oxford as the wise-cracking Benedict, and Anne Cecil, (his estranged wife), as Beatrice. Playwrights and actors, with their connections and rights of passage into the Court, the great houses and the families involved could readily pick up all sorts of stories and take a light-hearted jab, in the name of entertainment, at well-known figures on the "brightly lighted stage." There was a more sinister side to all this, of course; those writers and the actors portraying their characters had ample opportunity to observe the goings on in real life and become founts of illicit information. Walsingham found them very useful. They could be encouraged to spread propaganda through the plays and they could also be charged with keeping their eyes and ears open in the houses of known Catholic sympathisers.

Walsingham, more than ever now that she was a part of his world, used Frances to relay conversations heard at Court or elsewhere in order to build up an opinion of someone he had reason to doubt. Very occasionally, he asked her to instigate talk on a particular subject in certain company and to report what was said.

Much to Frances's delight, Brie, now almost fourteen, had returned to Court as a Maid of Honour. She had acquired self confidence and polish while with the Countess of Bedford, whose darling she had become. Thanks to Frances, she had also achieved literacy and was an avid reader. She was terrified to begin with, of the Queen, the protocol, the other Maids of Honour, and above all, the alarming Ladies of the Bedchamber. The Queen, however, took one of her rare and instant likings to her, showing unwonted kindness and patience which developed into deep affection. Brie had grown pretty and would be prettier still and she did her utmost to please, not for reward but because it was her nature. Her round little face had fined down, her skin was perfect and her sleek pale gold hair gleamed. Following the Queen's lead, but as much for herself, everybody loved her. She had no high-flying ambition unless it was to return to Rutland and marry her distant cousin and childhood friend, Robert Tyrwhitt of Kettleby, who had served the Queen as a page; she was clearly no threat to the ambitious in that overcharged world and she was known as "Brie, perfect Manners".

Frances spent as much time with her as her duties allowed, slipping easily back into the role of sister and confidante, while Brie, since knowing she was pregnant, kept a close watch on Frances during audiences and the occasions when she was obliged to stand for hours and sometimes felt faint.

This happened during a particularly lengthy audience to welcome a delegation from the Low Countries. Philip was nowhere near her; he was standing directly behind the Queen's chair from which she had risen and was pacing around before it declaiming in Greek to the bewildered Dutch who, not surprisingly, were completely lost for words. Frances was wondering, not for the first time, how on earth Her Majesty managed to move at all in such an enormous farthingale and weighted down with so much precious metal and jewelry, when she realised that Gloriana was fading into blurred darkness, the voice was receding to a whisper and that she felt empty and icily cold. A woman's arm came round her and a voice told her to lean back against her, or she would fall. The next moment, she was lifted very gently, barely off the ground, and knew nothing else. When she opened her eyes a most beautiful face was smiling at her, black eyes sparkled and Penelope Rich assured her that she, herself, was for ever fainting away in early pregnancy. A rich chuckle came from behind her, she turned her head and saw the gorgeous person of Essex, clad in japonica pink satin and realised he was seated on a low stool, cradling her. Between them, Penelope had managed to catch her before she fell in time for Essex to stealthily carry her away without causing any disturbance whatsoever. Frances was enormously grateful, sipped the sweet wine Essex held for her, smiled shakily and thanked them as gracefully as she could. What a formidable pair they were, laughing like children at the success of their mission. She had not known either of them had returned to Court.

Penelope's kindness, like most of her reactions, was instinctive and impetuous. She realised that she was no longer a part of Philip's life. He had made it clear that, once betrothed to Frances, he would not look elsewhere and she knew him well enough not to doubt it. Frances, however, intrigued her and while she grudgingly acknowledged her grace, she could not quite put her finger on what made her so enchanting. It was most provoking; one always liked to have the competition weighed up, and Penelope wished to know more. There was no golden hair, but the shape of Lady Sidney's eyes, slanting down at the outer corners and accentuating the sweep of dark lashes gave her a hint. As they were raised in smiling thanks, the pupils narrowed and the glimpse of grey, acqua and hazel shone at her like crystal and with extraordinary sweetness. She dragged her eyes away and rose petulantly, saying she would find Philip as soon as the Queen's peroration was over.

Essex, however, was in no hurry to let her go. With all the wisdom of an eighteen year old bachelor, he insisted she rest for a while for fear of damaging the child, fetched her more wine and chatted companionably while she drank it. He was one of Philip's greatest admirers and hung on his words, written or otherwise. He had pledged his allegiance to furthering Protestantism in Europe and was generally prepared to follow Philip over stick and stile for anything, particularly in the cause of courtly and military chivalry, preferably military. He had even begun to write a few verses himself and was rather pleased with the result. He had always admired Frances (among countless others), she was Philip's wife and, besides being a good friend, must be treated with every courtesy.

In the little firelit room, Frances smiled to herself and slid a hand across her belly. No sign of increase yet but there was content and a feeling of achievement in this first pregnancy; never mind the sleepiness and nausea, Philip should have his heir.

There was a tap at the door and Robert Poley, a newly employed manservant put his head round to tell her that Sir Philip was home and wished to see her. She was puzzled by this man. He did not have the bearing of a servant and, without a trace of insolence or familiarity, he made her uneasy. He had bold, protuberant brown eyes which never seemed to miss a thing and he had a way of anticipating her wishes which she did not like. She had walked into the Library one morning and found him going through papers in a table drawer. He moved quickly and deftly began to arrange them on the table top but not before she had seen his hands in the drawer. Now, she nodded briefly and rose as he pulled the curtain back and stood aside for her.

Philip was in their bedchamber, overlooking the courtyard. He had pulled off his doublet which was wet from the summer storm and shed his boots. Candles had been lit and she could see his heavy tawny hair was soaking his linen shirt. He opened his arms and gathered her in, laughing at her added weight and dripping all over her. His fairy was less fairylike, but still dainty by most standards. There was an air of suppressed excitement about him and she wondered what the day had brought.

While it was still in her mind, she asked him about Robert Poley. Who had employed him, from where and for what purpose? Whose man was he, her father's or his own? Or had he been planted in the house to spy on them all? Philip pulled down the corners of his mouth and looked speculatively at her, then replied that he was, in fact, all of these things, his uses and purposes were well known to Walsingham and himself, that he would not be with them for long and she was not to worry her head over him. He was clearly full of more important news.

The Dutch had specifically asked that he should lead men to the Low Countries to oppose the Spanish invaders. The request was for 1,000 horsemen and 5,000 foot soldiers. Walsingham had backed this adding "they are content to deliver into Her hands the towns of Flushing and Brill. It is thought that they will make no difficulty if my Lord of Leicester have the charge of the army and Sir Philip Sidney of Flushing."

Philip was ablaze at the thought of wielding a sword, at last, for the Dutch cause and for Protestantism in Europe for which he had worked so long. William of Orange had been assassinated in July last year, succeeded by his son Maurice of Nassau and the Dutch were both demoralised and destabilized. Philip was full of sweeping plans, but they did not appear to include his wife or the birth of his child, due in November. Eventually, he noticed the drooping little figure gazing at him forlornly, cursed himself for a knave and promised that as soon as she was safely delivered and could leave the baby, she should join him in Flushing if all was quiet there. With this, for the moment, Frances had to be content.

Christopher Carleill came storming in to Seething Lane very soon after this, his sights now on the New World and his enthusiasm unbounded. He still had not bothered with marriage but his children were legion and to be found in many of the countries he had visited or bombarded. He was now working at full stretch with Sir Francis Drake, Frobisher, Sir Humphrey Gilbert and Philip's friend from Oxford, Hakluyt, on the fitting out of a fleet bound for Santa Domingo and, possibly, further. Through the influence of Walsingham, he had been appointed Lieutenant-general of the land forces for this expedition. Walsingham and Philip were both involved in it and had invested considerable sums. On 7th July, Philip was granted his former request for 3 million acres of, as yet, undiscovered land.

On 21st July, he was given, at last, with his uncle the Earl of Warwick, the joint mastership of the Ordinance Office and this gave him a far freer hand in arming and supplying the expedition among other affairs. The fleet sailed from Woolwich to Plymouth at the end of the month, a magnificent sight with over twenty ships and two thousand men, one of the largest expeditions to leave English shores. They would finish out-fitting in Plymouth under the eye of Drake and Frobisher. With them sailed Christopher Carleill, commanding his own ship, the "Tiger."

Then came the blow. The Queen, very reluctant to let her still beloved Leicester lead her troops to the Low Countries in case harm befell him, flatly vetoed giving the Governorship of Flushing to Philip.

A very tense and difficult fortnight followed. Philip's anger, icily controlled, was hard to live with. For years he had tried to escape Court life by leading diplomatic or military missions to Europe, some with success and some aborted by a dilatory Queen, leaving him embarrassed and furious. This was a step too far and not to be borne.

One evening in August, Frances found him with Harry White, his body servant since Paris in 1572, hurling clothes and accoutrements into trunks, stacking papers and laying out boots and riding gear. Frances stood very still, her face expressionless and her heart pounding. Philip at once dismissed Harry White, took her hand and pulled her down to him. He was going to Plymouth to see the expedition off, taking Fulke and Harry White and staying with Drake until he sailed. The reason he had given for his sudden departure was that word had reached him, through intelligence, that his tiresome friend, Dom Antonio of Portugal, was headed once more for England, landing at Plymouth also. Philip was, supposedly, going to meet him and escort him to London. He would, in fact, be sailing a short way with the fleet, thereby provoking a panic with Queen and Court. Drake, for all his jovial and hearty exterior, would almost certainly send word to the Queen betraying his intentions. It would be supposed that he had sailed for the New World.

Philip promised faithfully to be back in good time for the birth of his child, come what might. His tight-lipped fury was gone; he was on the move and he was going to risk disgrace and the Queen's anger in order to force her hand over the matter of Flushing and to show that he would no longer be tied to unimportant posts in England. It was a gamble.

Frances knew she could not stop him. He had laid his plans, covered his tracks and speed was of the essence before word spread that he was gone. Frances could feel the unmistakeable hand of her father in the background, balancing the chances, gauging the reactions and calculating risks. She forced herself to smile, to laugh with him and to kiss him goodbye without a tear until they had clattered out of the courtyard at dusk. After all, it was only a charade. Nonetheless, heartache remained.

The charade, however, proved to be a long and nervous one. Drake and his lady entertained Philip and Fulke in their Devonshire estate; Drake at his most boisterous and welcoming, but, as expected, almost immediately sending messages to Court with information of their arrival and plans. Dom Antonio and his ships were nowhere to be seen. The fleet was nothing like ready to sail and Christopher Carleill was frantic at the delay, whirling like a dervish from ship to ship.

Amid the expected furore at Court when Philip's absence was discovered, Sir Christopher Hatton, now Vice Chamberlain, was ordered to write immediately to him commanding his return, to Drake forbidding him to allow Philip on any ship and to the Mayor of Plymouth to see that he obeyed. This last letter went further and added that if Philip had already sailed with the fleet, he was to be pursued and brought back. Amid the rumour pulsating round the Court, Walsingham gently fanned the flames.

One morning in mid September, Frances found him at his writing table, smiling sardonically to himself. He handed her a letter he had just written to Sir William Davison, smiling even more broadly as he did so. The letter contained these canny words:

"Sir Philip Sidney has taken a very hard resolution to accompany Sir Francis

Drake in this voyage, moved hereunto in that he saw her Majesty disposed to commit the charge of Flushing to some other which he reputed would fall out greatly to his disgrace to see another preferred before him, both for birth and for judgement inferior unto him. This resolution is greatly to the grief of Sir Philip's friends, but to none more than myself. I know that her Majesty would have easily been induced to have him placed in Flushing but he despaired thereof and the disgrace that he doubted that he would receive hath carried him into a desperate course. There is some order taken for his stay, but I fear it will not take place; and yet I pray you make me no author of this unpleasant news"

He knew perfectly well that his friend and colleague would immediately make this message known to those, including the Queen, who would take the desired action. Frances, despite her anxiety, could not help smiling too. Her husband and her father worked well together.

Although she had remained at home in Seething Lane, the stares, whispers and over-anxious questions from friends had been difficult to deal with; many had pitied her, believing she had been abandoned. She often found herself slipping quietly across the street to the little church of All Hallows and praying savagely for faith and, if need be, resignation. This small church, set below the street, made it necessary to step down into its shadowy depth, leaving the busy world behind.

Dom Antonio, whose timing was never perfect, had appeared in Plymouth on 7th September and, full of good cheer, joined Philip and Fulke at the Drakes' manor. He expressed a keen wish to see over the nearly completed ships in Philip's company.

Eventually, on 14th September, the great fleet pulled out of Plymouth harbour, the late afternoon sunlight shining on the ruffled water and the ships, like horses taking the bit, responding as the wind caught the sails and drove them westward. On board the "Elizabeth Buonaventura", provided by the Queen herself and commanded by Sir Francis Drake, were Sir Philip Sidney and Fulke Greville. Christopher Carleill, commanding the "Tiger", gleefully wrote in his journal that, after about an hours sailing, Sir Philip Sidney and Master Fulke Greville "went to the shore". It had been a near run thing.

A more senior messenger had arrived in pursuit of the ships, bearing two orders for Philip. The first to take up an instant appointment under Leicester in the Low Countries and the second to abandon any thought of sailing with Drake to the New World. Having been put ashore at Plymouth, Fulke Greville was detailed off to escort Dom Antonio to Osterley while Philip rode straight to London.

The plan had succeeded, much to Frances's relief. The whole enterprise had taken well over a month and the timing had been crucial. Had the fleet sailed earlier and the message of appointment never arrived, a small, unhappy part of her mind told her that Philip would indeed have gone to the West Indies with Drake, dazzled by thoughts of conquest and colonialism. How much would a young wife and a child have mattered to him then? She did not have an answer. During this expedition the cities of Santa Domingo, St.Iago, Carthaginia and St. Augustine were taken together with suitable reward.

Back in London, the next two months became a whirlwind of frantic activity. The Low Countries campaign had been so long delayed that the greatest haste was now needed. Levies of men, horses and ammunition had to be organised and transported. Ships needed to carry them from Gravesend required stocking and manning.

Philip was at the centre of it all, hardly at home and hardly out of the saddle. Brother Robert and brother Thomas, preparing to follow him closely to Flushing with late-comers, were also hurtling round the country from Penshurst to the Welsh marches, their progress made difficult as autumn slid into winter. The Ordinance Office was at full stretch and Walsingham House was permanently full of people. Fulke Greville, perhaps as a penance for aiding and abetting the fiasco at Plymouth, was forbidden to accompany them. For him, this was to be the hardest blow of his life.

For Frances, the excitement and stress of these weeks was ill-timed. As the baby grew and she became slower, heavier and more conscious of the small life within her, her need was for stability and peace of mind. She had neither of these things. Each day brought its own pressures and problems. Lady Ursula and Alice did their best to keep her out of the vortex, suggesting in vain that she remove to Barn Elms. She refused to leave Philip; every moment was precious and she could help him with lists and calculations of the more domestic kind. During this time, Mary Pembroke came often to visit. Her advice to Frances was first hand and excellent and her gentleness a balm. They had much in common and a shared love for Philip.

Frances was lucky in that she had inherited her mother's slight but tough physique. Her dresses and lacing needed no letting out until six months of pregnancy. After the first few months, she had been full of energy, riding and hawking often and she glowed with health; skin, hair and eyes shining and her face, perhaps, a little rounder. Amid the chaos surrounding her, she moved with assurance and an added beauty which managed to stop even Philip in his unrelenting tracks. He realised, abruptly, how sorely he would miss her but time was short, the ships were waiting and he must be gone.

On 9th November, he received letters patent for his appointment and Frances went into labour. The following day, the baby was born, a girl, fair, round and perfect.

Frances lay, at last, in a hazy peace which nothing could disturb, not even the knowledge that Philip was leaving the following day. The birth had been long and hard, even for a first child, but youth and suppleness were on her side. According to Thomas Moffet, a servant and doctor of Mary Pembroke, Philip "warmly greeted the little girl… no less gratefully and lovingly than he would have if she had taken the sex, as well as her descent, from himself. What more delightful to Philip than that face? What could be granted more charming than that daughter? What had he ever heard with a better will than that he had been made a father and that a little girl had opened the way for a son who would be his heir." He named her Elizabeth.

With his going, quiet, of a kind, descended on Seething Lane but not for long. Her Majesty, in a magnanimous frame of mind, announced her intention of standing Godmother to the child thereby throwing the household, once more, into crisis. The baptism, on 15th November, was to be in St.Olave's church, so often sanctuary for Frances, and the Queen would visit Walsingham House. Leicester, not due to embark until December, was to be Godfather, having generously paid six pounds each to Alice Poole and the midwife for a safe delivery. Mary Pembroke, who had sat with Frances during the early stages of the birth, was to be a Godmother.

Walsingham, full of doubts about the situation awaiting Philip in Flushing and not a few well grounded fears, nonetheless appreciated the honour done to his first grandchild. A family party, consisting of Pembrokes, Sidneys, Dudleys and Walsinghams and presided over by a smiling Queen was not an everyday occurence in his house. Frances appeared briefly, took her daughter in her arms, and curtsied gratefully to Her Majesty.

1586 – Low Countries, London

Like the ship carrying Theseus back to Athens from Crete, that which bore Sir Philip Sidney home to England in late autumn 1586, was black sailed. England had lost one of its most loved sons and was prepared to mourn him without restraint.

"The Black Pinnace" arrived on 5th November from Flushing and on its deck stood Lady Frances Sidney, the wind blowing dark wisps of hair about her pale face. Numb and exhausted by the events of the last six weeks, shock still held her in its grip, mute and unresisting. Grief lurked in the wings, but her mind refused to acknowledge or re-live the brutal happenings that had placed her on this ship, her hand on Philip's draped coffin, watching the white cliffs of England loom out of the silent, misty morning. She stood, straight and still, unable even to imagine the child she had not seen for so long.

Leicester had written one of the most moving letters of his career to Walsingham on Philip's death, unusually compassionate and gentle. It concerned Frances.

"Your sorrowful daughter and mine is here with me at Utrecht till she may recover some strength, for she is wonderfully overthrown through her long care since the beginning of her husband's hurt, and I am the more careful that she should be in some strength ere she take her journey into England, for that she is with child, which I pray God send to be a son if it be His will, but whether son or daughter, they shall be my children too. She is most earnest to be gone out of this country and so I could wish her, seeing it so against her mind, but for her weakness."

He was not thinking only of the possible heir to his own and Warwick's earldoms, but of Frances herself and her care of Philip before his death. She was now five months pregnant with their second child.

Events had moved with extraordinary speed since Frances joined Philip at Flushing in June that year. Even the months of waiting had raced by. Frances was entranced by her daughter, a beautiful child, who occupied a great deal of her time and whose care she was unwilling to relinquish, even to Alice or the wet nurse. Once the baby blue of her eyes had focused it was seen that they would be exactly the same shape as her mother's. Apart from that, she was a miniature of Philip. Frances spent hours gazing at her in wonder, seeing something new and familiar every day.

She missed Philip more than she could have thought possible, and this was sharpened by imagining what dangers he would unhesitatingly race towards, should there be fighting. News came in through her father and it was not good. Philip had arrived in Flushing to a perfect shambles; unpaid, unfed, unhoused troops, less than friendly Dutch and a quick realisation that, with the meagre means at their disposal, there was little hope of doing more than annoy the Spanish forces. Robert Sidney had joined him fairly promptly and been equally shocked. They managed to bring some order to the chaos assisted by William Davison who had already been sent to Flushing.

Leicester's arrival on 10th December had slightly improved matters though his departure had been overshadowed by Lettice provoking a Royal rage resembling the firing of muskets in a cupboard. It came to the Queen's ears that her hated cousin had come to London prepared, in some style, to follow her husband. His steward had unwisely let fall: "that my lady was prepared presently to come over to Your Excellency with such a train of gentlewomen, and such rich coaches, litters, and side-saddles, as Her Majesty never had such, and that there was such a court of ladies, as should far pass Her Majesty's Court here." Where she imagined the court of ladies would be housed and by whom was a mystery.

The Queen roared at Leicester that he was only going to the Netherlands for his own glorification, that he was a traitor, as was all his stock, that Walsingham was a rogue for having incited the Frog Prince to go to Brabant to his death and that no one else should go at all. Eventually, Burghley, Hatton and Walsingham managed to calm her down by telling her that Lady Leicester's proposed departure plans were untrue. She had managed to make herself quite ill with rage, feared she was about to depart this world and that Leicester must remain near her until she did.

It was a miracle he managed to leave at all. Leicester was over fifty, too old to deal with such histrionics, and needing every ounce of his declining energy to confront the Spanish.

Arriving with Leicester was an impressive array of young English blood. The Earl of Essex, now his stepfather's General of Horse, The Lords North and Audley, Charles Blount, later Lord Mountjoy, Sir William Pelham, Sir William Russell, another son of the Earl of Bedford, Sir Thomas Shirley, the very experienced Sir John Norris and the younger Sidney brother, Thomas, among many others. Peregrine Bertie, Lord Willoughby, a friend of Philip's was already in Bergen Op Zoom as Governor. An unwelcome, but later, addition was the Earl of Oxford, Philip's least favourite contemporary. His arrogance had been spiked by a most unfortunate happening. He had broken wind in the Queen's presence and was obliged to remain absent for several years. (When he did return her Majesty blisteringly remarked: "My Lord, I have forgot the fart.")

Gentleman of the horse to Leicester and now an officer in his cavalry, was a tall, swarthy young man named Christopher Blount and among those in Essex's train was a thirteen year old boy with a mop of dark hair and Irish eyes, Richard de Burgh, son of the Earl of Clanricarde, who had been brought up in the Essex household after his journey across Ireland perched before Philip. He had recently come down from Christchurch, Oxford and earned his place here with Essex because of his expert handling of horses.

With Leicester and his enormous retinue, came 3,000 troops. He was welcomed by the son of the deceased William of Orange, young Prince Maurice of Nassau, amid enthusiastic celebrations after which, accompanied by Philip, they set off on a progress round the country. They had an excellent reception, particularly in Delft and arrived at The Hague on a cloud of euphoria which was well reported to the Queen at home with the intention of calming her fears and her anger. This turned out to be a mere lull. On 9th January 1586, at Leiden, Philip was nominated as Leicester's deputy in negotiations with representatives of the Dutch States General and the States of Holland. He was in his element, he knew many of them personally and all his experience over years of Protestant diplomacy came to the fore; Leicester was happy to give him a free rein. On 24th January the Dutch formally asked the Earl to take the title of Governor-General, with the address "Your Excellency" which he graciously accepted but with no reference to his Queen. They also suggested that Philip should replace Prince Maurice as Governor of the Isles and become Colonel of a Zeeland regiment. When the news arrived in England, the "muskets in the cupboard" were as nothing compared to the cannonade that now came from London. Leicester's brief had been quite clear; he had far exceeded it and abuse was hurled across the North Sea in volleys. The Queen said furiously: "I will let the upstart know how easily the hand that has exalted him can beat him to the dust." Leicester was ordered to relinquish his position and his title.

Philip came in for his share of blame and Walsingham was, again, pushed into the breach to patch things up while William Davison raced back from Flushing with explanation and pacification. Walsingham was already engaged in the prelude to unravelling yet another plot against the Queen's person of such importance that it was to result in the ultimate downfall of Mary Stuart. He was at full stretch and he was a sick man.

Philip, keen for the role of the English forces to become more aggressive, attempted to take the town of Steenbergen at the end of February and failed. He had planned for Frances to join him in Bergen op Zoom, but after this and in view of further military action, the idea was ruled out. Frances tried to hide her disappointment but tears were shed and she hoped it was not a case of "out of sight, out of mind".

She was, at this time, trying to divert her mind by helping Walsingham in any way she could in order to lighten his load of work. He found her quick to learn and anxious to please him, often using memory as a tool to avoid committing sensitive information to paper, cyphers or no. In this capacity, the role of Mr. Robert Poley became clear to her. It was a complicated story.

He was, as Philip had hinted, her father's double agent and it was through the offices of Leicester's Gentleman of Horse, Christopher Blount, that he had been insinuated into the Sidneys' service with Walsingham's approval. This was to give him good working cover in order to impress a certain Thomas Morgan, Mary Stuart's main agent in Paris under James Beaton, her official ambassador. The aim of all this intrigue was to establish a communication channel, to be set up by Blount and Poley, between Mary and her agents to which Walsingham and Leicester would have full access. Poley's past was murky in the extreme but he had a family connection with Blount which he latched on to voraciously. Blount's mother was a Poley; his father was a landowner at Kidderminster in Worcestershire and the family had always served the Dudleys. Both he and Poley were Catholics. Blount had left Oxford and joined the Catholic college at Douai and went from there to Paris where he mixed with the supporters of Mary

Stuart, including Thomas Morgan. His credentials were good and he convinced Morgan that Poley's were also. Was the man not working in Sir Francis Walsingham's own house on their behalf?

Leicester had always been the Queen's Master of Horse and the Royal stud lay conveniently near Tutbury Castle, Mary's present place of imprisonment. At Morgan's suggestion, it was not long before Blount visited the stud to view the surroundings and make contact with Mary. He sent Poley, with a letter for Morgan, to Paris in June 1585. Morgan was unfortunately imprisoned in the Bastille due to information lodged against him but this did not deter the crafty Poley from managing to deliver the letter and by the end of the summer that year a link had been set up between Mary and Morgan, complete with cypher, which Blount had passed to Walsingham. The stage was set for the final act concerning the Queen of Scots.

All this was a distraction for Frances, revealing a great deal including the close working relationship between her father and her husband, but did not prevent her from longing to join Philip.

Sir Henry Sidney died suddenly after a particularly bad cold caused by a river journey to Worcester, although the month was May. He was fifty six, had lived through three Tudor reigns and three of his sons were fighting in the Low Countries. Philip had asked for immediate leave to return home and his wife's hopes soared. His request was refused and it was at this point, almost June, that she took matters into her own hands. Walsingham was now made aware for the first time of the steel that had been forged within his daughter. If Philip were not even to be allowed to attend his father's funeral, then she would go in his place, after which she would leave immediately for Flushing. Would he please make the necessary arrangements for the journey to Penshurst followed by travel to Gravesend, a ship to Zeeland and suitable accommodation in Flushing. She would take Elizabeth, with Alice, down to Penshurst and leave her there until her return. London was no place for a baby in the summer; he would remember Mary's death, among many, from sweating sickness, plague and mala-aria. Elizabeth was Philip's only child, as she was his, and precious beyond measure. It was time there were more, particularly a son. Francis Milles, who happened to be with them during this interview, was obliged to turn away to hide a broad grin. He had watched her grow up, loved her dearly, and was tickled to death to hear My Lady Sidney giving her orders to Her Majesty's

Secretary of State. It would be he who ungrudgingly made the arrangements she was demanding. Walsingham, after his initial surprise, agreed though with inward misgivings. He had often left her, but she had seldom left him or her mother. A few weeks later a Spanish intelligence report on the subject made him smile wryly. Philip, as he well knew, had been: "pressing the Queen urgently to let him return to England, but his petition has been firmly refused but his wife has therefore made ready to join him." She most certainly had and was on her way. There had been no nonsense about asking permission, from him, from the Queen or from anyone else.

Sir Henry had elected to be buried in a variety of places and his funeral obsequies were lengthy. His bowels were buried in Worcester Cathedral, his heart in Ludlow with his daughter, Ambrosia, and the rest of him was carried in an impressive funeral procession to Penshurst for interment.

Barbara was particularly delighted to see Frances at Penshurst and welcomed her help with the massive funeral arrangements and housing of guests for Sir Henry's burial. She was missing Robert as Frances was Philip but she had taken complete charge as their mother-in-law, Lady Mary, apart from the loss of her husband, was far from well. Lady Mary gave Frances her full approval for her decision to join Philip, remarking that she would have done the same herself. The Pembrokes were not quite so sure, the Earl having a better idea of the situation in the Low Countries. Much was made of Elizabeth who immediately joined the nursery party and Frances could see at once that she would be far happier here with other children, open country and a sprinkling of animals to play with.

Little did Frances realise how difficult it was going to be to part with her child, now six months old, and very beguiling. When the funeral was over and the moment of parting came, the baby wound her arms around her mother's neck, buried her face against her and clung frantically, her bright gold curls wet with tears. Alice, equally tearful, was obliged forcibly to detach her. Barbara put an arm round Frances and hustled her into the coach.

Thanks to Francis Milles's unfailing efficiency, she was in Flushing a week later, at the house of Louise de Coligny, the widow of William of Orange. She was a daughter of Admiral Gaspard de Coligny, the leader of the French Huguenots, murdered in Paris on St.Bartholomew's Eve, and she possessed a great deal of his charm. She had been married, like Frances, in 1583 and had managed to produce a son within a year, just before William was shot by an assassin in July 1584. Her little boy, already running around, brought tears to Frances's eyes when she thought that Elizabeth would be doing the same when next she saw her. By nature a happy extrovert, Louise was still overshadowed by the death of her husband and the truly hideous end meted out to his killer, involving red hot irons and pincers besides the mandatory disembowelling. It had been so extreme that the grisly details had been pored over even in London.

She warmly welcomed Frances and gave her what news she had. Communications to Flushing were not speedy but she knew that Philip, with brother Robert, Count Hohenlohe and Prince Maurice, was planning an assault on the town of Axel and was reconnoitring the area. That was enough for Frances. She had waited for six months with only scraps of outdated news of Philip and now that she was on Dutch soil she was not waiting any longer.

With Louise's help, horses, an armed guard and supplies for the journey were quickly assembled, maps looked over and within two days they set out. Going with her was a young maid of Louise's, Jane Rehora, agog at the chance of a little adventure. The Captain of the small troop, Louise assured Frances, was completely loyal and had served under William. They would go by barge to Sluys, then ride west towards Axel, hoping to find Philip and Robert this side of the town. It was not very far. Frances, not knowing whether she would be welcome or not, could not repress a feeling of rising excitement; fear did not come into it and she enjoyed riding through this strange flat country in high summer. Several miles before the garrison of Breda, they saw signs of a military encampment which, as they drew nearer, showed clear indication of being English.

They rode in, through the pickets and horse lines, Frances very straight in the saddle, her face emotionless but her eyes frantically searching the faces of the men gathering to line her path and stare in unnerving silence as she passed through them. She saw a knot of officers, some in foreign uniforms, outside one of the larger tents and headed for them. They turned and also stared, dumb and startled. Panic began to set in and her hands grew damp on the reins. What was she doing here?

Suddenly, there was a shout of recognition and Robert Sidney launched himself out of a tent and surged towards her. Her relief was so great she almost fell off the horse at his feet. He hauled her out of the saddle, one arm round her, and ran with her back to his tent. At the pinned back entrance with the Sidney arms fluttering over his head stood Philip. His face stony, he looked at her in utter disbelief, as if at a stranger. There was a long silence then his hands reached for hers, slid up to her elbows and pulled her towards him. She walked into his arms as if she had never left them, nor did she leave them very much after that. All would be well.

With no idea that Frances had left England, the shock of seeing her appearing like an apparition was, for Philip, as devastating as was the realisation of how he had missed her. This small, fairylike creature, so undemanding and loving, had wound her way into his being without effort or awareness. The great affairs of states, governorships, armies and religious causes could wait. This was their moment. The love for him that had brought her here unbidden would be returned in full.

They had only a few days in the small camp and they were among the most carefree and happy of Frances's life; they remained a yardstick in later years. She was not yet nineteen, she was with the man she loved above all else and he was making it quite clear that he did not want her out of his sight. She revelled in the excitement, the friendliness of Philip's brother officers, once they realised she was no camp follower, and the sense of boisterous expectancy. Greedy for glory, they joked, laughed and, like jostling boys, they could not wait for a chance to prove themselves in real action. Philip's mission here was reconnaissance before returning to Flushing for reinforcements but there was a brief military scuffle during which thirty horsemen of the Breda garrison were surprised and captured by the Sidney brothers and Count Hohenloe, Philip commanding a troup of English lancers. Frances watched them ride out in tidy ranks, spurs and arms jingling and, after a day with her heart in her mouth, seeing clouds of dust rising and dispersing, she watched the captured horsemen brought in, tired and angry. Watching with her was a young musician, Daniel Bacheler, a delightful boy who had come over with Philip to Flushing and was having the time of his life. He had been asked to play for Philip's guests, and occasionally for visiting Statesmen, he could turn his hand to anything, but every spare moment he had, he spent composing. Walsingham, recognising his talent, had employed him the year before and sent him off, at his request, with Philip.

The leadership of the Netherlands campaign was becoming increasingly fractured and difficult to co-ordinate. Leicester no longer had the energy or will to drive it forward militarily, he had very little support from home, only endless carping about expenses, and the Dutch were turning increasingly to Philip for leadership. Prince Maurice would no longer deal with Leicester at all and the seasoned campaigner, Sir John Norris, was openly contemptuous. Inspite of the initial goodwill, there were also sharp differences of opinion among the Dutch and English leaders.

After his return to Flushing with Frances, the plan to take Axel was put in train by Philip and Prince Maurice, now joined by Lord Willoughby from Bergen Op Zoom, with a further 500 men and Philip's Zeeland regiment. It was a surprise night raid, transport largely by boat and it involved the swimming of moats, scaling of walls with ladders and breaching of dykes. By the morning of 7th July, the town was in their hands. It was a brilliant, much needed military success with almost no losses. A week later a similar operation nearly ended in disaster at Gravelines on the north coast. Philip lost forty men and was nearly seized by the Spanish. Those captured were methodically butchered in the town square.

Frances, waiting in Louise's house in Flushing, did her best to conquer the fear that flooded her every time he rode off, always keeping a dazzling smile on her face until he was out of sight. There was nothing restrained, however, about the way she welcomed him back. She knew he always led from the front, that his courage was legendary and that he would do anything for the men serving under him. They were living life with great intensity heightened by danger and their love for each other; the highs were joyous but the lows were terrifying, especially the waiting for news. Gone was the well ordered existence of Walsingham House and Barn Elms or the strict pattern of Court life.

On 9th August, Lady Mary Sidney died. She was staying at Walsingham House at the time and, as Mary Pembroke was also ill, the task of removing her to Penshurst fell upon Walsingham and Lady Ursula. Again, Philip and his brothers were refused permission to return home for her burial and again it was upon Barbara Sidney that all responsibility for her funeral fell. Philip and Robert were heart broken, both parents lost within three months, and Frances found it hard to console them. By this time she knew she was expecting another child.

Philip was writing frantically to Walsingham and Burghley for food, supplies and money to pay his men. He feared a mutiny in Flushing which would totally undermine the campaign and mean they could not push further south. Nothing arrived until mid-August and Philip's own relationship with Leicester was becoming so frayed that Walsingham was being asked almost to circumvent the Earl and deal directly with Philip.

Leaving Frances, this time unable to restrain a flood of tears, in Louise's care but with a promise that she should join him at the first possible opportunity, he and Robert rode to meet Leicester where he was camped near Doesburg. This parting was the hardest of all and she watched him go with premonition in her heart. It was now early September.

The first news they had after this departure was that Doesburg had fallen. Philip, Robert, Hohenloe and Sir John Norris had all been in action but were unharmed and the next objective was Zutphen on the eastern bank of the river Ijssel. Zutphen was defended by two impregnable forts, both on the western bank and strongly defended by some of the Duke of Parma's best troops. Hohenloe had attempted to take them two years before without success. Most of Leicester's force was now employed in digging in for an ambitious attempt on the forts and Zutphen itself. The Earl of Essex, Lord Willoughby, Lord North, William Russell, William Pelham and Charles Blount were all with them.

On 26th September two lathered horsemen in dusty lancer's uniforms clattered through the streets of Flushing to the house of William of Orange and begged admittance to Lady Frances Sidney. She was sitting before the fire in Louise's small parlour, heard their coming and stiffened, knowing with sickening certainty what their errand would be. There had been hard fighting outside Zutphen in order to prevent Spanish supplies getting through to the town. Sir Philip Sidney had fallen and been taken by Leicester's barge to Arnhem, some miles up the river Ijssel. There was a musket ball lodged in his left leg, above the knee, and they had orders to escort her to Graves and from there to Arnhem; would she please make haste to come with them as soon as she was able. They must ride because a coach would take too long.

Once more, frantic preparations were made, food, drink, horses and men, Jane Rehora begging to be allowed to go again with Frances. A firm bond had been established between them, more than mistress and maid, and together with Louise, she had devotedly and quietly seen that Frances had the care she needed. Louise sent for the padded velvet saddle she had used during her own pregnancy and gave orders for it to be made ready for the horse Frances would ride. The tired troopers were fed and given beds for the night and the whole party set out the next morning. Louise kissed Frances fondly, hoping she would be back soon and Philip with her. Also going with them, at his insistent request, was Daniel Bacheler.

Whatever dread she might feel, the call to action was almost a relief to Frances, so sure had she been that Philip would not escape unhurt this time. He was, thank God, alive and all she wanted was to reach him. There was no time for lament or speculation and the troopers set a good pace. As they travelled, they told her all they knew. Neither had taken part in the action before Zutphen, but soldier's tales travel fast and they were well informed. Frances now had some of the detail they had been too exhausted to give her the previous night.

Philip had been encamped with Sir John Norris at Warnsfeld, across the river from the main force, just east of Zutphen, when he was asked to accompany Leicester to Deventer, a nearby town reputed to be disaffected. He had barely arrived when a report came with news that Spanish troops had been sighted approaching Zutphen. What nobody knew was that the Duke of Parma, then busily besieging Berck on the Rhine, had given orders for a large train of supplies with an escort of 600 horsemen to be sent to Zutphen to prepare for Leicester's siege and had also ordered the Commander of Zutphen to have ready a further 1,000 men from the garrison to resist a possible English attack on the supply train. Philip and Leicester returned hurriedly to Zutphen to find that a courier of Parma's had been caught and questioned and had confirmed that a large convoy was indeed approaching.

With no idea of the numbers of Spanish escorting the supplies, Sir John Norris, stationed that side of the river, was ordered to ambush them. He had 200 horsemen and 300 on foot only. On Thursday, 22nd September, some of the English officers, including Philip, and without orders from Leicester, had crossed the river to join Norris with some sixty men. They sensed approaching action and were not going to miss it. There was an immensely thick mist hanging over the river and its surrounds that morning which lifted suddenly to reveal the train of wagons, escorted by a very large force of Spanish troops and alarmingly close to them.

The English cavalry immediately charged and for an hour and a half fought with unprecedented bravery, backed up by their foot soldiers and against enormous odds. Three times they charged but were beaten back by musket fire positioned behind the Spanish horse. Even so, they managed to do a great deal of damage. It was what they had all been waiting for and they raced each other to get at the Spanish. Philip's horse was shot under him on the second charge but he found a re-mount, rallied the men with Essex, and charged right through the Spanish lines on the third attempt. Essex lost his lance in the first assault but proceeded to lay about him with an axe as did Lord Willoughby, unhorsing the Spanish cavalry commander. Sir William Russell fought with such ferocity that the Spanish yelled it was a devil sent against them and Lord North recovering from a wound, demanded to be hoisted on to his horse and charged with the rest. It was only a skirmish but it was the stuff of legend. Rigid with excitement, Richard de Burgh watched from the rear with Essex's spare horse.

It was on his return from the last charge that Philip was hit by the musket ball which shattered his left thigh. While arming with William Pelham that morning, he had noticed his friend was without cuisses, the protective thigh pieces, and had jokingly thrown off his own. (It was becoming increasingly popular for cavalry to be lighter armed than customary, giving them greater speed.) He had been carried back to camp, all forces being withdrawn across the river as more Spanish troops poured out of Zutphen to conduct the convoy into the town. Sir John Norris, blazing with fury that Leicester had refused to reinforce his troops on the eastern bank spat out: "You have had this day the honourablest day you ever had, for a handful of your men have driven the enemy three times to retreat this day." This from the most seasoned of soldiers. The English force had lost around a dozen cavalry and twenty foot soldiers while they had inflicted nearly three hundred losses on the Spanish escort. It was a triumph of which Philip was the hero, but it was a hollow one.

The troopers with Frances could give her no more news except that Philip was now in Arnhem with a Madame Gruithuissens, the widow of a judge. When they eventually arrived, after a hard ride from Graves, she was so tired and cramped she had to be lifted from the saddle and carried into the house. Madame immediately stripped her of her cloak, threw a warm woollen shawl around her and, at her adamant insistence, took her to where Philip lay. It was now September 28th, her nineteenth birthday.

Queen Elizabeth the First: By Henry Bone. After Zuchero.
By Courtesy of *The National Trust*.

Sir Francis Walsingham: By Henry Bone.
By Courtesy of *The National Trust*.

Sir Philip Sidney: By Henry Bone.
By Courtesy of *The National Trust*.

Robert Devereux, Earl of Essex: By Henry Bone after Marcus Gheeradts.
By Courtesy of *The National Trust*.

Lady Manners, Countess of Rutland. By Henry Bone.
By Courtesy of *The National Trust.*

Portrait of an Unknown Lady by Marcus Gheeradts the Younger.
Royal Collections Trust: By Courtesy of Queen Elizabeth II 2014.
This portrait is believed to be Frances, Countess of Essex in 1600.

Somerhill.

Rain Hoppers at Somerhill (Initials RCF).

Portumna Castle: by courtesy of the National Monuments Service,
Department of Arts, Heritage and the Gaeltacht. Dublin.

He was asleep and she noticed immediately how worn and thin he looked. She sat for a long time gazing at him until he stirred, opened his eyes and saw her. There was no mistaking the light in the smile that slowly spread over his face.

At the first possible chance, Frances questioned two of the doctors Leicester had sent with Philip, Dr. John James and William Clowes and endured the horrific account of the treatment he had undergone. His left thigh bone was in pieces and they had probed for the musket ball without managing to extract it, after which they had cauterised the wound and kept it covered in healing salves, dressing it every day. It had not, apparently, occurred to them to amputate, inspite of the state of the shattered bone and the presence of the bullet. Frances found, when they had finished their report, that her fists were so tightly clenched the nails had broken the skin. She asked them why they did not amputate the leg to which they replied that in his weakened state, it would probably kill him. They were clearly shocked that she, so young a wife, should have questioned their treatment. Frances, however, remembered reading in John Dee's library a book on surgery which stated that it was better to remove a limb if the bones were badly fractured or contained bullets. For Philip, it would have been no worse than the agony he had endured at their hands.

Robert and Thomas Sidney came as often as they could and she asked them for their opinion also. They were very perplexed and promised to ask for further medical advice. Robert had been knighted on the field for his part at Zutphen, a triumph overshadowed by Philip's injury. They were two of very many visitors to the house in Arnhem. Philip's friends poured in an out particularly the Earl of Essex, frantic for his recovery. With him came Charles Blount, William Russell and William Pelham. They were all immensely kind to Frances, bringing presents, wine and flowers, making her laugh and telling her that Philip would take a lot of killing. All these would remain her friends for life. Peregrine Bertie, Lord Willoughby, told her quietly that he owed his life to Philip for defending him on the return from their last charge only moments before he was hit. They all repeated the story that Philip, having asked for water when they carried him in, was in the act of drinking it when he spied one of his soldiers, wounded and crying out. He immediately passed the flask to him saying: "Thy necessity is yet greater than mine."

Madame Gruithuissens, who looked like a kindly sheep, was unfailingly hospitable to all these dashing English officers and had clearly fallen under Philip's spell, as had so many before her; she could not do enough for him or for Frances over whom she watched like a dragon, insisting that she eat properly and get sleep whenever she could. She could hardly bear to leave Philip's room and chose to watch over him at night when she had him to herself. These quiet hours, lit by a candle and the flickering firelight, listening intently to Philip's breathing, gave her some sort of peace, but if he moved she was immediately by his bedside.

Her mind was in limbo, dealing only with immediate necessity. She could not bear to think back on his suffering and she could not bear to think forward to what the future might hold. She found it hard even to pray, and trusted that the Lord would make allowances for her. Philip never complained and remained his gentle, courteous self. Jane Rehora took much of the nursing upon herself and proved invaluable; she was deft, gentle and efficient. Daniel Bacheler, knowing Philip's favourite music, played whenever he wanted it, sometimes through the night if he was wakeful. The soft sounds became a background to these night watches and would always remain in Frances's memory.

The Earl of Leicester was sending a barrage of encouraging letters to London on Philip's progress. Having waited five days before writing to Walsingham he assured him: "My grief was so great for the hurt of your son, my dear nephew and son also; as I would not increase yours by the discomfort of thereof... I do but beg his life of God, beseeching him for his mercy's sake to grant it. My hope is now very good." The following day he wrote: "I have received great comfort and hope from time to time, specially this day, being the seventh day, from his surgeons and physicians." He visited Arnhem on 29th September and was present on 30th when Philip made his Will, naming him as an executor in company with Warwick, Pembroke, Huntingdon, Walsingham and Frances. On 6th October, the Earl wrote once more that Philip was: "well amending as ever any man hath done for so short time. He feeleth no grief now but his long lying, which he must suffer." On 7th October, he visited them both again early before returning to Deventer where he was now camped. Sir John Norris, a far more experienced soldier, went away shaking his head.

When official news reached the Queen she sent a courier with "her gracious letters of Her Highness's own hand to comfort him (Philip) and to bring her word again how he doth as soon as he can."

All this optimism, tragically, was not well founded. Philip was sinking and Frances knew it and the loss of weight combined with the "long lying" described by Leicester, made it hard for him to find comfort in any position for long. On 9th October, it became clear that gangrene had set in. As a soldier, Philip knew exactly what that meant; he would not live and his passing would not be pleasant. He explained this to Frances although she could guess from the unfamiliar, sickening smell that something was very wrong. She would remain with him every moment possible. He had no fear of death, only that, at the last, his mind might be affected.

And so another terrible week dragged by. The visitors were no longer joking; they knew, now, what the outcome would be, but come they did and their presence was, for Frances, the greatest comfort despite the grief already lurking in their eyes.

Essex was distraught: Philip had been all he himself hoped to be and his only solace was when Philip called for his sword and presented it to him in honour of his courage at Zutphen saying: " I give to my beloved and much honoured Lord, my best sword." There was, possibly, a little more to the gift than appeared. They had talked at length and Philip had recognised the ardour in Essex and hoped that he would carry on his hopes for Protestantism in Europe.

George Gifford, one of Leicester's chaplains, was constantly with him and on the night of 16th October, as dawn was creeping through the cracks in the shutters, Philip made it clear he wanted to speak to him. He was exhausted after a painful night, but when Frances, who had watched the night through, rose to leave them, he took her wrist and made her stay. He told them both: "I had this night a trouble in my mind, for examining myself, methought I had not a sure hold in Christ. After I had continued in this perplexity a while, observe how strangely God did deliver me – for indeed it was a strange deliverance that I had. There came to my mind a vanity wherein I had taken delight, whereof I had not rid myself. It was my Lady Rich. But I rid myself of it and presently my joy and comfort returned within few hours." It was a confession, designed not to hurt his wife, but to assure her, before a chaplain, that Penelope had been a vanity, and that it was she he loved and did not want to leave.

Robert and Thomas arrived soon after and were given a number of instructions, codicils to his will and messages for those at home. He spoke clearly until his voice began to fail. The end came at 2.00pm that afternoon of 17th October and "The Perfect, Gentle Knight" slipped away, his hand not in that of the inspiration for some of the most beautiful of English verse, but in that of his wife, Frances.

ACT THREE 1

1587-1588 – Barn Elms, Penshurst

There followed a very dark year in the life of Frances Sidney. Looking back, she could recall very little of it, despite her unusual memory, nor did she want to.

The child she carried was born early, just after Christmas, at Barn Elms. It was a girl, stillborn, and baptised Frances before being buried beside her aunt, Mary, in Barnes Church. Walsingham had written to Leicester on 24th December 1586: "I thank God for it, I am now in the hope of the recovery of both my daughter and her child." It was not to be.

This had been Frances's one great hope for the future, a son of Philip's, and even that was now denied her. Despair took hold and she became so ill that she could not rise from her bed and it was feared she never would. The grief she had kept at bay for the sake of the baby swept in and overwhelmed her. Her mother and father suffered with her. They had loved Philip as a son but Walsingham was now pitchforked into the most unpleasant wrangling with Leicester and the Dudleys over the payment of his funeral expenses and his debts. This was most unedifying and did little for his health.

Frances was still too unwell to attend Philip's funeral on 16th February 1587. The whole country mourned him and it was a magnificent affair. A huge cortège of black-draped horses escorted the fourteen men carrying his coffin from the Minories Church, where he had lain for two months, to St.Paul's Church. Seven hundred mourners accompanied them and his charger followed the coffin, its rider none other than Daniel Bacheler, trailing a broken lance. It was a state occasion, the streets of the city so thronged with people that the cavalcade could hardly pass. No one, save the Monarchy, had ever been given such a funeral.

Philip Sidney's outstanding nature, which continued to shine through countless ages after his death, was, unusually, fully appreciated by the age in which he lived. William Camden described him as: "the great glory of his family, the great hope of mankind and the darling of the learned world." Legends and tales sprang up, some based on his heroism at Zutphen but many more on the story telling of ordinary men whose lives he had touched. Zutphen grew, in retrospect, from a failed skirmish to a glorious battle in no time at all and those who had fought with him carried the gloss of his fame for the rest of their lives. His poetry and prose were to keep his memory vibrantly alive but, for Frances, husband, lover and friend had gone and, except for one little daughter, she was once more alone.

The country certainly needed a hero and a triumph, none more so than its Queen, now impaled on the horns of a dire dilemma; the execution or the disposal of the Queen of Scots. This impasse had been brought about by the machinations of Walsingham and his agents. What better than a hero's burial to divert attention from the vexed question of the beheading of an anointed Queen, (both of France and of Scotland), by her cousin, another anointed Queen?

Mary, for all her vast experience of plots, agents and cyphers, had fallen headlong into the trap set for her. Her correspondence with Morgan and Beaton in Paris, carefully concealed in the bungs of beer kegs and as carefully extracted by Walsingham's men, had revealed a plan to murder the Queen by a few headstrong and exceedingly stupid young Catholics who had used the same methods of communication. Thomas Phelippes was in his element de-coding all their nonsense. They egged each other on to the point of no return, ably assisted and watchfully dogged by the ubiquitous Mr.Poley, the perfect double agent. Their leader, Anthony Babington, who had waited upon and been captivated by Mary Stuart as a boy, was a former employee of the Earl of Shrewsbury, Mary's host and jailor. The result was inevitable and their end at Tyburn, by orders of the Queen, was too severe even for the hardened London crowds to stomach; they turned away revolted, with Babington's prolonged screams of "Sweet Jesus, Sweet Jesus," ringing in their ears.

Walsingham, however, had what he wanted, Mary Stuart's signed approval of a mission to kill the Queen of England and seize her throne. Her days were numbered; she was tried, Walsingham being one of her judges, and found guilty but the Queen could not and would not bring herself to sign the death warrant. The prevarication that had served her so well in the past and had grown with the years, could not benefit her in this case. She twisted and turned, even suggesting that other parties should do the deed and so absolve her from any blame. A dagger in the dark or a twisted cloth around the neck, perhaps? Volunteers seemed to be strangely lacking and Walsingham stood firmly by the only possible outcome, execution according to the law.

Eventually, the much-tested William Davison, promoted to Junior Secretary of State, managed to get a signature on 1st February. Robert Beale, now Clerk to the Privy Council, and at their instigation, went down to the Castle of Fotheringay, Mary's final prison, carrying the warrant and accompanied by the Earls of Kent and Shrewsbury.

The Queen of Scots was executed with the maximum amount of drama on Wednesday 8th February before a very large crowd of prominent people. On the scaffold she drowned the Protestant Dean of Peterborough's prayers with an outpouring of Catholic incantation, disrobed down to a scarlet under-dress, the colour of martyrdom, and thoroughly unnerved the headsman when her wig came away in his hand. Her lips continued to move a quarter of an hour after his blows had severed her head and her tiny dog was discovered in the folds of the scarlet dress and taken away to be washed. The Queen of Scots would not easily be forgotten. She had retained her mystique and her dignity to the end.

Too late, the Queen of England suffered agonies of remorse which took the form of vicious swipes at anyone who could fit the role of scapegoat. Right in the line of fire was the unfortunate William Davison and, just out of range, were Sir Christopher Hatton, Lord Burghley, Robert Beale and Walsingham who had wisely, but with good cause, side-stepped into his bed before the execution. No matter that the bells of London were ringing out for joy at Mary's death or that the Privy Council were sheepishly trying to cover their backs, it was Davison who had allowed the warrant go to Fotheringay and betrayed her trust and it was Davison who was to be sent to the Tower. Incredibly, the Queen wrote to Mary's son, King James VI, in Scotland, denying knowledge of the execution, and an equally implausible account of her trial and death found its way to Philip II of Spain. Her brother-in-law, the late lamented Charles IX of France, had rightly commented of Mary's plots: "The poor fool will never cease until she loses her head."

After all this, the spectacle of Sir Philip Sidney's funeral and an outpouring of national feeling was exactly what the country needed; more bells, the firing of guns and the spread of legend.

Frances remained ignorant of the great events unfolding downriver from

Barn Elms. She was just becoming aware that the light was spreading into her room a little earlier each day and that she was now awake to hear the liquid magic of the morning thrushes; before she had not opened her eyes until almost noon. It was four years since Philip had swept her up from the mounting block and carried her off, in every sense. She knew her father lay gravely ill in Seething Lane, a result of overwork and gnawing worry. His responsibilities were enormous and he was suffering a physical collapse as a result of his kidney troubles. He had not been allowed to mourn Philip for long before the bludgeoning began on the subjects of his debts and the cost of his burial. Leicester, despite his soft-spoken letters, refused to meet even a part of them. In the end, it had been Walsingham, financially embattled by this time, who was obliged to pay out £6,000 for the funeral as well as being asked for a further £17,000 for expenses incurred in Flushing. These were huge sums of money and it led to very bad feeling between Walsingham and the Dudleys. The Queen refused, equally flatly, to shoulder any of the costs. After all that Walsingham had done to protect her person and prosecute her enemies, not to mention the removal of her "thorn in the flesh", Mary Stuart, this was hurtful and miserly in the extreme. Small wonder he took to his bed.

Leicester had returned from the Netherlands, a sick and embittered man, to a Queen who had undermined his efforts there, a domineering wife and no heir. In the absence of a son of Philip's, it would be Robert Sidney and his sons who would inherit the earldoms of Leicester and Warwick.

Meanwhile, Frances slowly forced herself back to health. Looking in her mirror one beautiful spring morning, with the pearly light full on her face, she was so appalled by the waif who looked back at her that she rang for Alice and scrambled out of bed, determined to be well again. Her knees refused to hold her up and she sank on to the window seat, shaking. Her clothes hung loosely on her, even with the tightest of lacing, and she could see her collar bones and the sharpness of her elbows. Was this the mother Elizabeth was brought in to see every day, who could not laugh with her, read to her or take her out to play? Enough! She would force herself to eat and drink, walk every day until she was well and then she would take Elizabeth down to Penshurst. She could remember her own solitary childhood and had vowed that Philip's daughter should not be brought up the same way.

Throughout her illness she had been aware of music, piercingly sweet or low and haunting, sometimes far away and faint, sometimes nearer and, occasionally, as if it came from below her window. Her mind had not been able to question who was playing or why, but looking out at the swathes of daffodils and the starry blossom, she caught sight of Daniel Bacheler playing a jig for Elizabeth on the terrace. The little girl was hopping up and down clapping her hands to the music, her cheeks rosy and her unbound curls bouncing around her glowing face. Now Frances remembered; now the comfort brought by that soft lute through the nights at Arnhem came back to her. For the first time in months, she smiled, leaned from the window and applauded them both. Daniel rose, blushing and grinning, and she saw how he had grown; he must now be about fifteen and she was deeply touched that he had chosen to stay with her, as had Jane Rehora, who returned with her from Flushing. When she was recovered, she must send Daniel and his lute back to her father at Walsingham House.

Once at Penshurst with Robert, Barbara and their children, spring bursting out all around her, Frances began to recover and to regain the close bond she had with her daughter. Like herself, Elizabeth was a small delicate person promising much of her mother's grace and a great deal of her father's charm. She was a golden child; eyes, sun-kissed skin and the mane of heavy hair were all Philip's and everyone at Penshurst loved her. Frances, too, was treated with the greatest affection and was known by the servants, as "Mrs. Philip." She would never be mistress of Penshurst now, but she had a sense of homecoming.

Mary Pembroke and her growing family came over from Wilton soon after they arrived. Frances had not seen her since the loss of the baby and together they had much to grieve over. To share the pain with someone who fully understood it, rather than to strive with it alone, was a great source of comfort for Frances. Mary looked so like Philip and they had been close all their lives, sharing the same love of writing and music. She had been devastated by his loss, so soon after that of their parents and she wanted to know all that Frances could tell her of events in the Low Countries. When she heard what had been said that last night, she looked sideways at Frances out of her tawny eyes and asked her if she had ever read "Astrophil and Stella", written while Philip had been head over ears in love with Penelope Rich. She had not, as yet, brought herself to do this although Philip had told her of it, and Mary now explained gently that she should prepare herself for its publication in due course. It was too beautiful a work to remain hidden, but, for Frances, it might have a painful sting in its tail. Mary was working on Philip's translation and version of the Psalms which he had left unfinished and she needed Frances's help and permission to publish these also when completed. Mary, like all the Sidney children, had been as thoroughly and classically educated as had Frances and her erudition was well known. She had not been well since before her mother's death, spending most of her time at Wilton, but she now intended to offer her patronage to as many of Philip's literary friends as she could, such as Edward Dyer, Gabriel Harvey and Edmund Spenser, and to encourage the revision of his "Arcadia." She was only six years older than Frances and her three children, William, Anne and Philip were now aged between seven and three. The fourth, Catherine, had died at small Philip's christening. She promised Frances that she would always treat Elizabeth as one of her own and begged her to bring the child to Wilton for a long visit.

While Frances picked up the threads of her life and basked in the spring sunshine at Penshurst, loyal, long-suffering William Davison was released from the Tower and resumed his duties, Walsingham rose from his bed as the threat of a Spanish invasion began to look like a certainty, and a new star rose in the firmament of the Court eclipsing all others in the eyes of the Queen. Robert Devereux, Earl of Essex, returning from the Netherlands with an added maturity and a reputation as a soldier, had caught Her Majesty's eye and held it. He had been honoured for his part at Zutphen and given the title of Knight Banneret and he had marched behind Philip Sidney's coffin at his funeral. He was tall, strikingly good looking and personified the careless charm of the Devereux. He was also well-read, ready-tongued and afraid of very little.

It was a strange relationship. For his part not entirely self-seeking, and for hers not entirely an infatuation with a beautiful and charismatic boy, although these were undoubtedly its main elements. The facts were bald. The Queen was now fifty four and Robert Devereux was nineteen; he was the youngest and the most impecunious Earl in England and the Queen held the purse strings not only to wealth but also to position and power. She had never had a husband, a lover, in the true sense, or a child; he would be able to have his pick of wife, mistresses, and as many children as he might choose. He was already going through the Maids of Honour like a wire through cheese, few of whom could resist him or the wicked satisfaction of knowing that they rivalled the Queen.

Much of his estates had already been mortgaged to the Crown long before he had spent recklessly on mustering men and equipment for the Netherlands campaign. The Queen knew well she had him over a barrel and that he depended entirely on her to make his way. She no longer had to contend with importunate foreign suitors and could please herself. Leicester had edged as close as any to marriage and she had almost succumbed, but now she was neither threatened nor tempted. She was old enough to be his grandmother and could play with him as a cat with a most attractive mouse. She had nothing to lose.

To begin with, he was diffident and slightly over-awed which, for her, had its own appeal. She was magnificent in every way and frighteningly intelligent, but as he began to realise that he had the wit and the learning, not only to keep up with her, but to amuse her, his confidence grew. Every courtier needed more than a little erudition to take his place at Court. The Queen set a very high standard.

They spent long hours together that spring; he was always near her on public and state occasions; she often whispering to him and touching his hand. Forgotten temporarily was his poor discarded stepfather, Leicester, now returning hopelessly to continue the Netherlands campaign, and forgotten too was the fact that his mother was her detested cousin, Lettice, or that his discredited sister, Dorothy, had so enraged her by her runaway marriage to Sir Thomas Perrot, a great "bête noir" of hers since his father, Sir John, was reputedly a bastard son of her own father, Henry VIII. She naturally considered this unsuitable marriage to be the fault of Lettice, described by her as "that she-wolf."

His most serious rival was the dangerous, freebooting Sir Walter Raleigh who, until now, had done his own social climbing very successfully through the Queen's good graces and who knew, as well as Essex, that he had been superceded. Raleigh was an unforgiving man and Essex was a heedless boy.

The Queen and her favourite made merry in the gleaming freshness of early summer; so much so that Robert Bagot, Essex's servant, wrote gleefully to his father: "When she is abroad, nobody near her but my Lord of Essex and, at night, my Lord is at cards or one game or another with her, that he cometh not to his own lodging till birds sing in the morning." What was the Court to make of that?

He hunted, rode, and danced with her, pouring out love (that much misused word) and admiration unendingly in a way that his mentor, Philip Sidney, would never have done. By June he was Master of Horse as Leicester had been before him, with an income of £1,500 a year.

In July, they quarrelled violently over the presence of his sister, Dorothy, in Lady Warwick's house where the Queen was staying. She ordered Dorothy to keep her room and Essex, exploding with rage, flung out of the house, sending Dorothy home before him, and made for Sandwich, in Kent, with the intention of taking a ship and returning to the Netherlands. He was overtaken and persuaded to return; this time all was to be forgiven.

The Queen had learned, however, that his temper was brash and violent enough to be heedless of the consequences of crossing her and, unfortunately, he had learned that it paid to bluster and rant.

Edward Dyer came often to Penshurst. He was more than twenty years older than Frances but he could not keep away. Looking at her with love, he could see how Philip's death had changed her; the gem clear profile was no longer roundly childish and the shining eyes appeared too large for her small face, but he could sense the inner resolve to take up her life again and live it fully. From him, Frances had rumour of the goings on at Court and could not help her smiles or her genuine gladness for Essex; that his giddy extravagance had now a chance of being paid for and that his schemes and dreams were being realised. She was, however, shrewd enough to be aware of the tightrope he was walking. She knew his temper and she knew how viciously the Queen could react, especially if jealousy was involved. It sounded to her as if an almost medieval charade of courtly love was being played out yet again; adoring knight and unattainable lady. She supposed the Queen did not know love for what it really was, but would soak up admiration and return it with favours for as long only as it pleased her. She would never have given her mind or body to any man; it was only a game. She had been too deeply scarred by her Mother's execution, her own enforced bastardy, and the dangers of her adolescent flirtation with Admiral Seymour to risk anything else.

But Frances was remembering the camaraderie and the deep understanding given her by Essex at Arnhem and, later, at Utrecht, when she was too stricken to feel any emotion at all. He had been there, suffering the same loss and grief, never far away. She was now uneasy for her friend; he had gone too far and too fast.

She had news of the Court, also, from Brie who wrote affectionately and fluently. She, too, was still basking in the sunshine of the Royal smiles but feared that she was to be elevated to "Queen's Carver", a great honour for one so young but an honour that would make a return to Rutland and her marriage to Robert Tyrwhitt recede even further into the future; she would not be able to refuse. Her brother, the young Earl of Rutland, was an admirer of Essex, so that the gossip, scandals and intrigues came first hand.

From Brie, she learned of the jealous quarrel and subsequent duel between Essex and Charles Blount. The Queen, perhaps to tease Essex, had shown particular attention to Charles, whose good looks and brilliant performance had attracted her notice during the joust. In his dark way, he was every bit as attractive as her favourite, and she had given him a golden queen from a chess set as a favour. This token he tied to his shoulder, in full view, provoking Essex to snap at him "that every fool must have a favour." Tempers flared and led to a rapid challenge, followed by a duel with rapiers during which Blount managed to pink Essex in the thigh. After this anti-climax, and because of their genuine friendship, humour got the better of them. They roared with laughter and went off to dine together. The Queen was delighted to have two such splendid young men, the cream of her Court, fighting over her and remarked of Essex that "it was fit that someone or other should take him down and teach him better manners."

Brie felt that Frances should make an appearance at Court; she longed to see her and, after all, she was the widow of England's hero.

Also suggesting that she should return to Court was Fulke Greville whose appearance and demeanour had cut Frances to the heart. She had never seen a man so devastated. Grief etched in every line of his face, he looked years older and it would clearly be a long time, if ever, before he recovered from the blow of Philip's death and the fact that he had not been with him. He was already writing a glowing biography in his memory and wanted, from Frances, every last detail of what had been done and said in the Low Countries and he was bitterly jealous that it was Essex and not he who shared the last charge with Philip and had been given his sword. Frances told him what he asked, but there was much she did not tell him. She was aware that his consuming admiration for Philip might turn the truth into a paean of praise that was not strictly accurate. All had not been plain sailing and the campaign far from successful.

Fulke wanted to keep his memory alive and his offer to escort Frances to Court was made because her appearance would be a reminder to those likely to forget. Frances promised she would return in due course but only when she felt well enough and that it would be in the company of her parents. She did not have the strength, as yet, to face the searching eyes, the speculation or the predatory pleasure so many found in the woes of others. The loss of a husband, two earldoms and vast wealth, not to mention an heir, was food for much comment. Neither did she want to face Penelope Rich, woven ineradicably and in verse, into the fabric of Philip's life. She would go first to see her parents at Walsingham House, and then she would go down to the Pembrokes at Wilton.

Philip's horses were now mainly at Penshurst and, except for those she used herself, Frances had loaned them to Robert and Barbara but she had particularly asked that the Andalucian stallion should be crossed with the small, lively grey mare, given her by Philip as a wedding present, which had an excellent pedigree and a very pretty head. Philip had loved his horses, not one of which was anything but excellent, and had never grudged their expense. Perhaps one part of his life, at least, could be kept alive for the future by a good breeding programme. Frances had learnt much from him, both horsemanship and horse management, and she wanted to begin making practicable use of the knowledge.

With this in mind, she and Robert went down one morning to the stables to make some sort of plan and were deep in blood lines and inspections when they heard the thud of hooves tearing up the driveway, shouts of greeting, Barbara's voice calling and the squeals of excited children. Into the stable yard charged the Earl of Essex, followed by Gilly Meyrick, his agent, Charles Blount, Brie's brother the Earl of Rutland, and William Pelham, all shouting greetings at once, tumbling off their horses and surrounding them like schoolboys. Frances had not seen any of them since leaving the Netherlands. She was delighted, unaware that her face was flushed, that there was hay in her hair and a smear down the front of the old dress she wore for the stables. They were like a concentrated blast of sunshine, Essex sweeping her up in his arms and kissing her, Charles Blount snatching her away to hug her himself, all of them asking how she did, was she recovered and when was she coming to Court? Their friendship and pleasure at seeing her warmed her heart and brought a glow to her eyes and she turned from one to the other laughing and answering their pelting questions. Catching up the reins of their horses and moving aside with smooth efficiency, was young Richard de Burgh, a large boy for his fourteen years, his blue eyes on Frances in curiosity and admiration.

Their reason for coming was that Her Majesty lay at Tonbridge, very close to Penshurst, on her way to inspect defences on the South coast. This was a fairly perfunctory expedition, because the Queen, dreading any form of further conflict and its inevitable expense, had chosen to believe that the Duke of Parma was preparing to open peace negotiations with her when, in fact, he was busily constructing a large flotilla of flat-bottomed barges to bring his armies across the Channel from the Low Countries in support of King Philip's huge Armada still assembling in Spain. Walsingham's intelligence had been most specific, but Her Majesty could not be brought, at this stage, to realise the extreme danger of leaving England's defence to her seamen. If the armies of Spain managed to land, there would be little or no defence. England was unprepared, as yet, to fight on land and there would be the danger of a most appalling slaughter. Lists were already being drawn up in the Escorial of those destined for the stake and Mary Tudor's reign would have been a picnic by comparison. The defence of England, excepting a heroic few, would be left to a be-smocked rabble wielding pitchforks and scythes.

On the strength of Walsingham's intelligence, Sir Francis Drake, at his own request, had been grudgingly permitted to conduct a scorching raid on Cadiz harbour in April, looting and burning a massive amount of shipping preparing there, including one of the Marquis of Santa Cruz's own galleons, and a further two dozen cargo and other ships. This was accomplished under heavy fire and despite a squadron of Spanish galleys resisting the attack. With Drake, and completely in his element, was Christopher Carleill, now a distinguished naval and military commander. It was an expedition after his own heart and wholly successful; it had probably set the Armada back by almost a year, since the raiders proceeded down the coast destroying supply lines from the Mediterranean.

Taking into account Drake's formidable sortie, Walsingham had a very fair idea that the Armada would be afloat by April or May the following year, 1588. He wanted as much as possible of England's armed force back from the Netherlands and held ready, not dispersed, and he advised a clear cut chain of command in charge of the defences. He was not getting very far with this, the Queen being anxious to demobilise as many as she could in the interests of economy while toying with the shameful idea of using the remaining holdings in the Low Countries as barter for favours from the Duke of Parma. Those bartered could have looked forward to a most unpleasant future. Tales of Spanish barbarity had circulated freely from troops returning from the Dutch campaign.

None of this was bothering the party in the stable yard, however. They were hungry and thirsty and they rushed Robert and Frances off to the house, beseeching Robert to do his duty as a host and at once. The children swarmed around them in the great hall and were heaved on to knees and benches, teased, made much of, and fed along with the guests. Discipline went by the board, sweetmeats were popped into small mouths as food was magically conjured up from the kitchens by Barbara, who had anticipated the need and knew how young men could eat. The wine began to flow.

Frances, coming down the main stairway having changed her dress for something more becoming than the grubby old stable gown, heard the buzz of chat and the roars of laughter before she descended, and thought how good it was to see them all again, particularly Essex and Charles Blount, now reconciled and clearly the best of friends. She smiled her lovely smile and floated down the stairs to rescue young Roger Rutland from Elizabeth who was climbing all over him, chattering and playing with his earrings.

Without turning his head, Essex reached out an arm to her and pulled them both down to sit beside him. Suddenly, he looked full at the child with an arrested expression and stayed so for several moments, taking in the striking likeness to Philip and the lion cub amber of hair and eyes. His gaze shifted to Frances's face, then back to Elizabeth's, comparing and assessing, almost with awe. A small part of Philip remained; all he had most revered was not lost. Smiling, he pulled them both closer to him.

Essex House. From the Mansell House Collection.

1591 – Essex House

The gardens of Essex House swept gently down from a long terrace to a wall into which were set wide steps leading to a landing stage, known as Essex Stairs, with mooring for a number of boats and barges. A brick arch at the head of the stairs was furnished with a handrail on either side to steady the steps of those who had been out on the water and, to the left, was a substantial boathouse which housed the rather grander craft, cushioned, canopied, and used for state occasions, river galas or visits to the many palaces along the Thames. Nonesuch and Greenwich lay downriver while Whitehall, Westminster, Richmond and Hampton Court lay upriver. Tucked into its bend of the river beyond Putney, nestled beloved Barn Elms.

A pack of children and dogs played on the green grass of the walled garden between the steps and the house, and the roses on the old brick walls were just beginning to burst into flower; their creamy pink buds almost more beautiful than the full blooms to come. Essex House had once been a bishop's palace and His Grace's gardeners had known what they were doing. It was one of many large mansions ranged along this bank of the Thames, very often named after their owners.

Two young women sat together in the shade of a cherry tree, eating fruit which neither had tasted before. A basket of dried figs, dates and pomegranates had been sent by Christopher Carleill after a confiscation of goods belonging to Spanish subjects in Ireland where he had been serving as Governor of Ulster. Penelope, Lady Rich, and Frances, Countess of Essex, had a great deal to talk, sigh and laugh over.

The children playing on the greensward were Lettice and Essex Rich and their brother, Robert, together with Elizabeth Sidney, and two very small boys, Henry Rich and Robert Devereux. Of these two, Robert was tottering around clutching a fig in one fist, while Henry sat on his mother's knee, sharing her fruit and sucking his sticky fingers. A red-haired baby of five months, Walter

Devereux, lay in a basket by their feet with a small, green parrot perched on one handle, making chirruping noises in imitation of the nurse. Through thick and thin, Greville had retained a privileged place in the household and was perfectly content to remain with his family, unfettered. He looked extremely sleek. Alongside the baby lounged two pretty little spaniels, one liver and white and one black and white. They were litter sisters, used for shooting and this was a rare moment of stillness for them. Frances had bred them at Barn Elms and was seldom without them. They sat now with their eyes fixed on her face, their tongues hanging out, poised for action.

This was a familiar scene since Lady Rich now had her own apartments in Essex House and sometimes brought a selection of children with her from Leigh's Priory, her Essex home. These numbered four, (a daughter born in November 1588 dying soon after birth), but, having secured the Rich succession with two sons, she considered her duty done.

The two elder Rich daughters were trying to stand on their heads with their feet in the air and, since they wore no underclothes except their shifts, this was being discouraged by their Mama. Elizabeth Sidney was attempting, with rather more success, to turn cartwheels and somersaults like the tumblers they had seen in the great hall yesterday evening. She was a small, lithe six year old, moving with her mother's co-ordinated grace and after each manoeuvre she ended with the tumbler's finishing pose; arched back, head tilted up and hands outflung in a gesture of triumph, the fingers pointing downwards; a fair imitation of what she had avidly watched last night.

The year was 1591 and a great deal of water had flowed past Essex Stairs since Frances had returned to Court for the New Year celebrations of 1588. Walsingham had, again, been bedridden, but Lady Ursula accompanied her daughter. As expected, this had not been easy despite the warmth of the welcome she was given from many friends, particularly those who had been devoted to Philip such as Sir Henry Lee, Fulke Greville, Edmund Spenser and Charles Blount. Brie was overjoyed to see her. She had grown quite beautiful, and was much admired, poetry being written in her name and several men offering for her hand. These she had, so far, managed to avoid, despite the best efforts of her uncle, Roger Manners, with his passion for family advancement. She was now a person of importance, the Queen's Carver, who waited on Her Majesty in her private apartments when she chose to eat there.

The Queen had been gracious enough to Frances, acknowledging Philip's part in the Netherlands campaign, regretting his death, and privately recalling that his funeral had distracted attention from the execution of the Queen of Scots. She also remembered to ask after the health of her goddaughter, Elizabeth. Frances thought that the years were taking their toll; even the quantities of ceruse on face and neck failed to hide the wrinkles and the brown spots of age. Nothing, though, had yet dimmed the Queen's mind, or her wits.

There were those who had overwhelmed Frances with protestations of pity at the loss of Philip, but whose speculative eyes searched for signs of regret that she was not now destined to be the Countess of Leicester and Warwick. There were unabashed enquiries about her financial position, since Philip's debts had been common knowledge, and an obvious sizing up of her value in the marriage market. She kept her head, answering enigmatically, but sometimes with chilling and depressing courtesy. She was obliged to deal thus with the Earl of Oxford, Philip's old enemy, who treated her with undue familiarity and two-edged sympathy. She stared at the hand he had laid on hers, then raised her eyes to his face with deliberation and surprise until he removed it, sketched a mere gesture of a curtsey and turned on her heel to greet Charles Blount with a brilliant smile.

Penelope Rich was not at Court, having just given birth to the daughter who had died so soon after. Her brother, Essex, was in close and constant attendance on the Queen and, although he greeted Frances with his usual careless affection, she saw very little of him.

Long before the huge crescent of Spanish ships was sighted sailing majestically up the English Channel that summer, Walsingham, with Burghley, had been working tirelessly to ensure that England was both prepared and properly defended. Intensive planning had taken a further toll on Walsingham's health. It was a long age since the country had suffered an invasion and there was a great deal to be done. England's isolation, since the fall of Calais, had bred in her people a fierce nationalism, and their attitude was that the invasion would never happen but, if it did, that Englishmen were invincible. By May, speculation on the size of the Armada ended when it was published in Spain that a hundred and thirty ships would sail. Their Commander, the Marquis of Santa Cruz having died in February, the Duke of Medina Sidonia, by his own admission no seaman and sadly afflicted by sea-sickness, was now appointed in his place. The Armada's destination and strategy was still undecided, but sail it must. The cost of its upkeep in harbour and that of its crews was proving too enormous to sustain.

The Queen was far too intelligent to share her subjects' view of any invasion and, in a private moment, confided her fears to Walsingham. He replied: "Madam, be content not to fear; the Spanish hath a great appetite and an excellent digestion; but I have fitted him with a bone for this twenty years, that your Majesty shall have no cause to doubt him: provided that the fire chance to slack which I have kindled; you will be ruled by me and now and then cast in some English fuel which may revive the flame"; a frank interchange between Monarch and long-time retainer.

The chain of beacons along England's south coast was found to be in a shocking state of disrepair. Duly refurbished, they were lit on 19th July as the tops of the Spanish masts appeared. The mood in the country was now rising rapidly from outrage to defiance, anger, and a grim determination to see the Spanish off. Men looked old enemies in the eye, clapped each other on the back and planned the defence of their cots, smallholdings and villages.

The Earl of Leicester, Supreme Military Commander of the Army, had fortified the old Roman camp at Tilbury and was encamped there. The Earl of Essex prepared to join him, having personally raised sixty foot soldiers and two hundred horsemen, and had escalated his expenditure by arraying them in the Devereux colours, an unbecoming orange and white. Thrilled to the core by the magnificence doled out to him, young Richard de Burgh had accompanied him with a string of horses from his family's estates in Ireland.

After much calculation and weighing of intelligence, Walsingham felt fairly certain the attack would be upon London via the Thames rather than the south coast. Tilbury and Stratford were strategically fortified, though a close watch was kept on the Isle of Wight and the Channel.

When the Armada eventually reached the narrower part of the Channel, to be confronted by the Lord High Admiral, Howard of Effingham, Drake, Frobisher, Hawkins and a phalanx of naval talent, it was discovered that Spanish seamanship, supposedly incompetent, was disciplined and effective. However, it was no match for the smaller, nimbler English ships with their seasoned commanders, and a mixture of foul weather, fire ships and a full gale ensured their tattered departure into the North Sea and, in due course, on to the fogbound rocks and treacherous tides of Scotland and Ireland. Some got blown as far North as the Fair Isles, made the shore and settled there, intermarrying with the islanders and using their inherited native weaving skills to institute the Fairisle designs which were to last five hundred years. They were last seen on 2nd August, having failed to make proper contact with the Duke of Parma and his landing craft.

The timing of the Queen's visit to Tilbury to rally and hearten her troops on 8th August was, therefore, not perfect. The enemy, already vanquished, had disappeared northwards, nobody seeming concerned that they might reappear.

Nevertheless, Her Majesty donned armour and rode her grey charger around the camp, famously declaring, as a parting shot, that she "had the heart and stomach of a King, and a King of England too." Her troops and the whole country were, by that time, in such a state of victorious euphoria that nothing could detract from the rejoicing. Triumphal portraits, poems, hymns and memorials flooded in; the Queen being portrayed as Gloriana, ruler of the waves, the Church, the Globe, and the mother and protector of her people. It was all very satisfactory.

For one man, it was a swansong. The Earl of Leicester was fading fast. Throughout the Armada crisis, he had maintained his role as the Queen's right hand man and the Commander of her land forces, rejoicing with her in her hour of victory, but at a cost; he was ill. Malaria had dogged him for several years, its recurring attacks leaving him weak, depressed, and its fevers giving him the high colour noticeable during his later years. With Lettice, he set off to take the waters at Buxton, but died at Cornbury House, near Thame in Oxfordshire, on 4th September. The Queen was heartbroken and shut herself in her room for days, grieving and inconsolable. Her "Rob" had been her great love, despite the many squalls in their relationship, and a precious link with her youth and happiness. She was an old woman now and the shadows were gathering fast. Even Essex was shut out.

Frances knew that there was another man who had paid a heavy price for England's salvation. Her father, comparatively unsung and unrewarded, had managed to remain on his feet during the crisis, planning, directing and anticipating. Now, he was again being crucified by his old enemy, kidney stones; still working from his bed, but a very sick man. Frances had remained with her parents at Walsingham House throughout the Armada conflict, helping him in whatever way she could, and it was at this time, while the Queen nursed her grief after the death of Leicester, that Essex came, once more, into her life.

Although he had been rewarded with the Order of the Garter for his loyalty and for his mustered men in orange, he was becoming impatient with his existence at Court; the easy conquest of giggling girls, the enforced grovelling to the Queen whose rapidly changing moods drove him demented, and, above all the lack of military action. The men he had raised to fight for her and his country had not been needed and, having once seen full-blooded action, jousting came a poor second. The sword that Philip had bequeathed him, and all that it signified, cried out for use, and in a good cause. Who else would follow Sidney's path as a chivalrous, Protestant knight? Although no promise had been made, the idea that he should, one day, give protection to that knight's lady and his child had lurked in his mind, prompted by seeing them both at Penshurst. He was surrounded by powerful women, all of whom adored him but never gave him any peace; his domineering Queen, his domineering mother and his domineering sisters. He needed a friend and ally to come home to and one who would act as a buffer. That the friend should be a lovely woman went without saying. As so often with him, the wish was father to the thought and the thought was father to the action. Knowing that Frances had returned to Barn Elms that August, following the Armada's defeat, he rode straight down, taking Gilly Meyrick with him.

For Frances, there was no respite from the intense courtship which followed; a battering which made her head and senses swim. She was not yet twenty one years old and Essex was in a league of his own with women. She held out for as long as she mentally and physically could, certain that he would never be faithful to her, but aware that marriage to a friend who would cherish Elizabeth for Philip's sake, besides ensuring the future for them both, would be better than to a stranger she neither knew nor cared about. The veil of friendship, however, was slipping fast and she was rapidly confronted with something far more potent. She still missed Philip with stabbing intensity, but her world dictated that she re-marry and the devil she knew seemed a wise choice. Physically, Essex played havoc with any decision her mind might try to make and he was not holding back. For so young a man, there was little he did not know about the art of love and he practised it with joyous abandon and laughing sensuality. He was, and knew it, irresistible, and he was making it plain that he found Frances irresistible too. None of this was lost on her and her body ached after his visits, while her mind struggled along in the rear, making it difficult to imagine any but one future with him. She managed to keep him at bay for four months without pre-empting marriage vows, knowing how horrified her parents would be if a child was expected out of wedlock. She sternly told herself that she stood in line with many other women in his life and wondered why this did not have the power to daunt her. From Brie, she had heard stories of his conquests and the dramas accompanying them. Perhaps it was lusty fun and not love that drove him to so much cherry-picking. He might find something better in marriage and with children of his own. She did not know the answer to that or to the vital question of whether she could love him enough to leave so much to chance, or even if she could love him at all. Never before had she felt so hopeless and confused. All Essex would do was pick her up, whirl her round till she was giddy then demand an answer while he kissed the breath out of her. How anything so wicked could look so downcast when she refused was a mystery until she caught the twinkle lurking in his innocent eye and knew he was perfectly sure of the outcome.

A different and rather material ploy used by Essex to persuade her into marriage was the acquisition of the lease of Englefield House where he and Frances had first met and hunted together and for which, he knew, she had a fondness. It would be, perhaps, a continuation of the Sidney legend and, for Frances, a return to happy memories of her childhood. His self-esteem did not allow him to wonder if she might not want to return there married to another man. The man was Robert Devereux; no more need be said. The Queen granted the estate to Thomas Crompton, Robert Wright and Gilly Meyrick as trustees for the Earl of Essex who then proceeded to spend vast sums on the house and land which retained the form he gave it down the centuries. It was also intended for the use of the widowed Lettice.

Four months later, in the dead of a freezing February night and with the greatest secrecy, they were married in St.Olave's Church, slipping out of Walsingham House wrapped in boat cloaks and knowing full well what kind of a Royal storm would be unleashed when the news became known. Kneeling on the icy stone with only a few flickering candles to show her the wondrous face beside her, Frances Sidney became the Countess of Essex. As his long, warm fingers closed on hers, she felt like a swift spreading its wings from a cliff face with nothing around her but empty air.

In a month's time, Essex was off on a very different mission, and one that was all too familiar to Frances. They were living, at this time, mainly in Walsingham House and Barn Elms, though Essex continued to spend most of his time at Court.

As a post-Armada spree, Drake was planning, once more, to raid Spanish waters. On the pretext that Philip's old friend, the deposed Dom Antonio of Portugal, needed a helping hand back to his throne, from which he had been ousted in 1581 by Spain, Drake proposed an attack on the Portuguese coast and the coastal forts held by the Spanish and, if they happened to be there, Spanish treasure ships, inadequately guarded by the remains of the Armada. This would teach them not to invade England and, from everyone's point of view, it was far too tempting a morsel to pass up. With him would go Sir John Norris, no spring chicken, but a favourite of the Queen. She had agreed, lending six of her ships and £20,000, but requiring a large reward for it out of the expected plunder. Then, as with Philip, the blow fell; she would not hear of Essex going with them.

Following in Philip's footsteps, he sent a very Falstaffian character, Sir Roger Williams, to outfit his ship "Swiftsure" at Falmouth. This professional soldier, who had served with him in the Netherlands and was as Welsh as he was himself, was devoted to him. Articulate, crude, alcoholic but efficient, he made sure all was ready by 3rd April. The main fleet was lying at Plymouth. Essex, or perhaps his wife, had learnt a few lessons; she had seen it all before. Leaving copious letters, some with Frances and some locked in his desk, he prudently joined his horses and grooms in St James Park under cover of darkness and rode the first stage like Jehu. With him went Sir Christopher Blount, that tall, dark soldier who had served with him in the Netherlands, now a tried and trusted friend. Fresh horses having been left for him along the route, he continued at breakneck speed to Plymouth, ascertained the date of the fleet's departure and rushed on to Falmouth without anyone discovering his identity. He had got clean away. Again, history repeated itself. The Queen, in due course, finding out where the truant had gone, sent letters ordering the arrest of the Captain of the "Swiftsure" and the return of Essex. Walsingham made sure they did not go in time. He had gauged the temper of Frances's husband and recognised the caged tiger he had seen before.

Unfortunately, Essex did not manage to join Drake's fleet off the coast of Portugal until 13th May, thus missing the taking of Corunna. He was greeted then by a barrage of furious letters, demands for his instant return and that Williams should be put in irons or executed. Sir Roger was well known to the Queen who had memorably told him to get out of her presence because "thy boots stink".

Well used to such letters, Drake soothingly replied to the Queen, that he could not "spare out of the fleet a ship of such good service as the "Swiftsure" and Essex remained to enjoy, with Williams, some rousing action which included wading waist high through the huge Atlantic surf to take a Portuguese fort, a long march to Lisbon under Sir John Norris, plundering churches as they went, but failure to take Lisbon itself. Utterly frustrated, Essex flung a spear into the bolted city gates with a challenge for any Spaniard within to single combat. This Homeric gesture got him nowhere. The Portuguese did not particularly want Dom Antonio back and were certainly not going to join the English invaders whom they regarded as pirates. Pirates they were, and Drake went on to plunder ships from Hanseatic ports putting in at Cascais, returning not with Inca gold but with practical and valuable merchant supplies.

In answer to a coldly threatening letter from the Queen, Essex cut short his escapade and returned to London by June. To his surprise, well elaborated news of his exploits had arrived before him and he found London prepared to give him a hero's welcome. He received no gold rope and red carpet treatment from the Queen, however, but he managed, after a thundering scold, to coax her into laughing at his adventures and returned to Barn Elms to find his wife pregnant with their first child.

She was not alone. Mistress Elizabeth Southwell, a Lady in Waiting to the Queen, was also expecting his child and made this clear to him soon after his return, which put him in a difficult position. His marriage to Frances was not known to anyone except their parents and his sisters and he was obliged to deal with Mistress Southwell as if he were the bachelor she thought him, though unwilling to wed her. The child was christened Walter Devereux. (Years later, in 1618, two young men, Robert, 3rd Earl of Essex and the illegitimate Walter Devereux, inheriting a shared love of music and drama, were both to take part in a performance of the " Corleorton Masque" at the home of the Beaumonts in Leicestershire, given to celebrate the marriage of a daughter of Frances). The wheels had turned, and remained interlocked, but the names were the same. Essex did not, at this time, feel equal to explaining the situation to Frances.

The Earl's women were certainly giving him trouble. His mother, Lettice, had no intention of remaining single and her eye was fixed upon none other than Sir Christopher Blount, her late husband's Commander of Horse, who had gone with Essex to Portugal and who had, earlier, helped engineer the downfall of the Queen of Scots with the aid of his kinsman, Robert Poley. He was nearer her son's age than her own. With what was considered indecent haste, she married Blount a matter of months after Leicester's death which gave rise to some nasty stories about infidelity and poison. Essex referred to it as an "unhappy choice." Lettice was, as always, impervious to public opinion and gave, as her reason, her need for a man's guidance through the complicated lawsuits that followed Leicester's death. She was, in fact, more than capable of fighting her own corner.

Her grief for Leicester did not prevent the Queen promptly taking steps to ensure that Lettice got no more from his estate than could be helped. His debts were enormous, especially to herself, and she insisted that a sale of his property and goods saw most of it re-paid, thereby depriving Lettice of any extra she might have had. Essex was given his stepfather's rooms in St James's Palace and some of his unencumbered land. He was also given Leicester's rights to the levy on "The Farm of Sweet Wines" for ten years, which produced a welcome and healthy income. Robert Dudley, (Leicester's illegitimate son by his former mistress, Douglas Sheffield), of whom he had been very fond, inherited Kenilworth. This left Lettice with his large house at Wanstead, Leicester House on the Strand and another estate at Drayton Basset in Staffordshire together with the remainder of his debts. She sold the London house to her son by 1593, although he and Frances were already living there and had re-named it Essex House.

Never far away and always at his elbow, urging and intriguing in his interest, Penelope Rich was also giving cause for concern. She had fallen deeply in love with Charles Blount and was finding it increasingly difficult to maintain the role of dutiful wife to Rich and mistress of Leigh's Priory. Her brother had made an apartment available for her at Essex House and here the lovers met in comfort and privacy. This put her into potentially awkward confrontation with Frances when both were in London.

The unexpected then happened. Penelope, never one to hide her light under a bushel and with all the cards of her life thrown in the air, turned to Frances for friendship and advice. She was impossible to resist. Completely forgetting that she had done her best to keep Philip by her side, she poured out her soul; love such as she had never known, passionate desire and single-minded determination to have Charles for her own. Frances put aside her wariness, met her at her own level, and realised she could no longer live in the past; Penelope was now her sister-in-law whether or not she had ever been Philip's lover in more than verse.

No two women could have been less alike. Penelope was an acknowledged beauty, flamboyantly wearing her heart on her sleeve. Frances, equally lovely in her way, was poised, outwardly gentle, and kept her counsel. Penelope leapt before she looked while Frances smiled serenely, very seldom leapt, and only acted after clear thought. What they shared was vitality, beauty and courage. In a surprisingly short time they became the closest of friends, mutual respect warming to laughter and the exchange of quick wits. Penelope was frequently outrageous but very good company and she was deeply generous and affectionate to those she loved. Lord Rich was not one of them and never had been. He knew well which way the wind was blowing, but chose to remain wrapped in rancorous silence, occasionally making snide remarks, but not daring to challenge Penelope's behaviour because of her brother's influence with the Queen and the military reputation of her lover. So far as she was concerned, he could do as he pleased. As early as November 1590, Charles had worn her colours for the Accession Day Tilt; her heart blatantly on his sleeve.

That occasion was a memorable one. Essex, still in some disgrace for absconding to Portugal, had made his entrance clad in "sable sad" and carried on a bier at the head of a mock funeral procession. This tongue in cheek effort to appease the Queen raised much mirth and a wry smile from Her Majesty. He subsequently fought with brilliance and panache.

Charles Blount, like Essex and Philip before him, became quickly bored with Court life. The Armada had been a boon to him and he had served and fought against the Spanish as Commander of a man-of-war, the "Lion". Despite his love for Penelope, his main aims were military.

Frances knew well that she would not be able to conceal either her own marriage or her pregnancy for long. Her father, worn out by the Armada and visibly sinking, had recognised her reasons for choosing to marry a man in such an exalted position and whom she knew well, and had given his consent, rather than his blessing. She could look no higher for a husband, but he, having spent most of his life reading men's thoughts and natures, did not feel optimistic about his new son-in-law's character. Despite the charm, he was mercurial and, therefore, unreliable. His motives and impulses were chivalrous, but they were all too likely to be blown away the moment he lost his temper. Walsingham had seen the tantrums and the sulks in his dealings with the Queen and was not impressed. What was forgivable in youth, would be tiresome and dangerous in later years. To him, however, Essex had always behaved with circumspection and respect and, despite his fluctuating fortunes, well known to Walsingham, he was not marrying Frances for money. There was very little left. Knowing that time was now short for him, he was glad to see her established in a second marriage.

He and Lady Ursula, (whom Essex had no trouble charming out of any doubts about the marriage), then received most unwelcome news. The Queen was planning to descend on Barn Elms as part of her 1589 Summer Progress, accompanied by a large part of the Court. This honour would be a financial coup de grace; the strain on health and resources would be enormous. Barn Elms might have to be re-furbished and enlarged, Robert Beale's house at Mortlake probably being requisitioned as well. The Queen had visited several times before, but only for specific reasons, for a day, and usually by boat.

These Summer Progresses were a well-established part of Court life and served several purposes. London, in the summer, became a stinking cesspit as the river sank and a mass of filth became stranded on the banks of the Thames. Many of the Queen's palaces and the houses of the great were particularly affected as they were situated on the river, London's aorta. The summer, besides the added stench, was rightly connected with the outbreak and spread of disease. Big households were obliged to move frequently in any case because they also became filthy; this accounted for the restless way life was conducted and the constant travelling and visiting which allowed houses to be cleaned and fumigated. The Queen's person had to be protected during the exigencies of the summer months, so the Progresses were an excellent way of killing several birds with one economical stone. Firstly, they removed the Monarch and the Court from the dangers of the city. Secondly, they were the platforms from which they could be viewed and admired by large numbers of the population. This had always been the practice of Kings and Queens. Authority must be seen, exclaimed over and acknowledged. (Henry II, whose rule extended over an area three times the size of Elizabeth's, since he held most of France and the Acquitaine, seldom spent more than two nights in any one place). The third reason for the Summer Progresses was that the Queen's subjects bore the cost of her Court for approximately three months of the year, and this was considerable. The Queen had a firm grip on domestic economy and was only too pleased to land her vast personal expenditure on a hapless subject. Those so honoured could neither refuse nor express anything but overwhelming joy at the thought of entertaining hundreds of people, their horses and their servants; entertainment on a grand scale was also expected, as were expensive presents. With ruin staring them in the face, her hosts pinned smiles on their countenances in the hope that a peerage at least might be round the corner after the last coach had lumbered down the drive.

This visit was, blessedly, to be a short one. Lord Talbot, writing to his father the Earl of Shrewsbury told him: "This day, Her Majesty goeth to Barn-Elmes where she is purposed to tarry all day, tomorrow being Tuesday, and on Wednesday, to return to Whytehall again. I am appointed, among the rest, to attend Her Majesty to Barn-Elmes."

Appointed with him was Brie who had lately received a strong missive from her brother, Roger Rutland. Knowing how she longed to return home and marry Robert Tyrwhitt, the Earl had written that he: "will heare no more talk of a marriage between thyself and our cousin Robert Tyrwhitt though some affection is naturel." She was to marry whom she was told; the decision would not be hers, but, inspite of her gentleness, he was to discover that there was a strong streak of obstinacy in Brie.

Frances, keeping very much in the background during the two day visit, welcomed Brie with open arms and urged her not to confront her brother, but to bide her time. Her pregnancy did not show at this stage and she was able to help her parents without drawing attention to herself. She felt well and full of energy; perhaps a son was on the way this time. Essex had managed to avoid accompanying the Court to Barn Elms but it was agreed that the Queen would very soon have to be told of the marriage. The visit left the Walsinghams exhausted though, mercifully, there had not been much time for entertainments, except a visit to John Dee, an old acquaintance of the Queen. All had run on oiled wheels.

When told of Essex's marriage to Frances, the Queen, as expected, threw the book at him. He knew what was coming and refused to let Frances anywhere near her, partly because he wanted to break the news in his own words and also because he knew the full blast of her anger would fall on his wife. Very clearly, he could remember the outrage that followed his mother's marriage to Leicester and the unremitting anger that had kept Lettice banished from that day. He let the storm break over his handsome head. The Queen shouted at him: How dared he marry without asking her, knowing she would never have permitted it? How dared he then flout her doubly by going on Drake's expedition? Like mother, like son, no doubt? The Queen then remembered that Walsingham's daughter had always seemed a threat and now she had been proved right. First, she had had the impertinence to dance La Volta so perfectly with Hatton; then there was her marriage to Sidney, the pride of her Court and, indeed, of England, and now she had ensnared Essex himself. Jealousy ripped her apart. The girl was not well-born, she was dark and small and had not even managed to give Sidney a son. She had rushed over to the Netherlands like a common drab, and without permission. The list of offences was dredged up and flung at Essex. It was two weeks before the Queen would listen to him and it took all his considerable address to convince her that marriage, for him, would always have been a necessity. He must have heirs, he was already twenty three, and Frances would be perfectly content to live in seclusion at Barn Elms, busily providing the necessary sons. She would not come to Court. Gradually, the thaw set in and the sun shone again.

Their unusual relationship was becoming more turbulent as time went on and the quarrels took longer to reconcile. He was, to the Queen, a mixture of recalcitrant son and ardent admirer, but the veneer was beginning to wear a little thin. He was becoming more rebellious and demanding and she was having to draw on the granite will that was hers in order to control him.

Frances had nerved herself, from the start, to accept that this second marriage was going to be a very different affair from the first although there were similarities. The undercover dash to the West Country in search of freedom and escape from Court was a repeat performance of Philip's although the aim was a bid for military action rather than a piece of arm-twisting. For Frances, the result was the same; the abrupt departure of a husband leaving her expecting a child. There was also the sense of sharing a husband; in Philip's case, with the memory of Penelope Devereux and, in Essex's case, with a far more permanent arrangement, his relationship with the Queen, on which his fortunes depended. Philip had treated her, from the start, with affection and courtesy which became something far deeper and more passionate while Essex had rushed in with the supreme confidence of one well accustomed to having his way with women. He was very beguiling and, indeed, a great friend, but Frances had few illusions about him as a husband. They spoke their minds to each other, and he was, almost always, excellent company, but there were hints of a darker side to his nature, and sometimes he would return from Court with his hair on end, breathing fire over someone playing fast and loose with his schemes or his position with the Queen, (too often Sir Walter Raleigh). He would find Frances and carry her off to some private place and pour out his frustrations. Without knowing it, he began to listen, and to rely upon her answers. Frances was, after all, Walsingham's daughter. Discretion was in the marrow of her bones and he could trust her as no other. He was able to pour out heart and soul in safety and be at rest when he was with her. He was also alarmingly attractive and in a very short time they had discovered that, physically, they were all too compatible.

Their first son, Robert, was born in January 1590 in Seething Lane and baptised in St.Olave's Church on 22nd January. He was a large baby with his mother's dark hair and grey eyes and he could not have been a greater contrast to the golden Elizabeth. Philip's daughter was inclined to view his appearance with jealousy and mistrust. He was the heir to an important father, where she had none, and he was taking far too much of her mother's time. The light went out of her amber eyes and her small mouth looked mutinous. Essex, who loved her, made the effort to charm her out of her moodiness, and do a little judicious spoiling when no one was looking. A visit to Penshurst, where she was the apple of every eye, did a great deal to restore her confidence. Robert Sidney and Essex were of an age and close friends so that, for Frances, the link with the Sidneys and Penshurst remained the same. She knew she was always welcome there though, unbidden, the memories rose to meet her in every corner of the old house, sometimes too sharp to bear. There was only one Philip. She had married something very different.

Penelope had remained with Frances throughout the birth of her son, keeping up her spirits with her chatter and proving herself a competent midwife. Even Lady Ursula, who strongly disapproved of her, acknowledged that she had more than made herself useful.

Walsingham's days were now numbered. He knew it and so did his wife and his daughter. For twenty-two years he had watched over, guarded and guided the Queen of England, at the same time fulfilling the gruelling position of Secretary of State and running a far-flung and highly efficient intelligence service, the like of which England had never seen. For this he went largely unacknowledged and scantily rewarded. He made his will on 12th December 1589 and died at Walsingham House on 7th April 1590 with Lady Ursula and Frances beside him. They buried him the following evening in the same tomb as his son-in-law, Philip Sidney, in St.Paul's, with a simple service and a few close friends. Walsingham money was now extremely short. Francis Milles and Robert Beale wept openly as did Daniel Bacheler for whom he had done so much. Also there were Essex, William Davison, Thomas Walsingham, Nicholas Faunt and his de-coding genius, Thomas Phelippes, all of whom had worked with him for many years. They shared a burning resentment that gratitude for such service seemed so scant. There were no processions, no flags flying, no grand guests and no presence of Majesty.

Frances was too exhausted to do more than watch, dry-eyed, the ceremony in the dim candle-lit recesses of St.Paul's, her heart lurching when Philip's tomb was opened to admit her father, the flickering light sending strange shadows across the gaping void and Daniel's superb voice chanting a requiem to the slow notes of his lute. Later that night, wrapped in Essex's arms, the tears seeped slowly into her pillow as images of childhood, music, gardening at Barn Elms, the beat of drums in the Paris night and his never-ending work, slid past her closed eyes. He had loved her more than most Elizabethan fathers did their daughters, not because she was the one and only child, but because she was akin to him in many ways and always a delight to his eye.

She believed she was expecting another baby and, feeling low and abysmally sad, wondered whether this was to be a permanent state of affairs.

Frances was left £100 per annum from Walsingham's lands in Lincolnshire in addition to the £200 per annum and the land in Wiltshire he had settled on her when she married Philip. He died owing the Queen some £40,000, largely the cost of running his agents and all that went with them. The debt was eventually waived by her successor, King James I. Frances and her mother retained the lease of Barn Elms, Lady Ursula retained Walsingham House which had come to her through her own family, the St.Barbes, and continued to live there, Frances often staying with her when she needed a respite from the fast-living Devereux family.

A second son was born to Frances and Essex earlier this year of 1591, in February, a beautiful child with golden-red hair, happily, not the flaming orange of the Devereux colours. Now, at five months, his eyes were turning from blue to the grey of Frances's own. He lay in his basket, crowing and reaching his fat little hands to Greville perched a respectful distance above him and croaking gently.

That joyous summer morning, Penelope had confided to Frances that she was expecting another child and that it was not Lord Rich's. She was delighted, had no fear of the future and no plans to re-establish herself in the eyes of the world. The dashing face and form of Charles Blount completely filled her horizon. She was his upon any terms but Frances was concerned for her and for the future of her children. The two heads bent together, speaking softly, the gold of Sidney's Stella contrasting with the shining darkness of his wife; eyes like black plums looked into the depth of changeful grey ones.

Interruption came with the announcement that the Countess of Leicester had arrived. Lettice had retained her title despite her marriage to Christopher Blount and had come to visit her daughter-in-law and daughter before retiring to Wanstead. She, also, had retained her rooms in Essex House and used them frequently. With her today was her younger son, Walter, visibly a Devereux, but without his brother's magnetism. She swept in, looking as she had always done, very much the "grande dame" and with the same air of self-satisfaction. Her interest in her grandchildren was limited, except for her son's heir, Robert, whom she picked up and kissed until she realised his face was sticky with fig juice and his hands were unspeakable. She put him down in a hurry. Robert then made bad worse by wiping the kiss from his face with both terrible little paws and Jane Rehora, watching from the terrace, came quickly down and carried him off to be washed.

Jane had remained with Frances throughout the past five years, both as her personal maid and as a nurse to her children and was now an integral part of their lives, as Alice had been with Frances. Alice had died the previous year, very overweight and lovingly tended by Lady Ursula and Frances. Leander remained at Barn Elms, now an old man, but majestically performing what duties he could. The late Royal visit had been the pinnacle of his career and he had risen to the occasion with true heroism, his expression from another sphere despite the cracking of his joints. After Walsingham's death, Daniel Bacheler joined the household at Essex House, a brilliant addition to what was to become a centre for arts of every kind and a source of generous sponsorship.

Essex spent lavishly on this and every other aspect of his life. It was an essential part of his existence and a part of his nature; houses, horses, clothes, barges, communications; nothing was spared. Added to this, he had gathered up a large part of Walsingham's intelligence service and was to use it, initially on behalf of the Queen and, later, as a power base run mainly from Essex House.

Frances was more than happy not to spend the majority of her time at Court, observing her husband's gyrations as the Queen's favourite, but to move between Essex House, Barn Elms and Walsingham House, with visits to Englefield, Penshurst and Wilton. She was able to be with her children for very much more time than most of her contemporaries and indulge her love of animals. Besides Greville, there were her two small spaniels, who accompanied her everywhere, and several favourite hounds. As Countess of Essex, she could call on quantities of staff and stewards in every residence to ensure her comfort and ease of passage.

Under Robert Sidney's eye, several good foals had been bred from Philip's horses at Penhurst, both for his use and Frances's. The Andalucian stallion had produced a beautiful riding mare for her as well as two big carriage horses inheriting the required amount of bone and muscle, but very much better looking than most. More knowledgeable than either Robert or herself was nineteen year old Richard de Burgh who, though diffident when asked for help, proved quickly that he had an almost uncanny understanding of all matters equine. He loved horses as Philip had done and could reduce the most difficult of them to sweetness and light in no time at all. He came down to Penshurst often to break and school the young stock and advise on breeding and it was a pleasure to watch him effortlessly handle the most fractious.

Frances had tried to keep Essex apart from this small enterprise, knowing he would try to take it out of her hands and use the horses for his own ends. He was very apt to appropriate anything connected with Philip, as he had, after all, appropriated her. This was a scheme in which she found a great deal of pleasure and which provided a good reason to spend time at Penshurst and to take her children away from London.

She knew her presence at Court, even had the Queen tolerated it, would have been a penance, and no hindrance to the gallivanting of her husband. What the eye did not see, the heart was less inclined to grieve over.

Well she knew the temptations of life at Court for Essex and the covetous glances aimed his way from many beautiful women who should have known better. Those glances had grown no less during his years as the Queen's favourite, nor had his ability or wish to resist them and the liaisons that went with them. Mistress Elizabeth Southwell, Lady Mary Howard, Mistress Russell, Elizabeth Brydges, Lord Chandos's daughter, had all, apparently, fallen or were falling, by the wayside. He knew that Frances knew what he was, and it was an accepted fact between them; they had few secrets and he did not lie to her about his women. He did, indeed, love her in his fashion, but true to her he would never be. He was generous to a fault, often surprisingly thoughtful, and would go out of his way, to the point of sticking his neck far out, to obtain favours for a friend, or to help those in need. He did not appear to possess that inbuilt warning that tells men when to draw back, either in speech or action. With Essex it was now or never, and, combined with an explosive temper and total fearlessness, he was regarded by some as a loose cannon. By others, including many of the common people, he was regarded as something of a hero.

The hero returned to Essex House that perfect June evening, after weeks of badgering and cajoling his Queen, and ecstatic with joy. She had capitulated and he had been put in command of a further English force, destined for France in support of its King, now Henry IV of Navarre.

Frances was in the garden, watching a heron on the river, its hunched shoulders and fearsome beak outlined against the afterglow, her thoughts flowing with the tide. He stole up behind her, slid his long arms round her and buried his face in her hair. He was shaking with laughter and she could feel the tension and excitement in him from head to heels; he was vibrant, so ablaze she could have warmed her hands on him. No need for words; she knew what he was going to tell her.

ACT THREE 3

1591-1592 – France, Essex House

The French Campaign of 1591 and 1592 was very nearly a disaster and it seared the soul of its Commander, the Earl of Essex, though it failed to dent his confidence. It was his first command of English forces abroad and it could very well have been his last. He had left the country without clear arrangements having been made with the wily Henry IV and, therefore, with no clear orders on how to proceed on arrival in France. This was the fault of the Queen and her ministers who had, none of them, got the measure of the French King and who had failed to extract the necessary agreements regarding money and military procedure from his representative, the Duke of Turenne. This equally wily gentleman, having assessed Essex, remarked wearily: "the difficult thing is to restrain him, not to push him forward." The Queen's grasp on matters of strategy, communications and foreign finance was not as sharp as it had been ten years ago, nor was her forethought. Age was creeping up.

Henry IV had succeeded Henri III, (the Duc d'Anjou of St Bartholomew's infamy). The personal habits of this last Valois King had been unpleasant and did not include the procreation of children, despite his marriage. It was a great relief to many, except the Catholic League, represented by the Guise family, when an assassin put an end to him. Catherine de Medici had not been a successful founder of dynasties. Three of her sons had ruled France without producing an heir and one had died unmarried despite a long courtship of the Queen of England. The jovial Henry IV came to the throne from Navarre, robustly Protestant and leader of the Huguenot faction in yet another of the "Religious Wars" so ruinous to France. In October 1590 a Spanish army had landed in north west France clearly planning to meet the Duke of Parma who was invading from the eastern Netherlands. This could mean a Catholic Franco-Spanish corridor along northern France, and an ideal launching opportunity for further attacks on England from Calais and Le Havre, with Rouen to the South, and all in Catholic hands. The Queen had been persuaded, despite her dislike of expensive foreign warfare, to make a push to prevent any further Armadas. The siege of Rouen was to be Essex's main objective. Sir John Norris, tough old campaigner that he was, and Essex's old crony, Sir Roger Williams of the "stinking boots", were already in France with some 3,000 men.

Listening to the frenzied plans before he left and watching the perfectly staggering array of clothing being laid out for packing, Frances thought it all looked more like a Papal visit than preparations for siege and battle. Amid the welter of orange velvet, much of it heavily embroidered with gold and lined with white satin, one of the few reminders that this was a military expedition was Philip Sidney's sword, at last intended to strike a blow for Protestant Europe. Essex was exuberant and Frances felt redundant in every sense.

She was fearful for him; he revelled in the thought of fighting and danger drew him like a magnet. She knew there was nothing he would rather do than challenge a man to single combat and fight until he dropped and that a siege would not suit him at all. Frances prayed that Rouen would fall speedily if it came to that; she also prayed for his safety, trusting that the Lord understood how little thought he would give to it himself. Her faith, drummed into her from babyhood, had grown somewhat faded since the death of Philip and she had a strong feeling that she was going to need it in the years to come.

Yet again, Essex had plundered his estates to muster men and horses, even threatening to terminate the tenancy of those who refused. He had also mustered his younger brother, Walter, who, having stood in Essex's shadow all his life, was more than willing to go with him in search of a share in fame and fortune. Walter had been married, very young, to Margaret Dakins, a dull heiress who had been brought up with him and his sisters, in the household of the Earl and Countess of Huntingdon; they were no strangers. Try as she did, Frances could not like Margaret. Despite her wealth, she was mean, small-minded and had absolutely no sense of humour. The young couple also had apartments in Essex House.

The brothers sailed in August, leaving Frances to reflect that her life appeared to be a series of anxious adieux interspersed with the birth of children. That she and Essex seemed to produce babies if they so much as looked at each other was a doubtful asset. She wondered whether their farewells this time would result in yet another Devereux; Walter was only seven months old.

Frances was left in charge of Essex House, Barn Elms, and Essex's estates in Staffordshire and Tamworth. She knew the stewards there would only call on her if there was any sort of crisis, but the management of Essex House with its permanent residents and many guests was a full time occupation. It was equivalent to running a first class and very full hotel. Besides Penelope and Charles Blount, Lettice and her new husband, Walter Devereux and his wife, and the children with their nurses, there were a host of staff and semi-permanent guests; artists, playwrights, friends, and those who had dined well and chosen to spend the night. Also with rooms of his own, was old Sir Francis Knollys, the father of Lettice and grandfather of Essex.

The house was something of a labyrinth and quite irregular in shape. There was a large forecourt for the arrival of horsemen and coaches and a paved inner court with steps leading into the galleried great hall, which was south facing. On this ground floor, also, was a warren of kitchens, larders, storerooms, armouries and servants' rooms. Above the great hall and also south-facing was the great chamber and, on the same floor, were the family apartments. Penelope, with typical panache, had made the most of hers. It contained a huge and splendid bed, draped in black, gold and silver and with a black velvet canopy trimmed with gold and black damask. It was the bed of a courtesan and it would have shocked the bible-thumping Lord Rich into fits had he ever seen it. Frances and Penelope collapsed in helpless laughter when it was delivered, together with black velvet stools and cloth of silver cushions.

There were 42 bedrooms altogether in Essex House and a picture gallery, also on the first floor.

The Earl and Countess and their family occupied rooms on the north and west sides of the great court, the children and their attendants on the ground floor, and their parents on the floor above. Frances had arranged her rooms with light, bright colours; creamy yellow combined with aquamarine and coral pink. Standing where it caught the maximum amount of light was the "great crystal glass" inherited from the Earl of Leicester and where, as she had done as a child in Walsingham House, she would practise new dance steps, strut out the old favourites and teach Elizabeth all she knew. Some of their happiest moments were spent here and it gladdened her heart to see how quickly and gracefully the little girl could learn. She had only to teach her the steps; the movements were instinctive.

On the third floor of the house were rooms for the steward, Gilly Meyrick, the Greek scholar and advisor, Henry Cuffe, Antonio Perez, a Spanish diplomat attached to the Earl whose past was extremely chequered, Daniel Bacheler, and Richard de Burgh when he was in London. It was a maze of small rooms, many leading into each other.

Separate from the house were the porter's lodge by the main entrance gate, the chapel, and rooms above the boat house down by the river. Also separate and further downriver were large stable blocks around a courtyard and the falconry. The whole establishment was staffed and maintained in the grand manner (there were seldom less than a hundred and forty servants) and was typical of the London houses of the nobility, especially those ranged along the north bank of the Thames. It ranked with Durham House, Sussex House, Arundel House and York House. Behind and dwarfing them all, stood the monumental St Paul's Church.

Having spent most of her twenty three years in London, the city was more home to Frances than anywhere else, but this did not prevent her feeling a great sense of freedom and release when she was able to go down to Barn Elms or Englefield and this she planned to do while Essex was in France. The country satisfied her soul in a way no city could; the stillness, wind in the trees, and, above all, the time to think. She loved watching and recognising birds, and the small creatures of field and woodland, with nature slipping from one season to another as it always had done. Her days of ferreting with Thomas Walsingham were not forgotten and she was determined that her own boys should have such memories of childhood. At this stage of her life, however, her place was within reach of Essex and mainly in London and Barn Elms. He was tied to the Court and the Queen and she was, indeed, a buffer for him against his women.

She had cleared the hurdle between herself and Penelope with surprising ease, due mainly to the fact that Penelope's existence was completely filled by Charles Blount and she had clearly erased Philip from her mind. When, as Mary Pembroke had foreseen, "Astrophil and Stella" was published earlier in the year, Penelope barely read it despite the fact that she was so clearly portrayed as the fair Stella. No one could mistake such lines as:

"Rich in the treasure of deserv'd renown'
Rich in the riches of a royal heart,
Rich in those gifts which give th'eternal crown;

Who though most rich in these and every part,
Which makes the patents of true worldly bliss,
Hath no misfortune, but that Rich she is."

There was also mention of her golden hair and dark eyes and, forcing herself to read it, Frances suffered a stab of terrible jealousy. Philip had never written poetry for her or murmured the sweet nothings that tripped off "Astrophil's" pen so smoothly. Then, unexpected, came an answer. "Astrophil's" lust for "Stella", self-parodied in places, had been unfulfilled. Philip had been laughing at himself. With Frances, it had been no laughing matter, and what was whispered to her in the dark hours before dawn, had no need for clever verse or ridicule, neither was there anything unfulfilled. Penelope had been to him what John Wickerson had been to her, a great love, but a prelude. That was her answer and she would live with it. Nevertheless, Mary Pembroke had been right; though full of innuendo, it was beautiful verse.

Her dealings with Lettice, still obstinately Countess of Leicester, had not been so easy. "Robin" was the apple of her eye and no woman would have been good enough for him, but one who brought no fortune with her, had already been married and was not nobly born, was very far from good enough. The fact that her father had held one of the highest positions in the State, and her husband had been England's "perfect knight," did not weigh with Lettice. Birth and fortune were what mattered and beauty helped. This, Lettice was forced to admit, was not lacking although it was, in her eyes, not comparable to that of her daughters, Penelope and Dorothy, whose fair good looks perfectly suited the standards of their age. They were, after all, cousins of the Queen, and their colouring matched hers. Her gaze, however, as did that of many others, focused on Frances almost against her will. Her movement alone drew the eye, her carriage was regal, and when that small figure entered a room, the regard of many followed her, involuntarily demanding closer inspection. Lettice grudgingly admitted that she was lovely, the crystal clear eyes with their down-swept lashes, lighting when she did smile with no coquetry, but unfeigned delight. Lettice admitted that she might be a worthy Countess but determined that there was to be no encroachment on Robin's affection for herself, or upon what influence his mother still had with him. She attempted, several times, to assert her authority over Frances only to find, on later reflection, that though the new Countess had smiled disarmingly and clearly not opposed her mother-in-law, no headway had been made at all. Commands that she had given were somehow not obeyed and, eventually, she began to find that her orders to servants, if they ran counter to those of the Countess, were deferred to her. To one of her autocratic nature, this was insupportable, but when she swept down the corridor to Frances's rooms to attempt a confrontation, she found, again, that her anger was diffused. Frances gently pointed out that Lettice was to be spared the running of Essex House since she already had the fatigue of managing the Wanstead and the Staffordshire estates. Frances would ensure that her wishes were to be granted and that she was as welcome as she had always been in her old home, but would it not be better if they discussed matters first, so that there was no confusion over the question of command? This suggestion was delivered with the greatest courtesy. Robin would be most distressed if there was friction between his wife and his mother, whose comfort and well-being were of paramount importance to him. In her own absence, Lettice was to order things just as she chose. At the end of this interchange, Lettice found there was little left for her to say; Frances had been sweetly reasonable and it was impossible to take offence. Very gradually, and with a few jealous lapses on Lettice's part, mutual respect grew up between the two women and they began to enjoy each other's company. Frances found Lettice's selfishness refreshingly straightforward; she knew exactly where she stood with her. But if Lettice attempted to interfere in Essex's plans and policies, she found she was being carefully side-lined or that decisions had already been made, sometimes contrary to her advice and without her knowledge.

Penelope, who was a great meddler and intriguer in her brother's life, and, indeed, wielded a certain amount of influence through her own contacts, had already found that her efforts met with the same results. The new Countess had proved herself the cushion so much needed between Essex and three, at least, of his women. The fourth was beyond her reach; all she could do was to pick up the pieces from that direction; she had nothing at all to do with his mistresses. She had also proved that despite their best efforts, and despite her gentle ways, she could not be bullied or led by any of them. At the same time, they found that it was impossible not to respect her and, eventually, to hold her in great affection. Not for nothing was she Walsingham's daughter who knew exactly how to: "Speak no more than you may fully retreat from without danger, or fairly go through without opposition." She had a far better brain than any of the Devereux and although she was at pains not to demonstrate this, it was a fact that, in time, became clear to all of them.

Essex's campaign in France was bogged down almost from the start and through no fault of his own. After landing with his forces in Dieppe, he found that his allies, under Henry IV, were nowhere to be seen but that the King was encamped at Compèigne, some hundred miles away with hostile forces between them. Sir Roger Williams, who knew his stuff when it came to French wars, advised him to make the journey, dangerous though it was, in order to pin the King down on strategy and terms before attempting any other action. Essex was only too pleased with such a hazardous plan, selected an impressive entourage, and raced across to Compèigne through enemy territory before anyone was aware of his presence in France. With him went Richard de Burgh, now nineteen, and longing for action.

Henry was delighted to receive him. When he set eyes on the entourage, his eyebrows flew up and down and his large mouth curled in an appreciative grin. Six mounted pages were followed by six trumpeters and twelve squires all decked out in orange velvet while Essex himself was dressed with the greatest splendour in a cloak embroidered with jewels matched by his horse's harness. Compèigne had never seen anything like this mass of orange magnificence.

Hiding his mirth, Henry made them extremely welcome and entertained them with the best his camp could provide. Sitting at ease, having consumed a large dinner and copious amounts of excellent wine, the firelight flickering on their two remarkable faces, Essex and Henry of Navarre took stock of each other. Henry, his heavy-lidded eyes missing nothing, saw himself, at twenty-five, mirrored in the handsome face before him, recognised his own careless charm and his unfailing love of women, but saw, also, the thwarted longing for action. He would make use of that.

Essex saw, as Philip Sidney had before him, a man whose huge love of life and wicked humour was matched by a fearlessness similar to his own. After two days, with very little achieved except goodwill, Henry bade them a fond farewell and rode off in the opposite direction to drum up support from Germany. Essex was expected to take Rouen and hold it with no apparent French assistance. That would keep him busy. He had been nicely hoodwinked by the delightful French King from whom he had got nothing but splendid hospitality. Nevertheless, a bond had been forged between them which would remain; a recognition of kindred spirits.

After this pleasant interlude, things went from bad to appalling. Having ridden back through Catholic-held, and now forewarned territory, to Dieppe, a hair-raising journey involving great risk and speed, Essex succumbed to the fever that, together with malaria and dysentery, was decimating his troops. Still too ill to rise, he was brought the terrible news that Walter had been killed while approaching Rouen with the vanguard intended to make the first move against the city. A bullet had struck him in the cheek and he died almost at once. Essex was prostrated with grief and guilt.

He was unaware that the Queen, now really roused, had recalled him on 24th September. She had waited at Portsmouth for some time in the very unreasonable hope that Essex would bring King Henry over to discuss terms and, having been made to look ridiculous, her wrath knew no bounds.

The news of his recall did not reach the Earl until early October, by which time the French King had unpredictably decided, after all, to send a large force to Rouen; the death of Walter may possibly have changed his mind. Essex joined them en route for the city, and, after a united effort, the fort of Gournay, near Rouen, fell on 27th September.

When Essex, still ill and melancholic, received the news of his recall, he committed, with typical flamboyance, the one act calculated to further provoke the Queen. Flourishing Philip Sidney's sword, he proceeded to knight twenty-four of his officers, not one of whom had taken part in any major action, let alone a victory. Her Majesty, he well knew, had been enraged by the number of knighthoods granted by Leicester in the Netherlands, and had vigorously cut down their distribution.

On his return, his reception in Whitehall was markedly frigid and his return to Essex House in the dusk of a murky October evening, bearing Walter's body to be laid in the chapel, was sombre. As the clatter and rumble of the cortège came past the porter's lodge, Frances, waiting, seized a torch from its sconce on the wall, and ran to the entrance of the great hall. She was horrified by the sight of her husband as he rode in out of the gloom. He was gaunt and grey; there were lines in his face she had never seen before and she noticed that when he dismounted, he staggered slightly. He saw her, standing straight and small, in the light from the great hall door, the bright torch held high in her hand, and he made for her as for a beacon. She had guessed, from the dire news brought them from the palace, what kind of a reception he would get there and she longed to see him warmed, sheltered and fed.

Only much later, when Walter's body had been laid in the chapel, four men at arms set to guard it, the proper condolences and explanations made to his wife, his mother and his sister, and a glass of strong, warmed wine in his hand, did she get the full story of the failure in France from him. They sat in the firelight of their own room, he sprawled in the comfort of a cushioned chair, she on a stool before him, his long fingers playing with hers and occasionally thumping her hand on his knee to demonstrate a point. Truly, most of it had not been his fault. The knighting of the twenty-four most certainly had, but now was not the moment to tell him so. Even if she did, what were the chances that he would not commit the same, or an equally extravagant folly, in the future? He had endured his brother's death, the disintegration of his army and the jeers and sneers of his Queen. Whatever was to come, tonight was an oasis of warmth, comfort and peace. She would not spoil it.

Frances had spent the last weeks trying to console Walter's permanently lachrymose and prostrated widow, Margaret, and the far more stalwart Lettice who, though badly shaken by her son's death, did not allow it to disrupt her life. Frances could not help but admire her fortitude but felt that, as with her cousin the Queen, there were very few things or people who could penetrate her self-sufficiency. She had a young and virile man to divert her; Christopher Blount had merged seamlessly into the Devereux clan and what was to become the Essex House set. Penelope, with the same toughness of fibre, had been able to deal with her distress in the comfort of Charles Blount's arms though Blount, himself, was extremely restive, despite his preoccupation with Penelope, and was longing to join Essex in France and pursue the military career he had thrived on under Sir John Norris in the Low Countries and had always hankered after. As in her dealings with Philip Sidney, the Queen had given him post after post, but always domestic. He wanted to lead men in battle not in politics.

Within the walls of his own home, his family and his dependants around him, Essex quickly recovered and began to climb back on his pedestal. He was not given very long. On 14th October, he was summoned to Court and peremptorily sent back to France. His orders, this time, were clear. Rouen was to be taken, with or without French Protestant assistance. He had begged to lead the English force, now he must prove that he could do it.

The sorry story continued when he arrived back in France. Sickness and desertion had robbed him of most of his army, and although reinforcements were sent and Rouen was besieged, it did not fall. There were sharp and often heroic skirmishes fought with the troops within the town when they showed their noses beyond the walls, but without much of the expected French support. In all these, the English, led by Essex, showed exemplary courage, but the end result was a return to England in January 1592, leaving what was left of his army under the command of Sir Roger Williams. It was an inglorious departure but what had been learned from it and would he ever again be asked to command an English army in the field? Charles Blount, unable to contain his thwarted longing any longer, then took up the baton, absented himself from Court, and joined Williams to fight a rearguard action against the Spaniards infiltrating North-Western France. He was eventually hauled back with the inevitable harangue and given the post of overseeing the New Forest, much to the relief of his mistress, Penelope.

Frances had kept Christmas and New Year at Barn Elms with her children, Lady Ursula and with Alice and Christopher Hoddeson, together with their daughter. It was a quiet, family gathering and gave her a feeling of cocooned content despite her anxiety over the situation in France. Decorating the hall with holly, ivy and garlands of mistletoe and berries, singing the Christmas songs in the glow of the yule logs, with Daniel Bacheler making the music, and watching the wonder on her children's faces as they absorbed the story of Christ's Nativity, the delight and excitement of gifts, given and received; all these brought the peace rarely found in her life at this time.

Walter, now nearly a year old, could pull himself to his feet and stand, swaying like a drunkard, for a few moments. Watching the look of achievement on his perfect little face as it appeared over the top of the stool he had clung to for support, was one of many joys for Frances that Christmas. He was a child of great beauty, and his smile lit a room like a Renaissance angel. His elder brother, Robert, was darker, more demanding, and jealous of the attention Walter always attracted. Frances took pains to draw out her elder son, curb the impatience he had inherited from his father and give him as much of her time as she could. The Hoddeson's daughter, another Ursula, now almost fifteen, needed watching also, especially in her dealings with Elizabeth. She was restive, adventurous, and longing to escape into a wider world. She rode like a gypsy, encouraging Elizabeth to follow her, tried skating on water not completely frozen and was beginning to make eyes at any personable male. Her mother, the gentle Alice, bewailed the fact that she had not been born a boy and hoped to get her speedily married.

Mary Pembroke had suggested that they all go down to Wilton for the twelve days of Christmas, but Frances did not want to be too far from London this year, in case news came from France. What tidings she did receive came from friends at Court, particularly Brie, who faithfully passed on any information concerning Essex. She thought of him with apprehension, fearing a recurrence of his fever in the cold discomfort of camp life with its dirt and miserable food. Physically, she knew that he was tough, but, mentally, it might be another matter. The shadow of his brother's death outside the walls of unconquered Rouen would lie heavily.

He returned in mid-January 1592, chastened but determined to put the fiasco in France behind him, and equally determined not to relinquish his post as Commander of English forces. He had matured considerably and his ambitions had widened. He had begun to use his mind as well as his sword, and it was at this time that two highly competent brains swam into his orbit. Anthony and Francis Bacon were the sons of Sir Nicholas Bacon, Keeper of the Great Seal during the early part of Elizabeth's reign, and were two exceptionally intelligent men. Both had spent time in Burghley's household (his wife, Mildred, being their aunt) but while Francis had weaselled his way to Court and influence through Gray's Inn and various Parliamentary seats, Anthony had ranged through the courts of Europe as a gentlemanly spy, reporting to Walsingham and other patrons, and coming to rest in Montauban, the home town of Henry of Navarre who had proved a true friend to him. Both brothers were known to be homosexual, a fact deplored by their mother, the forceful Lady Anne Bacon, who complained ceaselessly from the family home of Gorhambury, bewailing the lack of marriages and grandchildren. Burghley had not gone out of his way to befriend them, seeing in them a threat to his own son, Robert Cecil, whom he intended should step into his shoes. They were not wanted in that camp. What more natural than that they should ally themselves to the Queen's favourite who had birth, money and military influence and in return for whose generosity they could offer brains, hard work and ambition. It was a partnership that would be difficult to beat.

Frances had never met Anthony Bacon, except as a small child in Paris, but his brother had worked with Walsingham and was known to her. She did not like him and, with an intuition inherited from her father, she did not trust him. She told herself her instincts were unreasonable and biased; his intellect should be respected, he was already proving useful to Essex, so why did she always wish to leave a room as soon as he entered it?

A month after Essex's return, these and all other thoughts, were driven out of her head. Her beautiful baby, Walter, the picture of health, developed a virulent fever, accompanied by a rash. Frances was no over-careful mother, but she could see at once that this was more than a childish winter complaint. The best doctors were summoned and gave her varied reports. They bled him, applied hot bricks to his feet, fomentations to his chest and shook their heads. His bright gold hair dark with sweat and his body burning, he clung to life and to Frances for four days. She could feel him growing cool and prayed, as she had never prayed before, that the fever was leaving him, but cool turned to cold and he died in her arms one arctic February morning. He was just a year old.

They buried him on 19th February in the church of All Hallows by the Tower, the little coffin disappearing with horrible speed into the dark earth, as if his brightness had never graced their lives.

ACT THREE 4

1594-1597 – Calais and Cadiz

By 1594 Essex House had become a glittering centre for "The Brilliant Stage" and its company of extravagant characters. It was very far from a domestic retreat from Court.

Frances was now presiding over an establishment which shone ever more brightly on the northern bank of the Thames, gathering to itself the stars of a generation. Poets, musicians, actors, soldiers and spies met, made merry and rubbed sparks of genius off each other.

At the centre of the circle were those most closely bound by ties of kinship, marriage, love and lust. Essex, himself, was the magnet, married to Sidney's widow. His sister, Penelope Rich, Sidney's "Stella", was the mistress of his greatest friend, Sir Charles Blount. Lettice, their mother, was married to Sir Christopher Blount, Leicester's former Master of Horse, and now stepfather to the Devereux clan, and Dorothy Devereux, Essex's younger sister, was married, for the second time, to the Earl of Northumberland. Robert Sidney, Frances's brother-in-law, was a close friend of Essex, as was Henry Wriothesley, Earl of Southampton and Roger, Earl of Rutland, the brother of Brie.

The outer circles saw Sir Roger Williams, soldier of fortune, Anthony Bacon, now running Essex's intelligence service, his brother, Francis Bacon, lawyer and advisor and Henry Cuffe, with his origins in an apple farm in Hinton St.George, Somerset, a clever intriguer who had, like so many, hitched his wagon to the Essex train and who worked with the Bacon brothers. There were also Daniel Bacheler, now writing music performed at Court, the Earl of Southampton's protégée, William Shakespeare, a frequent visitor, as was Frances's cousin, Sir Thomas Walsingham, sponsoring the young poet and spy, Christopher Marlowe. It was a kaleidoscope of talent and energy, a collective of diverse dreams covering imperial expansion, foreign warfare and political and monetary power together with all forms of art. Those dreams and the ambition that went with them were pinned on Essex; charismatic, generous and the ticket to success. Like many of that restive throng, he moved ceaselessly from palace to palace, at the heart of the Summer Progresses and a champion of the joust.

Frances did not sit idly waiting for him. She loved the dancing, the masques and the music, the challenging arguments and the constant arrival of guests, so many now her good friends. She had no yearning for the more rigid protocol of the Court, the back-stabbing and the vicious power-play under the auspices of an ageing Queen. That was her husband's world and what had been created in Essex House was much more enjoyable. Certainly, debates became heated in the Great Hall; the age was volatile and crude at times. A protein charged diet washed down with quantities of alcohol and accompanied by sugary excess did not make for even tempers. Spleen rose quickly on such fare and most men carried knives.

Frances kept her unspoken promises to Essex but did not expect the same in return. She accepted that he spent half his life elsewhere, dancing attendance on the Queen, to whom his existence was so closely bound, and from whose presence she was excluded. She ignored his mistresses, and made quite sure they in no way intruded into her own world; she simply did not allow herself to think of them. She ran his households with their gardens, she entertained his guests and the permanent members of his train and she bore his children. Whatever vacuum his absence created was filled with their care and education. Her life was by no means the self-effacing retirement at Barn Elms, so airily sketched out by Essex to divert the Queen's anger over their marriage.

The terrible void left by Walter's death had been speedily, though in part only, filled by the birth of a daughter, Penelope, in May 1593. She was a comical child and something of a clown. Her dark hair curled furiously over her head and her round blue eyes looked permanently surprised. Even as a baby, she laughed more than she cried and Robert, now four years old, christened her "Hedgepig". Essex was too engrossed with his own affairs to be more than an indifferent father, but, true to form, he loved the girls more than the boys.

Despite her small form, Frances found childbearing comparatively easy but she could not allow it to interfere too much with her life; she was active from morning till night. Rising early, there was, first, the usual household bustle, the arrangement of the childrens' routine, the orders to the steward and housekeeper for the day and the doling out of the more exotic and expensive spices and herbs needed for cooking; then she would ride out, taking her dogs with her, or go hawking. There were formal and prepared hunting days which would mean being out till dusk, probably having travelled first to a nearby forest or a good stretch of country. Then, coming home, she would join and entertain the usual large party of people who danced, sang, and debated far into the night. She had inherited her mother's constitution and added supple fitness to it by constant exercise. Perhaps the clean sea air of Appuldurcombe in her early days and a bouncing, healthy wet-nurse had contributed to her toughness. She was a survivor but she knew what it was to be seriously ill and she would not let it happen again.

In November 1593, Christopher Carleill died at Walsingham House. He was only forty two, but a life lived at such a furious pace had simply worn him out. Following a severe heart attack, he slipped away quietly in his sleep, something no one had ever expected. He died a renowned sea and military commander whose one great sadness was that he had been stationed in Ireland at the time of the Armada and so had taken no part in the most famous of English naval battles. He had been more of a brother to Frances than any of actual blood tie, and she was with him when he died.

Penelope Rich had produced a daughter in March 1592, the first of many children she was to bear Charles Blount, and also named Penelope. Charles had unexpectedly inherited his father's title this January, his elder brother having died only a few months after the demise of their sire, and was now Baron Mountjoy. This little girl, born at Essex House, was given the surname Rich, and christened in St.Clement Danes immediately opposite. The situation was not easy. As Mountjoy, Charles wished to establish a line of legitimate children but he loved Penelope too much to abandon her and it was not in his nature to do such a thing. He was a delightful person with a strong sense of honour. Besides being a dedicated soldier, he was a scholar, interested in mathematics, philosophy and divinity. Subterfuge was not in Penelope's nature either and there were no more marital relations with Lord Rich, who continued to snipe from the sidelines. Nonetheless, Penelope often took parties of friends down to her husband's home in Essex and, if he needed her for legal or property matters, she dutifully went to him. Charles, at this time, was Governor of Portsmouth where he was able to hone his military and naval skills.

Walter Devereux's widow, the heiress, Margaret, had been besieged with offers of re-marriage within weeks of his death. That she entertained such thoughts at all was both offensive to the family and awkward because Thomas Sidney, the youngest of Philip's brothers, was among the principal suitors, another being the dreadful Thomas Posthumous Hoby who had so disgusted Frances long ago at Englefield. Hoby had redeemed himself, in part, by translating Castiglione's definitive book, "The Courtier," upon which every hopeful member of the Court modelled himself, but it was Sidney who won and married Margaret only three months after Walter's death, to the outrage of the Devereux. It was a hollow victory, however, since, at Thomas's death, four years later, Margaret did exactly the same thing, and to the family's fury, married Hoby. Frances was delighted that she was no longer obliged to have her in the house. She whined incessantly, mainly about fears for her own future and speculation over her next husband. Now poor, patient Barbara Sidney was going to have to put up with her at Penshurst.

The year 1593 saw a bad outbreak of bubonic plague in London and other parts of the country. Frances hastily bundled as many of her household as she could down to Englefield. Barn Elms was not far enough. As they rattled through London, the houses of the infected were already being pitilessly boarded up, the screams of the inmates drowned by the hammering and those trying to escape being thrust back inside; death would come soon enough, if not from plague from starvation. Already a stench was beginning to spread through the city, a compound of rotting matter and burning sulphur. All theatres were closed and poets and playwrights went back to their scripts.

One poet, however, would never return to the London stages. May 30th that year also saw the stabbing of Christopher Marlowe in a house in Deptford, purportedly an accident but a focal point of many strange and inter-related circumstances. There were three other men present, one of them the ever-recurring Robert Poley, the others being Ingram Frizer and Nicholas Skeres. The house belonged to a Mrs.Eleanor Bull, a relative of the Queen's oldest and dearest friend, Blanche Parry, her nurse and lady in waiting. Poley was working for Essex, Marlowe and Frizer for Thomas Walsingham, and Nicholas Skeres was a marginal character working on the shady sidelines of espionage and with several masters. Marlowe had sailed close to the wind on several occasions and had more than one brush with the authorities under his belt. But for his towering talent, his death would have been just another drunken, possibly homosexual, brawl; his work rivalled Shakespeare's and remained an inspiration to many. He had often been with Thomas Walsingham at Essex House and Frances had read his "Dr.Faustus" and, with horrid fascination, "Massacre in Paris", recognising that a writer of exceptional power lay beneath the desire to shock and the "bad boy" image.

A year on, this spring of 1594, there had been a serious falling-out between Frances and her husband which resulted in her removing herself and her children, first to Lady Ursula at Walsingham House and then to Mary Pembroke at Wilton. It was not a result of Essex's philanderings, but the hounding to death of the Queen's Portuguese physician, Dr.Lopez.

Anthony Bacon, working from Essex House, had uncovered some suspicious goings-on between the ever troublesome Dom Antonio, exiled ruler of Portugal, his Portuguese agents , and one Tinoco, a Spanish agent in Brussels. Both Essex and Robert Cecil, with Burghley's permission, examined Tinoco who proved, indeed, to be in possession of letters and money which needed explaining. They managed to extract from him an admission that he had been sent to get Dr.Lopez to "do service for the King of Spain." In triumph, Essex had the poor little doctor arrested and hustled to Essex House while his house was searched. Robert Cecil, unconvinced and rather more astute, rode straight to the Queen at Hampton Court and laid the case before her. Essex, who had not seen fit to tell her anything as yet, furiously chased after him to pour out his own suspicions. He was hardly allowed to open his mouth before being bawled out as "a rash and temerarious youth" who had dared to arrest Her Majesty's doctor without her knowledge or permission and with no real evidence to support his charges. She then dismissively waved him out of the room, leaving Robert Cecil, his small misshapen rival, holding the floor.

His pride in tatters and his rage mounting, Essex stormed back to London. Frances saw him coming and ran along the gallery round the Great Hall to meet him. He shoved her out of his way and strode down the corridor to his own chamber where he slammed and locked the door. Never, in their five years of marriage, had he treated her so. He emerged, all smiles, a day later and called for Anthony Bacon. The rest of the story was utterly shameful and marked, for Frances, a turning point in their marriage. She would never fully trust him again.

Tinoco and another agent were tortured mercilessly until they accused Dr.Lopez of intending to poison the Queen. Knowing they had done so, he capitulated under questioning and the threat of the rack. He was old, exhausted and frightened. He was also a Jew and their popularity was at a low ebb since Christopher Marlowe's play, "The Jew of Malta" had been performed. He and Tinoco were condemned, hung, drawn and quartered. Tinoco, young and burly, managed to give his would be butcher a hefty clout when cut down from the gallows and fought for his life, to the delight of the crowd, but was overpowered, castrated and gutted. Essex, in an attempt to save his own face and his pride, had sent two innocent men to a disgusting death.

Frances's cold outrage when she pieced the story together was so great that she gathered the children and their nurses, called for her coach, and drove immediately to Walsingham House. Her mother, stalwart as ever, took them in and suggested they all go down to Barn Elms together. For Frances, this was not far enough and she sent word to Mary Pembroke at her London house, Baynards Castle, that they would like to go to Wilton.

Mary insisted on accompanying them with her own children. She also knew the real story of Dr Lopez's death so that Frances was able to pour her heart out without any disloyalty to her husband. The Devereux family had, naturally, taken a rather different view, applauding the loyalty and enterprise of its favourite son.

As the two young women walked through the stone-vaulted galleries or the length of the great flower borders, Mary, very perceptive and, more from what Frances did not say than from what she did, guessed how the land lay with this favourite sister-in-law so near her own heart. Outwardly, Frances's life was a pageant of excitement and glamour, full of action in many fields, but there was a quiet sadness at the heart of it all and a deep fear for the future. Watching Elizabeth, the image of Philip, running from the great towered eastern entrance towards them, she suddenly kissed Frances and promised that this child would always be loved as one of her own.

Brie also came briefly to Wilton although it was always difficult for her to leave Court for more than a few days. She had been present when Essex was harangued by the Queen over his first arrest of Dr.Lopez, had seen the towering rage in which he departed and understood perfectly why Frances had left London. Her own affairs, however, were at a crucial crossroads. She was in a state of mingled despair and excitement and needed advice. She had served the Queen devotedly for ten years, she was twenty two years old and no nearer to marriage with Robert Tyrwhitt. So far she had managed to fend off her other suggested suitors including Lord Wharton, Walsingham's charge in Paris, and Henry Wriothesley, Earl of Southampton, and she really longed, as she always had done, to escape from Court to a quiet country life. Robert had loyally remained unmarried in the hopes of winning her. Her faithful maid, Mary Harding, with her all the years since she was sent from Rutland, suggested that she should "fayne the messelles" and get leave to "ayre herself" in Rutland where she could marry Robert and face the music when the deed was done. This doughty dame, who was both literate and vocal had managed to make her voice heard and Brie's Mother, the Countess of Rutland, had consulted both the ever attentive uncle, Roger Manners, and Burghley himself on the matter and, strangely, they did not oppose the plan. Perhaps there had been a mellowing of ambition over the years. As things stood, there was little chance that she would be allowed to marry anyone, the Queen being too devoted to her willingly to let her go.

Frances had, herself, lived through the consequences of a bid to marry for love and also of a clandestine marriage. Both had been harsh. John Wickerson had simply been whisked away and she had been banished from Court for her union with Essex. Banishment would delight Brie, but imprisonment would not. She must face the possible results of the Queen's wrath, she had witnessed it often enough, and decide whether her courage was equal to what might come. She would also have to face the opposition of her young brother, Roger, Earl of Rutland.

Brie's courage and resolve did not fail her. She obtained a month's leave from Court, pleading the onset of measles and a five year lapse in seeing her home and family, and married Robert Tyrwhitt at Belvoir Castle in July. As foreseen, the Queen was far from pleased but fortunately decided that Brie's mother was principally to blame. The unhappy couple were ordered to return to London, where Robert was imprisoned in the Tower and Lady Bridget was returned to her grandmother's custody. Robert Cecil was asked for help and by November they were both released. For Brie, there remained the ordeal of a bitter confrontation with the Queen, and she did this with exemplary fortitude. Straightforward and quiet, and without any excuses, she bowed her shining head, and took all blame upon herself, asking only that others should not suffer. The Queen was disarmed, her anger melted, and she embraced Brie fondly, pardoning them both and giving them leave to return to Rutland where, in blissful domesticity, they raised two sons and a daughter. It had all been worth the wait.

Frances did not return from Wilton until June and then it was to Barn Elms. Essex was away on that year's Summer Progress and Essex House would be emptied of its inhabitants and fumigated in the usual way. She rejoiced to hear that Brie had married but remained anxious about her future. She had to wait for news while the Court, her husband in the midst, was still progressing round the southern counties, a huge snaking dragon of people, horses and baggage, at least two miles long.

These years, 1594 until 1597, were, for England, dire. The rain fell in curtains, harvests failed for three years, livestock died in droves, and winters were bitter. Men suffered, died, or were prosecuted for no other fault than minor theft, trying to stay alive and to keep themselves and their families from starvation.

Gloriana was no longer glorious, an old woman who had lost touch with her people and would not help them or move with the times. Folk began to look elsewhere for leadership and, inevitably, talk turned more and more frequently to the subject of succession. Who had more appeal, the unknown, but reputedly uninspiring James V1 of Scotland, son of the hated Mary Stuart, or a man they cheered in the streets of London; a tall, dashing soldier, loved by their Queen and her people?

When next Frances set eyes on Essex, he was ebullient. The Summer Progress was going well, despite the weather, he was back in the Queen's favour, forgiven and constantly by her side, dancing in overdressed splendour with her every night and full of plans for the future. He had clearly been far too occupied to have missed Frances, but, equally clearly, he knew he was under a cloud. She had never withdrawn herself from him in this way or shown such blatant anger. Once back at Essex House, he found he missed her sorely. Penelope had opened a most unwise correspondence with King James of Scotland in his absence and Lettice was plaguing him to get the Queen's permission for her return to Court.

His younger sister, Dorothy, was also trying to make her way back to favour.

After a dramatic elopement in 1583, at the age of seventeen, followed by a shotgun wedding, performed by an abducted cleric and with drawn swords guarding the church, she had been banished in disgrace as a Maid of Honour to the Queen. Her husband, Thomas Perrot, was sent to the Fleet prison for his presumption. He died in 1593, soon after his father Sir John Perrot, and Dorothy, having inherited a substantial amount of property from her father-in-law and her husband, including beautiful Syon House near Kew, had just been snapped up by Henry Percy, Earl of Northumberland. As beautiful as Penelope, she was every bit as wayward and headstrong and, like Penelope, she adored her brother. As the Countess of Northumberland and the sister of Essex, she felt she now had every right to return to Court and was badgering him to put in a good word for her.

Essex needed Frances with him, to fend off his women and give him freedom from all these family importunities. The Devereux ladies, unlike Frances who avoided committing very much to paper, were all great letter writers and kept in close touch with each other on both important and domestic matters. Their missives were, like themselves, impulsive, unguarded and very affectionate.

Essex, therefore, was prepared to take time and trouble to bring Frances back. Rowed down by barge to Barn Elms on one of the few lovely days in June, he found her just riding in, his heir on a small pony attached to a leading rein trailing along beside her. Frances, herself, was mounted on one of the beautiful mares bred at Penshurst, and, together, they presented a charming picture, graceful and elegant. Philip had taught her painstakingly, and she had helped school the horses she rode well enough to perform some of the simpler movements taught in the Austrian equestrian schools.

She pulled up at the mounting block, handed Robert's rein to a groom, and looked down into a blinding smile on the face of her husband. He had pulled off his elaborate, feathered hat and swept her an exquisite bow before holding out his arms to catch her. Her own face expressionless, she slid from the saddle where he held her round the waist a moment before setting her on her feet. She had a moment of vivid recall, seeing a fourteen year old girl standing on that block, swept upward by another man on to the saddle of a horse which had sired the mare she now rode. So much was the same, but so much had changed. She was not going to make this reconciliation easy for Essex, but, as with her marriage, she knew what the outcome would be. Only too pleased to be left in the stables, Robert made a hasty bow to his father and scuttled off to help stable his pony.

Frances was now twenty seven and had born five children but she looked very much the same as had the girl on the mounting block thirteen years earlier. Time had dealt kindly with her. Her face, because it seldom demonstrated emotion, had remained almost unlined. Her lucid eyes were unclouded, their whites as clear as ever. Her small frame was supple and firm from constant activity and nearly as slim as it had always been. Rigorous lacing had controlled her waist after childbirth and Jane Rehora had given her a secret salve for tired muscles.

Looking at her speculatively, Essex sensed the steel in her, and rightly decided not to beat about the bush verbally. He would be as honest as he knew he had to be. Frances, like her father, could find the truth in every lie he told, and even if she said nothing, he knew exactly when she ceased to believe him. He, therefore, walked with her through the rose garden, where two very young lovers had joyously joined hands, through the herb-strewn hall to the library, and there he admitted every fault and begged her to come back with him. She listened in deafening silence.

When he had run out of words and began to repeat himself, she made a gesture to quieten him, turned her back and looked out of the long windows and across the gardens. Then she swept round, with a swish of skirts, and informed him that if ever again he did anything as cruelly despicable as engineering the death of Dr. Lopez, she would retire completely to Barn Elms, as he had promised the Queen she should. He would then be left to the demands of his mother, sisters and, she added, his mistresses. His wife would no longer be a part of his existence.

He could have told her to go; he could have told her he would take his children and abandon her, but she knew he would not. She was the most constant thing in his life and easily the most reliable. He moved like a cat across the room to her with his hands held out.

By the end of the year, big schemes were afoot in the corridors of power in which Essex was central. King Philip of Spain, still smarting from the devastation of his Armada, was not putting up with any more depredation from English pirates. He had concentrated thought and money on his ships and their deployment. No longer did vast treasure ships thrash around in the Atlantic unattended. His convoys were escorted by sleek, efficient men-o-war with enough fire-power to repel marauders. The gallant old tars, Drake, Hawkins and Frobisher, were slow to realise this and got badly mauled while trying to raid Spanish fleets on the South American run in 1595. Hawkins died as his ship approached Puerto Rico, followed soon after by Drake, who died of dysentery. They had served Queen, country, and themselves, for three decades and were giants of their age. Was it possible that their mantle would be taken up by a valiant young military commander who knew his way around a ship as well as a battlefield?

The Portuguese raid to which Essex had absconded in 1589 had not been more than a jolly romp. Something far more serious was now afoot and Anthony Bacon's agents, among others, were reporting a great deal of naval activity and a serious build-up of war ships in Spanish ports. Another Armada was surely on the way and defence on a much larger scale than Drake's raid on Cadiz was going to be called for. Essex, as expected, bombarded the Queen with calls for an aggressive and positive move against Spain. His ally and friend of many years, Sir Roger Williams, had recently died, but this time, he was backed up strongly by Lord Howard of Effingham, old Burghley himself, and the Privy Council. Plans and ships began to move.

By New Year of 1595, preparations were, for once, going quite well and Essex was able to escape from Whitehall and join his family on 3rd January for "The Gray's Inn Revels," one of the elaborate entertainments given by the Inns of Court. It was a glorious evening of real pleasure. These entertainments had evolved from the law students "singing for their suppers" and became increasingly sophisticated, incorporating plays, masques and music. The cream of London society was to be found there, as it was on this night, and the suppers were renowned.

The first play was Shakespeare's "A Comedy of Errors" in which Will Shakespeare himself took part, as did Henry Wriothesley, the young Earl of Southampton, his friend and patron whose stage presence was eye-catching. The second was both funny and bawdy, the food superb, and Frances and Penelope were looking their best. The writer of this second piece, Bartholomew Young, also acting, wrote later how "their honourable presences... graced and beautified these sports." It was slightly unusual, too, in that the entire Devereux household, including Mountjoy, were present, as was Lord Rich. Frances was six months pregnant, but not very apparently so. She was, by now, fairly well able to predict what the infant would be and was hoping for another son.

She was right. He was born in the comparative peace of Walsingham House in early April and baptised, Henry, at All Hallows by the Tower on 14th April 1595, amid much rejoicing This baby immediately showed a strong resemblance to his aunt, Penelope, with the same fair head and dark eyes. Essex was genuinely delighted, as he had been when he persuaded Frances to come back to Essex House with him. He was, for him, treading very carefully and attentively; the physical bond between them was still extremely strong and alarmingly procreative.

By July that year Frances was, once more, pregnant and really rather resentful; the next arrival was due in March 1596, a mere eleven months since Henry's birth. There must, she reflected, be some safe way to stave off these endless pregnancies: the Chinese Court ladies were reputed to eat angelica. She would consult her old friend Dr.Dee and his library and see if history could throw any light on the matter. She remembered reading that the ancient Egyptians had devised something effective while the Greek Hetairae also had their secrets. Meanwhile, she knew a fellow feeling for the brood mares at Penshurst.

This feeling was not improved by the knowledge that Essex had embarked on an energetic affair with Elizabeth Stanley, Countess of Derby. The dutiful husband had not remained very dutiful for long. Frances was used to these flights of fancy, but found this one particularly insulting.

With Essex and Charles Mountjoy completely pre-occupied with the Court, the Council and the Ordinance Office, Frances, Penelope and Dorothy decided they would make an expedition to Staffordshire and visit Lettice who was then at Chartley, the Devereux home. They took with them a young cousin, Elizabeth Vernon, one of the Queen's Maids of Honour who had fallen dangerously in love with the arresting young Earl of Southampton. Absence from this spellbinder would, they thought, be good for her. At her urgent plea, they also took Elizabeth Sidney, now ten years old and always a pleasure. All three of the Essex ladies were pregnant in varying degrees, but thought nothing of a long ride north. Their children were in good health and could be left under the careful eye of Jane Rehora who had overall charge of the nurseries. They had an armed guard of several men with them in case of trouble from the many vagrants and bands of thieves resulting from these hard times. For two years now, the harvests had all but failed and many were starving, even in summer.

It was the kind of journey they all enjoyed, going in easy stages and visiting friends and family on the way. Riding was more comfortable than the hideously rocking coaches which so often broke down or got wheels stuck in ruts and ditches and they were lucky in that they did not often have to unwrap the heavy over-cloaks rolled behind their saddles in case of rain. Two coaches did accompany them with servants and mountains of baggage.

As they neared journey's end, they rode through the small town of Market Drayton and stopped for refreshment at an Inn. The head groom went in to speak to the ale-draper while they all dismounted, their arrival, with baggage train and spare horses, causing quite a stir. People called out to each other to come and see such fine folk riding in and before long their identity was known. The Devereux children had grown up here and were, famously, a part of the county, their exploits well-known and much admired. No-one had yet seen the Lord Essex's lady and her daughter. The crowd grew larger and greetings were called out.

Hearing them, a man in his thirties with curling brown hair and a deeply tanned face, turned sharply from mounting his horse, tethered it to a hitching post, and strode forward through the throng of people. He saw the group of richly dressed women and, like a magnet, his eyes were drawn to the smallest of them. Upright and graceful, her long riding habit draped over one arm and her eyes shielded from the sun by a wide hat, he could not mistake the girl he had loved so greatly and for whose sake he had suffered. When she slowly turned, searching for something, and raised her face, the well-remembered eyes smiling with peculiar sweetness, he let his breath out in a long sigh. She was looking at a child with tawny hair who moved, as she did, like a dancer, and now ran towards her. So that was Philip Sidney's daughter. John Wickerson gazed, rooted to the spot, until she mounted her horse and the whole party rode off in the direction of Chartley. He was not remembering the filth, the stinking darkness, fear and icy cold of the Marshalsea Prison, but a girl under an apple tree in late summer.

Philip II of Spain was nearing the end of his life but his work was not complete. He had failed to return all Europe to the Catholic faith and he had not, as yet, fully subdued the Dutch. He must make peace with France and above all, he must conquer and eliminate that terrible old woman, the Queen of England, his demon for so many years, and her heretic country. He worked incessantly and with frantic purpose, therefore, from his eyrie in the Escorial Palace, high in the Guadarrama hills. His room, which he seldom left, was perched like an opera box above his private chapel and gave him constant access to the Holy offices chanted below him. He was now an old man, and a most unattractive one. He was riddled with disease, but gout, skin canker and a debilitating form of paralysis, could not stop his pen moving ceaselessly over the paper. Holy and horrible, he wrote on.

He would send a further force to north western France from where they would invade and take Calais so that, when his great new Armada sailed, the attack on England could be reinforced. The reason that Spanish troops remained in France was because Philip II had refused to accept the conversion to Catholicism of Henry IV in 1593. That perspicacious monarch had realised that his country, shredded by years of deadly religious strife, would have to be ruled under one faith and, in order to have peace with most of its population and with Spain, it must be Catholic. Philip was disappointed to find that Henry had no intention of persecuting and burning, in scores, his lifelong Protestant friends and allies, the Huguenots, and strongly suspected that his faith, despite a few masses and "Hail Marys", remained unchanged.

On 26th March 1596, with final preparations under way for the fleet now preparing in Plymouth to set sail for Cadiz, Frances was awaiting the birth of her child in Essex House with Lady Ursula and felt familiar pain begin. It was more continuous and intense than anything she could remember and, in an unusually short time, a son was delivered. He was stillborn. There had been no warning; no hint that things were amiss. She had been well throughout and her pregnancy was almost full term. Frances was devastated. A messenger was sent to Essex at Whitehall, but returned with the news that he was daily expected in Plymouth and could not come. His baggage had already gone.

The baby was committed to the dank earth at All Hallows, next to his brother Walter, without even being given a name; his birth being registered only as "a man child."

A few days later, as a result of King Philip's mistrust of the French King, Londoners woke on the morning of All Fools' Day 1596 to the distant but definite sound of gunfire from across the channel. Calais was being attacked.

Essex, leaping out of bed like a rocket in his rooms at the palace, and with an army of attendants hurriedly dressing him, went immediately to join the Council and by 3rd April a ship was sent across the channel to see if the Spaniards had taken the town. They had not, and what followed was the worst farce ever endured by a commander of forces. Orders were given for 6,000 men to muster at Dover ready to cross and snatch Calais from the Spaniards. Three times the order to sail was given and subsequently withdrawn as the Queen frantically haggled with Henry IV over costs and length of occupation. The final cancellation came on 15th April as Essex, having finally embarked his troops, sat down to a hasty dinner on board ship before sailing. Calais had fallen to the Spanish and could not be re-taken. The price of indecision had been paid in full; penny pinching and dithering age had lost this vital opportunity for the Queen. It was a sad foretaste of what was to come and the blame could not even be shared or shifted.

The confusion that followed did not bode well for the expedition to Cadiz, which would now have to be postponed while the troops, cursing and swearing, and the ships were moved from Dover down to Plymouth where the fleet was preparing to sail for Spain. Essex and the Lord Admiral set sail immediately from Dover and found perfect pandemonium awaiting them; it was greatly to the credit of Essex that he achieved sufficient order, including the provisioning and distribution of troops, for the fleet to be ready by the end of May. The Queen finally sent official sealed orders to sail on 24th May together with a neat and sweetly worded blessing for her "Robin."

On 5th May, while Essex was still struggling to restore order in Plymouth, Henry, his year old son, developed smallpox. Cold with horror and not fully recovered from the birth of the dead baby, Frances rose from her bed and rushed to the nursery where Jane Rehora, in tears, assured her the diagnosis was right; she had seen it before. The little boy was limp and pale and when Frances picked him up, his head dropped back showing livid blotches on his throat and chest. She wrapped him in warm blankets and took him immediately to Walsingham House, and, like a wounded animal, made straight for the small tapestry room which had always been her sanctuary. She left orders that all the other children in Essex House were to go directly down to Barn Elms with Jane Rehora and Lady Ursula, and that anyone remaining in the house should be aware of the danger and also leave if the present crisis allowed. Two kitchen maids and a groom were then found to be infected and the carrier was suspected of being an oarsman off one of the barges who had been fed in the big kitchen buttery.

Frances allowed no one at Walsingham House to come near her. Anything she asked for was left at the head of the stairs and she nursed her son herself. She knew there was no antidote or herbal medicine that would alleviate or cure smallpox, so she made up the fire for warmth and tried by every trick she knew to get him to drink as much as possible. She believed that heat should bring the horrible rash out and prevent the infection turning inwards. Henry never burst out in the usual sores and despite her frantic efforts, he died on 7th May late in the evening, his black eyes fixed on her face and his little fingers gradually loosening their grip on hers as his breathing became harsh and intermittent. Within six weeks, she had lost two sons.

Completely exhausted in mind and body, Frances remained shut in the tapestry room until she was perfectly sure there was no risk of infection for herself or anyone else at Walsingham House. Henry's small coffin was carried to the chapel at Essex House to await the possible return of his father. There was no comfort anywhere for Frances and the black void of grief once more threatened her. The crazy tapestry began to spin around her in a mad cacophony of sight and sound; foxes chasing hounds, hounds chasing men until, in desperation, she shut her eyes, leaning her head against the wall.

This time, however, there were too many people dependent on her to give way and as soon as she thought it safe, she returned to Essex House, to assure herself that there was no further sickness there and to gain news of Essex. She did not yet dare go down to Barn Elms.

Anthony Bacon, compassion in his eyes, met her and told her at once that Essex had gone directly from Dover to Plymouth, never returning to London, and that the fleet would sail for Spain on 1st June. He, himself, could not leave Essex House as news was constantly coming in from the Continent. (His friendship with Henry IV was deep and of long standing. He had been accused of sodomy long ago in Montauban and Henry had moved quickly and effectively to protect him from the threatened stake.) He was a gentle, kindly soul, far less ambitious and more self-effacing than his brother Francis but with a brain every bit as formidable. He had his own apartment now on the third floor of Essex House, to which he was somewhat bound by gout, but he often came limping down to chat to Frances. He was also a great favourite of Lady Ursula and sometimes stayed with her at Walsingham House. He looked now at Frances's shadowy eyes and ashen face, put an arm round her and called for wine to be warmed. Many of the servants had leave of absence because of the risk of smallpox and Essex House was short-staffed.

From him she learned that of her own circle, Charles Mountjoy, Christopher Blount, Gilly Meyrick, Henry Cuffe, Sir Francis Vere and the poet John Donne had gone with Essex. Sharing the leadership of the expedition with him was Lord Howard of Effingham, old stalwart of the 1588 Armada, and under their command were Lord Thomas Howard, the brother of the Lord Admiral, Sir Walter Raleigh, Sir Thomas Egerton and Sir Edward Hoby, the brother of Thomas Posthumous, among many others. There were well over a hundred ships, almost half of them men-o-war and at least a thousand men at arms, both soldiers and sailors. Many were Dutch who had not forgotten English help in the Netherlands and were keen to strike any blow at Spain after years of cruel occupation. It was a huge enterprise in which the Queen had invested heavily. Anthony did not think hair or hide of it would be seen until August at least.

He was right but the return did not bring with it the triumphal success story hoped for. The expedition had started with a loud and successful bang and ended with something of a whimper. There had been the inevitable disputes among those leading it, misunderstandings leading to loss of men, ships and treasure although Cadiz had, indeed, been taken, burnt to a crisp, and with many of the ships gathered there blasted out of the water. Unfortunately, three of them, laden with treasure, had been fired by the Duke of Medina Sidonia to avoid capture; about the most effective act of his career. Equally unfortunate had been the meandering voyage back to Plymouth, via the islands of the Azores, in the hopes of picking up further largesse. They had missed, by two days, huge cargoes from the New World unloaded in Lisbon and there were few returns to show for the vast expenditure. Essex braced himself for recriminations and got them, in full view and hearing of the whole Court on 12th August. It was bitter and degrading and the grievances were mostly fiscal. The Queen had paid out £50,000 with very little in return and she was sure that others had done better than she. Little mention was made of Essex's heroism at

Cadiz, which had not been lacking. He had, as always, led his men with huge courage and success. Cadiz had been in English hands until it was burnt to the ground but he had, yet again, scattered knighthoods on those serving under him with deplorable abundance.

It was very far from a hero's welcome and these grand missions were beginning to assume a pattern of high expectations and poor results.

He found an ally, however, in the Archbishop of Canterbury, John Whitgift, who ordered a thanksgiving day to be celebrated by the whole country, in honour of the victory at Cadiz, and in praise of Essex. The people responded jubilantly despite the fact that the Queen did her best to restrict any celebrations.

Frances was at St Paul's Cross on the thanksgiving day to hear the sermon preached by the Archbishop's chaplain. Henry had been buried at All Hallows on 26th June, his mother, Anthony Bacon and Penelope Rich being the only mourners. All was well at Barn Elms and there had been no spread of smallpox either there, or at Essex House.

Today, there was a huge crowd around her sedan chair and she was glad of its six hefty bearers. It was a grey day, but the throng was in a holiday mood and prepared to enjoy themselves; there had been precious little else to enjoy this summer. They listened quietly enough to begin with but began cheering loudly as praise was heaped on Essex. When, however, criticism of his detractors began, they roared in earnest, angry and indignant. This was dangerous; Essex was out of favour but they were clearly showing him loyalty, angry at his critics, including the Queen. Ever since St.Bartholomew's Eve, Frances had been nervous of noisy crowds. She asked her bearers to take her back to Essex House, but with an unquiet mind.

She could see, as Essex could not, the path that he was treading and Her Majesty's reaction to it. Despite her love for him, the Queen found him increasingly unruly. He was constantly trying to expand his position and he appealed directly to the people whether he knew it or not. He was a soldier and longed for the military and naval campaigns that she now had neither the will nor the money for. He had little subtlety; as Henry Cuffe had rightly said: "He can conceal nothing; he carries his love and his hatred on his forehead." He was also, perhaps, becoming a little less sincere in his compliments and the declarations of love were flowing less freely. The Queen would be on the look out for this, as the signs of age inexorably progressed, and sharp to recognise anything suggestive of the familiar. Frankly, she had spoilt him and was paying the price. If she vetoed his wishes, he should, by now, be able to see that she was often playing him like a trout, and to respond by being conciliatory instead of immediately picking up the cudgels. This had happened several times, notably over the proposing of Francis Bacon for the post of Attorney General in 1593 and he had failed in his sponsorship of this appointment, and others. Most significant slight of all, was the recent confirmation that his rival, Robert Cecil, was to succeed his father, Burghley, as Secretary of State the most powerful of all posts in Government. The quiet, competent little cripple, the antithesis of Essex, had been working in tandem with his father and fully deserved to take over from him. Burghley was fading and this was his dearest wish.

There were going to be rocks ahead and Frances was not the only person to recognize them. The cold, viperish eyes of Francis Bacon had seen them long ago and he was carefully laying the ground for a change of scenery. He had repeatedly warned Essex against confrontation with the Queen, but to no avail, and was to hint gently that, if Essex did not listen to him, others would. Essex was beginning to embarrass him and Francis would be a very dangerous opponent. His brother, Anthony, on the other hand, was bone loyal to Essex and could find no fault in him.

Now was not the moment for personalities, however. King Philip of Spain was again on the warpath. Enraged by the sacking of Cadiz and with the whole of Spain in uproar, he gathered the rest of his Armada together and, unwisely, gave orders for it to sail in October 1596, the month of storms, and also some time before he had intended. News of a large fleet leaving Lisbon was received in England in November and the country was galvanised into action. The Earl of Essex was given the command of a Council of War, the alarm beacons along the South Coast were dusted down and made ready and a force of 70,000 armed men were divided and concentrated where the Spanish might be expected to land. Tension mounted but there was no time to gather another naval force.

Essex was in his element, flying between Whitehall, the Ordinance Office, of which he was now Master, and the coast. Then, all went very quiet and the look-out ships in the Channel had nothing to report. This sinister pause had a very fortunate explanation. Once again, the weather had come to England's defence. A huge storm in the Bay of Biscay had virtually wiped out King Philip's second Armada. Would there be time for a third? The old man in the Escorial wondered whether God, Himself, was against him.

ACT FOUR 1

1597-1599 – Azores

Whatever King Philip's failings may have been lack of perseverance was not one. A third Armada had been resurrected from the ruins of the second and another invasion planned for the spring of 1598. The unholy and unruly kingdom of England must be crushed; it was cold, rude and heretic and he had not enjoyed being married to its former Queen, Mary Tudor. The knowledge that he was not long for this world drove him on relentlessly; undaunted, he was prepared to risk Spanish lives, ships and money.

While he and Spain laboured, Essex had managed, by sheer force of will, to persuade his Queen to put him in command of yet another expedition, via Spain, to the Islands of the Azores, the mid-Atlantic stopping and re-commissioning point for the Spanish treasure fleets where the heroes of Cadiz had meandered about after their successful raid. The main mission, this time, was barefaced piracy but the qualifying proviso was that they should first deal with the Spanish fleet assembling around Ferrol and Corunna and, if information was received that the Spaniards were ready to sail, they were immediately to deal with this threat before proceeding. Although intelligence said otherwise, it remained a risk that England and Ireland could be attacked while Essex's ships might, hopefully, be stuffing their holds with treasure in the Azores and it was one that should not have been taken.

This Islands Voyage seemed fated and was, if anything, a worse mixture of jealous quarrelling and lack of co-ordination than had been Cadiz and, ultimately, with much less to show for it. They sailed in late June and, this time, luck was not with them. Summer storms hit the English ships before ever they left the Channel, de-masting some, capsizing others, drowning men and ruining stores.

Frances was at Englefield with friends and family when the storms hit and their late evening music was ruined by screaming wind, lashing rain and rolling thunder. She was just returning from a visit to the nurseries to reassure the children, and was halfway down the stairs, when a forked flash lit the hall, followed by the most terrible tearing sound and a crash that sounded almost beside her and took the air out of her lungs. For a moment shock held her rigid then the outer hall doors swung slowly open to reveal part of a huge tree lying across the entrance steps. It had missed the house by a matter of yards.

Frances flew across the hall to the music room and very soon the men of the household had pulled on doublets and cloaks and rushed outside. Richard de Burgh, back from his estates in Ireland and one of the party, took charge and assessed the damage.

By morning the tree was cleared from the steps and he came to find Frances. Aware of what the storms might be doing in the south, the west, and throughout the Channel and feeling that the felled tree could be a portent, she had spent the remainder of the night on her knees in the chapel, her prayers punctuated by crashes, bangs and the rain drumming in ferocious bursts on the roof. Essex had described to her what havoc a storm at sea could create and her imagination ran riot, bringing visions of broken masts with men clinging to them, splintering, heaving decks and the terrible inrush of water. If such a force had destroyed the great Spanish ships in 1588, what might be happening to him at this moment? Richard wrapped a warm cloak around her, put a drink of hot ginger into her hands and blew up the fire in the music room. She had no need to tell him her fears. He had been with Essex since he was a child, had gone with him to the Netherlands and to France, and his thoughts were an image of her own. They talked quietly in the grey dawn.

Their fears were fully justified. The fleet was scattered, some vessels having got as far as the Bay of Biscay where mountainous seas prevented their return, others eventually limping back to Plymouth and Falmouth in total disarray. The seamen were exhausted, the soldiers were sick, and food was running out. Although they had been at sea for nearly two weeks, some ships had barely left the Channel. By any standard, it was a terrible start to an expedition.

Frances went back to London to meet Essex after he eventually made port in Plymouth on 20th July and returned wearily to London. He had lost weight and looked thin and gaunt. Worry and foul food had taken their toll and his moods swung from ferocious planning to frustrated grievance. She was more disturbed by his mental state than his physical condition which was easier to deal with. Proper food and sleep in a comfortable bed could work wonders if he would let them. The diet on board a warship, after the first few weeks, was grim and played havoc with men's health. Many seamen developed painful and revolting boils, their loosened teeth making it hard to chew the tough, salted, meat and fish provided and the almost total lack of fruit and vegetables resulted in irritating skin diseases. It was not a romantic life.

Essex seemed to his wife a changed and driven man. He was impatient with her, short-tempered with both his household and his sisters, and he virtually ignored his children. Occasionally he would turn to her with some of the old charm and passion but most of the time his thoughts were on another plane, deeply concentrated on the pursuit his own ambitions.

Young Robert, who should have had three brothers looking up to him, was moody, demanding and craved his father's attention. When the Rich cousins were with him he was happy; he led and they followed, but Eton was looming and Frances was aware of his insecurity. She had firmly held out against the practice of sending children to a bigger, possibly grander, establishment for upbringing as Lettice had sent hers to the Burghleys and the Huntingdons. The Essex household was as splendid as any and there were almost continuous visits by young cousins, both to Essex House and to Barn Elms.

While Essex was away, Frances would sometimes take her children down to Wanstead, or, if Penelope needed moral support on her "duty" visits to the Rich home, Leigh's Priory, she would go with her. This was never so popular as the religious practices were puritanically strict and prayerfully lengthy and Barn Elms remained, as always, their favourite house for retreat from London.

Penelope had given birth to a son in January this year, blatantly naming him Mountjoy and leaving no ambiguity about the identity of his father. In April she had contracted smallpox and, though very ill, emerged unscathed and without a mark on her lovely countenance.

Faced now with Essex in a vile frame of mind, which included strangely uncharacteristic vacillation, Frances began to suspect that he was far from well. Certain things, overheard in the past, purposely ignored at the time, now dredged themselves from her memory and caused her alarm. There was a pattern somewhere that she did not want to discover.

By mid-August, the English fleet was again seaworthy and Essex, restored in body, but uncertain in mind, bid Frances a preoccupied farewell and set off, yet again, for Plymouth. As he and his escort formed up and clattered out from

Essex House on a hot, hazy summer morning, that promised an even hotter day, her heart lurched at the thought of the many miles he had to ride before ever he reached his ship and, after that, the cramped discomfort, dangers and violence he would be faced with. What was driving him to these extremes of living? What was he trying to achieve and did reason have any part in it? Surely he had gained enough glory and acclamation for one lifetime to take the edge off his craving for it: and where would it lead him? A trickle of fear crept up her scalp and she turned away, her little spaniels pattering beside her, to walk down to the water's edge. Here, so close to the beating heart of London, the Thames was turgid, brown and oily with nameless bits of flotsam bobbing by. The spaniels' questing noses spoke of untold treasures in the dark water and Frances saw four rigid cloven feet sail along, the body beneath the surface. London was no place to be in August. She would go down to Penshurst, to Robert and Barbara, and see her horses and the new foals. She could do no good by fretting in London.

Essex had with him many of the companions of the Cadiz raid; Howard, Mountjoy, Vere, Raleigh, stepfather Christopher Blount, Gilly Meyrick and Henry Cuffe of the old brigade, together with many of the young bloods so generously knighted by him after Cadiz, and recklessly ready for anything. This present venture appeared to be doubly be-devilled. When the fleet eventually hobbled off to sea, the wind was non-existent and the ships had to be towed out into the Channel to catch what breeze they could.

Frances had plenty of family and domestic matters to occupy her before setting out for Penshurst. One particularly near her heart, though not immediate, needed thought.

Elizabeth was now thirteen years old and marriage would soon have to be thought of. A position as Maid of Honour to the Queen had been suggested to her, but she was adamantly opposed to the idea and Frances had no wish to force her. She was presented at Court by Robert and Barbara Sidney, none of the Devereux ladies being able to show their faces there, and she had aroused a great deal of interest so like was she to Philip. Frances had unerringly chosen deep cream for her presentation dress, the kirtle and sleeves embroidered with pale green and white daisies; a perfect foil for her golden hair and eyes. The Queen had smiled upon her and so had the Earl of Rutland.

She was a vital, sensitive child, expecting perfection from herself in all she did and this included the writing of verse which delighted Frances. She was, in all respects, very much Philip's daughter and she moved, as her mother did, with elfin grace. Also like Frances, whose greatest asset was her passive face, it was hard to guess her thoughts although she was always outwardly charming and considerate. Frances had, however, secretly observed her talking to Greville in the garden one day, a large daisy between them, from which they were pulling the petals one by one, Elizabeth chanting "He loves me, he loves me not, he loves me, he loves me not." Greville had ended the interlude by squawking loudly, "Roger loves me," which rather gave the game away. Brie's brother was only ten years older than Elizabeth and the Earl of Rutland would be a worthy match. Frances could remember him feeding her sugar plums from his plate at Penshurst. Greville may well have seen more than Frances had and his memory was embarrassingly good; she would spend a little time with him and see what could be learnt. The little green parrot had survived as a cherished friend all these years and was well able to contend with the many dogs so often with them, not to mention the attention of countless small children. He was very much a part of their lives and marched around, dignified and pigeon toed, never having to be confined. He often roosted in an ash tree during the summer months and he was very fond of the small cherries that grew in the garden of Essex House, now his permanent home.

Her other concern was Jane Rehora, for over ten years now her maid, friend and in charge of her nurseries. She had unexpectedly fallen in love with a recently employed body servant of Essex, John Daniel. Jane was the same age as Frances, had never appeared interested in a man before, but had remained the same sweet, quiet, and deeply trustworthy confidante whom Frances had relied on since Philip's death at Arnhem. Jane did not want to leave the Essex household and neither did John and they asked whether they could remain after they were married. This seemed the obvious course; Frances was devoted to Jane and would have hated to lose her though she would never have constrained her to stay.

John Daniel, however, was another matter. He reminded her too strongly of the ambitious Robert Poley, her father's double agent, who had subsequently worked for the Bacon brothers and for Christopher Blount. She had seen him from time to time at Essex house and he had never been a favourite. John Daniel had the same bold, inquisitive eyes and ready tongue, his manner verging on sycophancy. She worried whether Jane would be happy with him and had suggested they wait for at least six months before marriage. Time, perhaps, would tell.

The Islands Voyage, meanwhile, continued to be stalked by bad luck. There was no getting away from the immense storms that hit northern Europe that year. Caught by yet another Atlantic monster, Essex and Raleigh were blown apart and their force separated, neither of them able to attack the Spaniards massing at Ferrol, as ordered, with insufficient ships. They managed to muddle through to the Azores but thereafter failed to capture any treasure worth having. Eventually, having blundered round the islands, tripping over each other and with hostility mounting between them, they set sail for England on 9th October. It had all been a shambolic waste of time, lives and money.

There was to be no peace, however, for Essex or anyone else limping home from the Azores. King Philip of Spain, having heard of the dispiriting fortunes of the English fleet, gave orders for the immediate sailing of his latest Armada and for his troops, with reinforcements from northern France, to be flung at England before Essex and Raleigh's ships could return and stop them. For him, this was rare impetuosity and it must have been the only time in his long life that he had done anything so out of character. It ought to have succeeded, and the Queen should never have allowed the Islands Voyage fleet to sail when it was known he was planning another attack. King Philip's commanders, summoned to Ferrol, went down on their knees to dissuade him. It was, as with the last Armada, the month of storms, in a year of unprecedented storms, and they begged him to wait. He was adamant. They must go immediately and attack England, starting at Falmouth, the plan being to land the troops after which the warships would destroy the English fleet as it straggled, unprepared, up the Channel. From Falmouth, the soldiers would fight their way to London. It seemed a sound idea.

England was flung, once more, into panic. The militia along the southern coasts were called up, the beacons prepared and folk squared their shoulders for a third time while English troops in Picardy were hurriedly recalled. There was a very real danger of invasion.

Having got all possible information from the Bacon brothers, Frances, unable to bear the tense waiting any longer, resolved to ride down to Plymouth, even Falmouth, to meet Essex wherever he should land and whether or not the

Spaniards managed to invade. She again sent her household to Barn Elms with Lady Ursula, leaving Penelope and Lettice to wait for Mountjoy and Blount at Wanstead. She then called on Richard de Burgh to immediately gather a party of men and horses for the journey and they set off one peerless October morning, the sun rising out of the mists slanting on gold, red and green in the shivering trees, lighting up the shining fields of stubble and the cattle, standing like statues, their feet in the mist.

Once clear of London, they rode hard down the route so often travelled by Essex and Philip Sidney before him. Frances was well aware of the risk she was taking and that wisdom dictated she should remain at home with her children at a time of national danger. In her heart, and just as her father had done, she did not believe that England would succumb to the Spanish, now or ever. In any case, she had steeled herself to welcome a frustrated and possibly sick husband, so better sooner than later. Her decision, now, not to wait and console after the customary, gruelling audience with the Queen, but to ride down to the West Country in time to meet him, was very similar to that which had sent her impetuously off to the Netherlands to join Philip eleven years earlier.

As the miles went by, she became aware of the unobtrusive care with which she was being treated. They were travelling at almost the same speed as had Essex and, by late afternoon, she was aching in every limb, her hands cold and slipping on the reins, and her back, usually so straight, becoming a bow of pain. Always, before she asked for it, there was a quiet suggestion that it was time to stop for the night, and a pair of hands to lift her from the saddle, holding her just long enough to prevent her staggering, but no more. Richard knew the route well, had carefully planned the journey with its changes of horses so that she was spared extremes of exhaustion and he rode just behind her, rarely taking his eyes off her, anticipating her every need and coming abreast now and again to direct her, explain the course they were taking, or just to talk. It was very companionable and easy. She had known him since the Netherlands campaign, as a part of Essex's household; he had been at Arnhem in attendance and now, at twenty-five, though still devoted to Essex, he was spending more and more time on his vast estates in Ireland as his father's age began to tell and Irish affairs became more threatening. He still took an interest in Frances's horses at Penshurst, their breeding and schooling, and she had learnt a lot from him. She was riding two of them on this journey and their pace and the comfort of their stride made a great difference to her own endurance. As they talked by day, or dined together in the evenings, Frances became aware of how very like Essex Richard had become, both to look at and in the way they moved and spoke; long gone was the Irish brogue. Both were unusually tall, with the same generous freedom of stride and bearing, Richard being slightly broader and darker than Essex, with intense blue eyes that appeared planted in his face by a sooty finger, so black and thick were the lashes. Essex's hazel eyes reflected exactly his moods; laughter, anger, introspective brooding, all on the surface to be read. This basic similarity was not really surprising. They had lived together since the respective ages of six and twelve, the younger boy inevitably imitating the elder, they had campaigned together, shared cold, fear, hunger and pain with, until now, Essex always the leader and giving the orders. Richard, educated at Christchurch, Oxford was, outwardly, more English than Irish. As the son of a "loyal" Irish peer, he had been taken to Court by Essex and made his bow to the Queen. Her Majesty had been distinctly interested in his history, his bearing and his good looks, remarking immediately on his likeness to her "Robin". She was inclined to single him out for attention and favour which sent him off hot-foot to Ireland on some pretext. He had seen the hoops through which men jumped if smiled upon over much by their Sovereign and he had no ambitions as a courtier, only as a soldier.

Essex had written to Robert Cecil on his behalf this year, of Richard's "fitness in himself to do Her Majesty's service. I will therefore entreat you to countenance him well for my sake, and to grace him so much with my lord your father that the favourable letters of my lords make way for his advancement with my Lord Deputy of Ireland."

As they passed through Wiltshire and neared Somerset, Frances found her muscles were becoming accustomed to the rigours of the ride and she was actually enjoying it, just as she had before on her way to find Philip at Axel, not knowing what she would discover at the end of the journey but revelling in the beauty of the country and her own sense of purpose. She had often been this way to the Pembroke's at Wilton, but never at this pace.

Little did they know that, as they left Stonehenge behind them, there were two fleets converging on Cornwall. King Philip's huge Armada, as large as his first, was on its way to a rendezvous at Blavet to pick up soldiers and galleys from Spanish held France from where it would descend on Falmouth, and the battered remains of Essex's fleet, leaky and unsuccessful, heading for Plymouth. By the grace of God and the diversion at Blavet, Essex arrived first, on 26th October, to be met by the news that he was about to be embroiled in an immediate battle. With typical bravado and courage and all to play for, he expressed himself delighted to take the Spanish on: "though we eat ropes ends and drink nothing but rainwater." It was about all they had on board at this stage. The Queen confirmed him as Commander of her forces but could not resist planting the blame for the current crisis firmly at his door for not attacking the Armada in Ferrol harbour as she had ordered.

Frances and Richard had arrived on 23rd October while the crisis was at its height, no one knowing whether Spanish or English masts would be the first to be sighted. They went straight to the house of Sir Ferdinand Gorges, the Governor of Plymouth, who had originally sailed with Essex, but was too ill, or fainthearted, to join him on the final attempt on the Azores. He had been optimistically knighted by Essex at Rouen and, for this, had always been grateful.

It was not until the evening of the 27th October that Frances saw her husband and his astonishment and unfeigned delight as he marched, unaware, into the house made her every ache well worth it. He looked like the wrath of God, worn and dirty, but greatly exhilarated by the danger of the moment and the chance to rise to a tense and dangerous situation after a depressing homeward journey full of resentment and failure. His arms closed hungrily around Frances, his hazel eyes once more alight.

He marched out again very soon after, shouting orders, dictating despatches and deploying the returning troops from Picardy, his mouth still full of good food and his spirits reviving by the minute. Richard rose and went out with him, their lofty heads topping those around them.

Once again the heavens opened and did their worst, this time fully to the advantage of England. Their fleet almost all safe in port, yet another vast storm blew up on the French coast, catching the Spanish fleet full-on at Blavet, decimating its ships and eventually forcing it back to its own ports in a terrible state. It was the last of the great Armadas.

The remainder of that year was spent by Essex in feuding over precedence, mud-slinging and monumental sulking. He seemed unable to resist giving any ladder under his feet a sharp kick. His judgement sometimes seemed impaired to the point of lunacy and Frances's fears for him increased.

When the Queen created his comrade at sea, Admiral Charles Howard, Earl of Nottingham, thereby giving him precedence over Essex, he retired to Wanstead pleading sickness and, never one to understate a grievance, descended into depressive self-pity as hard to live with as it was to ignore.

His relationship with Raleigh, never good, was at breaking point after the fiasco of the Islands Voyage and he was daily obliged to acknowledge the seniority of Secretary Robert Cecil, Burghley's brilliant little son.

Eventually the Queen, truly missing him by her side, devised a solution to his sulks and bestowed on him the title of Earl Marshal of England. Essex considered that he had emerged victorious from the confrontation and had won the Queen's submission. No such thing, as Frances rightly guessed; the Queen had merely found an easy way to stop his petulant behaviour and again to make him useful without any cost to herself.

As Earl Marshal he was, as much as ever, subject to her will and a servant of the Crown. She knew, as well as did Frances, that his moods concealed vaulting ambition, a lust for power and a craving for warfare during which he could exercise his own authority regardless of the consequences. The results of this authority had been seen at the end of each campaign. Lack of real achievement and a shower of unearned knighthoods, given to reinforce his popularity and present an impression of success.

A boy's charming waywardness had become, as foreseen by Walsingham, tiresome in maturity and it did him no credit as a capable and reliable statesman such as Robert Cecil. The Secretary, due in France for negotiations with Henry IV in February 1598 had, with great acumen, persuaded the Queen to temporarily appoint Essex as Secretary in his place with the proviso that the Earl would do nothing to harm his position or favour during his absence. Essex was gentleman enough to agree and to stick by it.

He did not, however, do as much for his marriage vows, but promptly renewed his old liaison with Elizabeth Brydges, daughter of Lord Chandos, his "fairest Brydges". This thoroughly naughty girl had been briefly sent away from Court for daring to watch him play at "ballon" without the Queen's permission and, before long, she went on to do a great deal more than that. Her previous activities had included leading on a rich admirer with promises of marriage in order to get her debts paid. To Frances, this diversion came almost as a relief. There is nothing like a torrid "affaire" to banish depression.

Her unquenchable mother-in-law, Lettice, saw Essex's temporary step into Robert Cecil's shoes with the gimlet eye of opportunity and began, again, to pester the life out of him to get her received by the Queen and once more returned to Court. The Queen, in her element, deliberately prevaricated, once leaving Lettice standing hopefully in a gallery and once refusing to turn up at a dinner given by Essex in her honour where Lettice was standing by with a good sized jewel for presentation. Frances had declined to attend this dubious treat; the Queen's feelings for herself were no more cordial than those she harboured for Lettice. Both women had married her favourites and without her permission and it would not have been a comfortable evening. Eventually, Lettice was granted a peck on the cheek at a formal audience. Peace had by no means been declared but the Countess had managed to get her iron-shod toe in the door.

Affairs in Ireland were now becoming crucial. Hugh O'Neill, Earl of Tyrone, whipped up by the hope of Spanish help and backed by the Church, had managed to drive out most English settlers beyond Dublin. A new Lord Deputy was urgently needed and a fearsome wrangle on the question of the appointment arose on 1st July 1598 between Essex, the Cecils and the Queen. Losing the argument on all counts, Essex also lost his temper. He turned his back on Her Majesty who was effectively demolishing his case and, when thoroughly goaded by his rudeness, she fetched him a clout on the ear, he whipped round and half drew his sword, swearing that he would never have accepted such an insult from her father any more than he would accept it from her. After that, he turned on his heel and stalked off. There was a deep and deadly silence. Never, since her accession, had such a scene occurred. Steel had been drawn against the Monarch.

The strangeness of their relationship then became apparent to all. He was not sent to the Tower but, sweeping up Frances and his children, he retired to Barn Elms to indulge in another fit of brooding; it had, he believed, succeeded before. Frances knew perfectly well that there was a limit to such behaviour as a strategy and that it might already have been reached. However, in answer to all correspondence, he continued to push authority to the edge in a way that terrified her and ran counter to every instinct she possessed. Where would this end?

4th August 1598 saw the death of Burghley to the Queen's immeasurable grief. He had spanned three Tudor reigns, always managing to remain on the side of the angels, no easy feat, and he had been her tried and tested ally since her accession. She sat by his bedside during his last days and wept openly at his passing. His son, Robert, as he had wished, would remain her constant guardian until her death.

Also ending his life's journey, King Philip of Spain lay dying in the Escorial. Covered in putrefying sores, tormented without and unfailingly holy within, he lay for fifty days and nights on a raised bed in his oratory surrounded by incense, relics, perpetual chanting and the highest in the Church of Spain, a fifth Armada only a dream. He had been godfather to Philip Sidney and, according to the historian Cabrera: "His smile and his dagger were very close to each other".

Frances could not enjoy Barn Elms as she usually did in such a situation. At any moment the Queen might decide to send her husband to the Tower for his appalling behaviour and in the meantime he was not fulfilling his roles as Earl Marshal of England, Master of the Ordinance and many others. Furthermore, he was in no state to even think about succeeding to any of Burghley's vacant positions. She found she could not sleep at night and took to wandering round the familiar rooms, in and out of the nurseries listening to the small night noises of children and animals, her night robe whispering over the polished boards.

Nothing appeared to come between Essex and his sleep until he genuinely became ill with a fever which she could not help feeling he fully deserved.

The terrible news of a major Irish uprising proved the catalyst which ended his present stand-off with the Monarch. A very large English force from Armagh, marching to relieve a small outpost on the Blackwater river, was ambushed by the Earl of Tyrone and over two thousand of the Queen's troops were massacred at Yellow Ford.

Ireland went up in flames, smoke, and violence and before long Tyrone had gained virtual control of the whole country.

Fulke Greville was sent down to Barn Elms to make overtures to Essex, and Frances was wholly delighted to see such a familiar face, particularly as the Queen had sent her own physician with him. Fulke took her in his arms and whispered in her ear that he would do his best. He also told her that Edmund Spenser, Philip's old friend, who had settled in Ireland after serving there and writing his great work "The Faerie Queene", had been forced to flee when his house was fired. (Frances had featured in this work as "Pastorella", a fair foundling carried off by brigands.) Fulke was a good ambassador and Essex returned to Court on 10th September to a surprisingly warm welcome.

He was, however, still kicking the ladder beneath him and after attempting to take over Burghley's posts of Lord Treasurer and Master of Wards, he plunged into argument over the best way to deal with the crisis in Ireland. The Queen called his bluff. If he did not like those proposed as Lord Deputy or the Council's treatment of the Irish crisis, he should go himself and deal with them.

ACT FOUR 2

1599-1601 – Ireland

It was a brave cavalcade that rode through London on 27th March 1599 bound for Ireland. For miles the streets of the city were lined with people, laughing and cheering. Essex was on top of the world, waving his hat to them, his face alight with the grin that had endeared him to so many; it was a hero's send-off.

His wife's farewell had been more muted. She was again pregnant and she did not trust his judgement or his motives. Once out of England and his own master, what dangerous, even treasonable, schemes might not be hatched if encouraged by the kind of hot-headed young men he was taking with him. She was thankful that Fulke Greville, Mountjoy, Blount and Richard de Burgh were also going.

The return was very different. A mere six months later, early on the morning of 28th September, a group of horsemen, spattered with mud and drawn with fatigue, thundered through London to Westminster. Leaving their horses to follow in a groom's care, they leapt on board the ferry to Lambeth, commandeered more horses found tethered on the South bank and covered the four miles to Nonesuch Palace at breakneck speed, arriving in the inner forecourt at 10.00am. This bruising ride from Dublin had taken them a mere four days including the passage by ship. None must know of their coming or their errand.

The tallest rider flung himself off his horse and raced up the wide outside steps, past the Renaissance columns with their many statues, across the hall and up the stairs to the State Apartments. Shoving aside the guards, he banged on the door to the Queen's own rooms, but waiting for no answer, burst in through the Privy Chamber, full of women, and marched on into the Queen's bedchamber. There, he had the grace to go down on one knee, hat in hand and with his unkempt head bent.

The old woman seated before a crystal glass froze, then slightly inclined her head. Her grizzled hair was undressed, the elaborate ginger wig still in the hand of a Lady of the Bedchamber, her lined face, unpainted, was a curious shade of ochre and her teeth, visible through her parted lips, were brackish. She was not yet dressed and wore only a loose robe.

She did not move but her mind had begun to race. Was he here as a threat or as a suppliant? If a threat, how many were with him and how many more on the way from Ireland or, if a suppliant, what folly had he committed or what catastrophe had occurred to bring him here unheralded and clearly determined to get his word to her before any other.

She therefore played for time, smiling upon him while she swiftly assessed all possibilities and calculated whether she stood in danger from him. She listened as he began to blurt out his errand and his explanations for it, then she told him to go and refresh himself; she would finish dressing, they would meet later and discuss the matter further. He kissed her hand with such impeccable grace that it was easy to forget the mud and dust that covered him. His hat had protected the top half of his face but there was a line beneath his eyes under which he was brown with grime and sunburn.

As he came downstairs, grinning broadly, his companions, stiff and sore and grimly waiting in the hall, let out sighs of relief. He had got there first and he had worked his magic yet again. It was what they had counted on and they went off to a merry meal and a great welcome from their friends, believing that all would be well. As they went, a door into the great hall closed softly; Robert Cecil was asking himself some questions too.

When Essex had gone, the Queen continued to sit gazing into her glass. To break into his Sovereign's bedchamber was quite unpardonable and she had not missed the shocked surprise in his eyes when they lit on her grey, wispy hair and raddled face. Her pride had been lacerated and for that impertinence alone he was going to pay.

She received him later therefore, at her bidding, and in an official but friendly manner; no need to put him on his guard. The full story came pouring out, well-rehearsed and with the worst of it glossed over. She did not think there were treasonable motives, but knew him well enough to guess that the thought had been there. He had failed in his mission, had made unacceptable terms with the Earl of Tyrone, and had deserted his army in order to put his case to her himself. The audience lasted over an hour, she probing his reasons for leaving Ireland and whether a force was to be brought against her, and he in a welter of self-justification.

The next audience, later that day, was not friendly at all. By then she knew there was no immediate threat, she had marshalled the facts and she flung them back at him one by one, icy and unanswerable. He was cross examined and found wanting; it was a total "volte face" and he was left without a word to say and furiously dismissed.

He was then questioned by those Councillors available at Nonesuch that day who later sent their report to the Queen. By 11.00 o'clock that evening, he was forbidden to leave his room.

Frances, whose birthday it was, was daily expecting the birth of her baby at Walsingham House. For this, she preferred the comparative peace found here to the endless bustle at Essex House and the swarms of people coming and going. The summer heat had left the city and the air had a welcome freshness. Unable to ride, she was watching the swallows lining up on the rooftops, listening to their squeaks and burbling chatter and trying to identify the babies hatched this year; they were rounder, their forked tails were shorter than the parent birds and their chestnut bibs were paler. They would soon be gone. How far would they travel until they returned next year and how many of her family would be here to welcome them?

On 5th March this year, just before the departure for Ireland, Elizabeth had been married to Roger, Earl of Rutland. She had not deviated, since the stage of pulling petals off a daisy with Greville, in her resolve to wed him, and Frances had happily done all she could to further the match. Elizabeth had known him since early childhood and gazed shyly at him as a she grew up. Though younger, he was an unswervingly loyal friend to Essex, had accompanied him on several campaigns and was the brother of her beloved Brie. He was also a close friend of the gifted but volatile Earl of Southampton with whom he had acted and written plays. His only fault appeared to be incurable extravagance. He spent like a sinner though luckily he had the wherewithal to do it. Frances had counselled her daughter to wait another year but Elizabeth was gently adamant. Roger was following Essex to Ireland, he might be killed in action, why not be happy while she could. Frances could hear herself exhorting her father on the subject of marriage at the same age, using much the same words and she capitulated. Life was, indeed, too short.

Elizabeth was married at Barn Elms, as her parents had been, looking so lovely that the harsh March day seemed to light around her and so like Philip that Frances felt time stand still. Her heavy, dark gold hair hung down her back and her honey-coloured eyes glowed unashamedly at her bridegroom. At fourteen, she had all her mother's grace and, like her father, the soul of a poet. Frances adored her and so did Essex, perhaps more than his own children. She and Roger would go first to Belvoir Castle but she had promised to return when he left for Ireland. Frances counted on Brie, who had known her from birth, to welcome her to Rutland as a daughter as well as a sister-in-law. In fact, Roger had returned in June and they then remained at Belvoir before joining the Court.

Of the five children Frances had born Essex, only ten year old Robert remained. Her confidence had been tragically shattered in June this year when Penelope, her small, dark clown, had ridden her pony at a tree trunk too large for them both in an effort to keep up with Robert. The pony had scrambled shakily to its feet, but the curly head had never moved again. She was five years old and Frances wondered bleakly why she was being punished in this way and whether she could bear the loss of another child and keep her reason. Penelope was buried at All Hallows by the Tower on 27th June and, for Frances, there was no sharper pain. Perhaps she suffered more than most because she knew the loneliness of growing up an only child and treasured her own children more than most. It was an accepted fact that only one in three babies grew to adulthood.

These sombre thoughts were interrupted by the swift entrance of Robert Sidney into the courtyard. He and Barbara had remained among her closest friends and, over the years, she and Elizabeth had spent much time at Penshurst in the heart of their enormous family.

He put his arms around her and told her to be calm; then gave her every detail of what news he had of Essex's untimely return, that he was confined to his room at Nonesuch Palace and expected to be transferred under guard to York house subject to the jurisdiction of The Lord Keeper, Lord Egerton, and following a further examination by the Privy Councillors. He would again be questioned by the Council in Star Chamber in due course and his fate decided later. For the moment neither she, nor anyone else, would be allowed to see him. His page, Henry Tracy, was with him and one other servant only.

She remained quite still, her face a mask but her eyes fixed on his face, and there was a long pause. Then she looked down at her hands, thanked him for coming and smiled at him with great sweetness and affection. Irrelevantly, he thought no other woman he knew bore children with such dignity and ease as she did despite the many blows life had dealt her. Her face glowed, her eyes shone and she looked many years younger than she was. He also wondered anxiously if she would immediately go into labour; shock could do strange things to women near their time.

She asked him whether he had seen Essex himself, who were his companions and how they had seemed, apart from exhaustion, after the ride from Dublin. Lastly, if he had asked for her. Robert had eaten with him and his friends, Southampton and Sir Charles Danvers among others, soon after his arrival; all of them seemed in excellent heart. Essex had asked whether the child had yet arrived. He had not seen him since then, but he knew that Francis Bacon had managed to gain entry. Frances also wanted to know if Elizabeth and Roger Rutland were at Court.

Robert eventually left, reassured by her calm; that she seemed preoccupied was hardly surprising. He said he was fixed at Nonesuch for the moment and she must send word if she needed him, then he kissed her and left.

On her own in the quiet courtyard, her mind, like the Queen's, raced around what she had been told. Had he turned his back on failure, left his army to rot, and staked all on convincing the Queen that he had no other course, that it was really no failure at all, and then let his winning ways and his hold over her do the rest? Or was there a hidden hint of rebellion in this jigsaw and, if things went against him, would he be mad enough to attempt bringing his army from Ireland and threaten the Crown? God forbid!

She then sent for Jane, now Daniel since her marriage earlier in the year, and together they went to her bedchamber where Frances unlocked a cupboard in the wall and brought out a casket containing several bundles of letters. She gave the casket to Jane asking her with urgency to keep it in the safest place she could think of until she asked for its return. Essex had stressed their importance, that she was not to read them, and she feared now that both Essex House and Walsingham House would be searched. She charged Jane not, on any account, to read the letters or to allow anyone else to know that she had them. Jane promised faithfully and quietly withdrew as her mother came scurrying into the room. She had just heard the news of Essex's return.

Lady Ursula was made of stern stuff and had remained a pillar of support to Frances throughout the last hectic decade and she now gave her forthright opinion of Essex's manners, morals and behaviour. Nothing was spared though Frances knew well he had only to slide an arm round her and she would melt. She then gave Frances a swift look and said that the baby would certainly be born the following day.

She was perfectly right. On September 30th 1599, Frances Devereux, future Duchess of Somerset, was born at Walsingham House. She was baptised that very day in St.Olave's Church, Elizabeth and Southampton standing as godparents. Frances was taking no chances. The following day, October 1st, her father was conveyed by coach to York House in the company of Lord Egerton and surrounded by an armed guard.

Lady Ursula then wrote directly to the Queen asking that Essex should be allowed to see his wife and his new-born child, or, at least, to receive letters. The reply was an unequivocal "no". Furthermore, it was made clear that the visitors thronging Essex House, awaiting news of the Earl, especially the direct Devereux family, should disperse immediately. Lettice, Penelope Rich, Dorothy Northumberland, Elizabeth Southampton and Elizabeth and Roger Rutland, beat a strategic retreat, mostly to Wanstead, not far away. York House was all too close to Essex House and, almost immediately, there were loud-mouthed protests from the citizens of London and demands to know why their hero had become a captive. They were joined by a large number of soldiers deserting from Ireland who were much ruder and even more violent. They cheered riotously as they passed York House and there were noisy gatherings, placards posted and mayhem in the taverns.

The waiting days that followed were anxious ones.

Cut off from the world and after months of intense activity culminating in the punishing ride from Ireland, Essex succumbed to a recurrence of dysentery, known as "the Irish flux" which had plagued him in Dublin. Depression set in again and he became extremely ill, mentally and physically.

Rumours of his collapse soon reached Seething Lane and, as soon as she was able, Frances left her bed and, assisted by Jane, began walking up and down the stairs at Walsingham House. Time and again she forced herself to go a little further until she had the strength to move freely without touching the stair rail. Then, with Jane's help, she was laced very tightly into the stomacher of a plain black dress of figured silk, made high to the neck with lace, the skirt and plain kirtle arranged over a modest farthingale. A black mantilla draped above a high comb covered her hair which had been washed in rainwater, and polished. She did not paint her face; the glow had gone from it and her reflected eyes looked back at her, huge and grave, from a countenance that might have been a widow's, and that was precisely the effect she wanted. She wore no jewels except her wedding ring.

The Queen was now at Hampton Court so that she had no need to cross the river and as soon as her coach arrived there she went in search of Lady Huntingdon. She was not in her room, so Frances sat down to write a note begging her to intercede with the Queen in allowing her to visit her husband. She knew that the sprightly young Lady Huntingdon was a Lady of the Bedchamber and very much a favourite. She also knew that Essex had cast an eye in her direction. Lady Huntingdon returned a message that she dare not see Frances, but would deliver her plea.

This was the first of several visits Frances made to Hampton Court, repeating her request for permission to see Essex. Each time was more difficult for her than the last and only her own vitality forced her to continue. She saw many people she knew and used her excellent memory to mentally list those who avoided her, those who rudely cold-shouldered her, those who looked at her with pity but dared not do more than wave and the very few who whole-heartedly greeted her regardless of their reputations and did their best to help her, repeating her request to the Queen. Among these were Mountjoy, just returned from Ireland, Southampton, Fulke Greville, Robert Sidney, the Danvers brothers and her son in law, Roger Rutland. They had not deserted the Earl and were working quietly to further his interests, but, for Frances, it was a salutary lesson in human nature that she would not forget and, each time, it took every ounce of her courage to get out of her coach. She did not go there in the guise of an imploring little ghost, but as a reasonable suppliant seeking access to a sick husband, and those who watched her graceful figure with its regal carriage and deliberate movement were aware of the support she carried at her back. The common man was behind her. She had listened to the cries of London and she knew it. When it became known that Lady Essex had been turned away and told "that she must attend her Majesty's pleasure by the Lords of the Council, and come no more to Court", there was a furious outcry, rumours spreading that Essex was to be sent to the Tower, and it was plain that some reason must be given to the people of England for the Earl's incarceration.

On November 29th 1599, the Privy Council met in Star Chamber. All Essex's shortcomings were pored over, the same list of accusations levelled at Nonesuch now made known, and accompanied by endless carping over the huge amount of money spent on a failed campaign. He did not appear but his reputation was hammered publicly into the ground.

In his temporary jail at York House, Essex became sicker and sicker, his only pleasure being mental and religious self-flagellation, but it was a repeat of past performances. He longed for death, he said, and seemed to be galloping towards eternity with remarkable speed.

By 10th December, he was reported to be dying and bells began to ring all over London. This greatly irritated the Queen, who had seen this kind of act before and failed to believe it; he had cried wolf too often in the past; sickness and sulks had gone together. However, when her own doctors, sent to report, confirmed that he was too weak to rise in his bed, that his guts were ulcerated and in a terrible state, and that his only utterances were prayers, she changed her mind, sent him a special broth and announced her intention of visiting him if he became any worse.

Frances was still denied any form of access to him and Christmas and New Year 1599 and 1600 were a miserable prelude to the new century. The bells of London had shaken her badly, but she rode and went hawking and hunting with Robert as often as she could, trying to remain cheerful, though her quiet, dark boy was clearly as worried as she was. She could see him growing up by the day.

Altogether it was a horrible start to the year. Another and extremely pressing worry was beginning to keep her awake at night too. John Daniel, the new husband of Jane Rehora, had found the casket of letters sewn into a spare mattress under their bed, taken them, and read them. When Frances asked for their return and realised some were missing, he offered to "get them back" for a sum of £3,000. Frances sold some of her jewels to raise this enormous sum and paid him £1,700 but he refused to return the missing originals, sending her only forged copies. She realised she was dealing with a particularly slimy criminal and promptly discharged him from the Essex service. Knowing the hold he now had over her, she was not going to see him smirking round every corner. Jane, in floods of tears, implored him to give the original letters back, together with any other forgeries she suspected he had made, and he then showed his true colours by writing to her and saying he proposed to send the letters to the authorities, even the Queen, but would try first to blackmail Frances further. This very unpleasant state of affairs continued as a backdrop to the saga of Essex's future and sat, like a dark cloud, at the back of her mind. She did not know the contents of the letters herself. Essex had charged her not to read them because they might endanger her also, but she guessed they were being kept for some purpose and were highly compromising. She also knew that she had to deal with this herself without adding to Essex's troubles; they had, after all, been left in her care. He would be in too fragile a state to be burdened with anything but his own recovery for many months.

As if that were not enough, Penelope Rich who had also been besieging the Court with pleas for her brother's release, took it into her head to write, at New Year, an extravagant and thoroughly impertinent letter to the Queen on his behalf. The letter began with sycophantic praise and descended into vague threats and warnings that her brother's enemies would, in turn, bring down Her Majesty. This was done without Frances's knowledge and the repercussions could not have been worse. The Queen was seriously enraged and Penelope was called to appear before the Lord Treasurer and Robert Cecil. Even worse, the letter was printed publicly and Penelope was threatened with imprisonment and commanded to keep her house. Lettice then entered the fray and attempted to give the Queen "a most curious fine gown... which will cost her £100 at least." The Queen neither accepted nor refused it, but made it clear it was not going to influence her decisions on Essex's future.

In the meantime, on February 7th 1600, Mountjoy was sent back to Ireland to replace Essex as Lord Deputy, a most unwelcome and awkward appointment for him since he and Christopher Blount had taken over Essex's negotiations with King James in preparation for his succeeding to the English crown on the Queen's death. The Irish appointment would mean the end of that and any thoughts of using the Army in Ireland to force an issue. Others would have to carry the flag to Scotland.

It was not until March 1600 that all the Devereux and their acquaintance who had seeped back into Essex House were told to leave, as were most of the staff. Lady Egerton had died in January and the Lord Keeper felt unequal to any further invigilation of his noble prisoner. Essex was to be moved back to his own home under the charge of Sir Richard Berkeley. The one notable change in his situation was that Frances would be allowed to visit him.

It was now almost a year since she had seen him, when he left her to ride so splendidly through the streets of London, bound for Ireland, and she braced herself for the stranger she might find. It was not a pretty sight. He was painfully thin, a wreck of a big man, with sunken cheeks and wasted muscles; no warmth in him mentally or physically. Defeat did not suit him, he looked years older and the sight of him brought stinging tears to her eyes. He was pathetically glad to see her but she hoped she could keep him at arms length and their relationship platonic for a while, never easy with one of his temperament. Some things, however, she could amend and she sought an audience with Sir Richard Berkeley.

Sir Richard was not acquainted with Lady Essex and his composure was somewhat unsettled when he was confronted by a lovely, diminutive and determined lady whose arresting eyes swept over him cursorily before she presented him with a comprehensive list of the medecines she would procure for her husband and which were to be properly administered as she instructed. There followed a strict diet with the recipes that should be followed in preparing the ingredients she specified. How, she would like to know, could the Earl be expected to appear before Star Chamber in his present state, let alone stand upright when summoned before their Lordships? Was he to be carried in on a stretcher and how would that reflect on the man who had charge of him? Sir Richard, knocked sideways, agreed to her demands and a regime which included daily exercise in the garden began. There was much of Lady Ursula emerging in Frances.

Recover he did, slowly and with various set-backs, and by 5th June 1600 he was able to appear before a Special Commission in York House, presided over by his erstwhile gaoler, the kindly Lord Egerton. The trial at Star Chamber had been cancelled by the Queen, after receiving a series of humble, if not abject, letters from Essex. The hearing took all day but in the long June twilight, the conclusion reached was that the Earl should remain a prisoner in his own house until Her Majesty was pleased to release him. He was utterly exhausted, having been obliged to stand for eleven hours, only Archbishop Whitgift suggesting he should be allowed to sit.

His release finally came in August 1600 but the conditions were that he was to retire to the country, not setting foot at Court. His wings had been clipped and his days of glory gone. So, also, had his wealth. He had very little income left, except the "Farm of Sweet Wines" due to expire that very month. Nothing would now be due from his former positions as Earl Marshal, Master of the Ordinance and the Queen's Horse and a member of the Privy Council. After the furious spending of the last ten years, the future, financially, looked very dark.

Hugely relieved, nevertheless, Frances packed up what remained of her household, gathered up her husband, her son and her baby and removed immediately to Barn Elms.

The tranquil familiarity of the place, the lack of drama and the quiet of the sunlit house that had always been her favourite worked powerfully on mind and body and she began to relax for the first time since the dire return from Ireland. The question of the casket of letters still weighed heavily, but she would not let it intrude into the first peace she had known for almost a year. Memories of childhood, first love, betrothal to Philip and the courtship of Essex were all around her; doubt, wonder, giddy happiness and pain were woven here into the weft and the warp of her life. Where would the finished threads lead?

She was again pregnant, very much to her annoyance and something she had tried to avoid, but it showed proof of Essex's recovery and if he were not as sulky as a bear, she would have been glad of such a positive sign; looking back, she could not help laughing and wondering how on earth they had managed it, under guard at Essex House.

The family then began to descend on Barn Elms in droves which was a mixed blessing. Though good to see the house full of children and laughter again, with Robert climbing back on his perch as head of the troupe, she could have done without the gossip, intrigue and the constant plotting and manoeuvring to restore Essex to a position of power. She did not want any part of that life again. It was over and so was the grandeur, the unlimited wealth, and everything that went with it. She thanked God fasting that Essex was restored to them and she would be content with a far simpler life. The Essex ladies, however, would not. They were all devoted to the Earl, but he had been their ticket to high positions and Court contacts and he had always been unfailingly generous to them. They wanted him back where he belonged, at Essex House and at Court.

But it was not so easy to withdraw either. There were already creditors making heavy demands and his financial future hung on the renewal of the levy on "The Farm of Sweet Wines". He had no time to reinstate himself in the

Queen's good graces and panic set in accompanied by a series of letters to her whose desperation was thinly veiled. He was a year out of touch, no longer a force of any kind, and he had antagonised the only men who could have helped him. After so long a time of inactivity, he had lost his way, his contacts and his power. Francis Bacon, for one, had definitely switched direction and loyalty. He had advised him, at their last meeting at Nonesuch to grovel unreservedly to the Queen, with no attempt at self-justification, and that was as far as he would go. He was to prove a very dangerous adversary.

But Essex was not on his own. Those kindred spirits so devoted to him were mulling the situation over and did not accept his defeat. They convinced themselves and the Earl that they were victims of a plot hatched to destroy them by the Court faction opposed to Essex: Robert Cecil, the Howards, including Nottingham, Raleigh and Cobham and the bad-tempered Lord Grey. They must act to save themselves. Henry Cuffe and Gilly Meyrick were among the most vociferous, urging Essex to take up arms to defend himself and accusing him of faintheartedness. Mountjoy, beginning to make an impression on the chaos he had found in Ireland, could not and would not aid them further. Richard de Burgh was serving under him, defending Galway and the province of Connaught, both containing swathes of his own land; a thoroughly difficult situation for an Irish absentee landlord.

But at the end of October came the last ounce of salt in the wounds. The grant to Essex on the "Farm of Sweet Wines" was not renewed. The Queen would keep it for herself. Though not unexpected, this was the worst that could have happened and the drums began to roll for the final act.

Gone was Frances's fragile peace, nor was she to regain it for many months and then the price was going to be high. Her husband appeared to have lost his mind as well as his fortune; what talk she heard was sinister and smacked of insurrection. Much communication followed with James of Scotland, Henry IV of France, the Essex estates in Wales, and even Mountjoy in Ireland to whom Daniel Bacheler was sent as a courier with letters from the Queen, but also carrying letters from Penelope to her beloved.

Frances was now seven months pregnant; she felt the weight physically and, mentally, the heavy threat of blackmail continuing to cast an added shadow. She had heard no more from the odious John Daniel but she knew he was lurking somewhere in the wings, waiting his moment, the letters still in his possession.

Essex had not asked for them and she prayed he would not. Jane wanted nothing more to do with John Daniel and remained, staunchly loyal, with Frances. It had been a very brief and unhappy marriage and it had aged Jane sadly, but, for Frances, it was the greatest relief to have one person in whom she could confide.

She felt powerless. In the past she had been able to influence Essex, to argue or laugh him out of some of his wilder schemes, or discourage some of his outrageous behaviour. Now she felt like a leaf on the river being swept towards the falls.

Though brought up almost puritanically Protestant, she turned, for the first time, to the intercession of the Mother of God. Her prayers for those she loved had not protected them in the past but Our Lady would surely watch over her children.

With the roll of drums sounding louder and louder, Christmas and New Year 1600 and 1601 approached.

1603-1631 – Somerhill, Portumna

The last of the Tudors was gone. Queen Elizabeth had reigned over England for forty five years and her death on March 24th 1603, though daily expected, sent a tremor through her country. Like most of her major decisions, death had taken time. She would not succumb, but stood for long hours in silence leaning against a wall, refusing food or drink. Eventually she sank upon a stool and only very near the end would she allow her ladies to put her to bed. Archbishop Whitgift was kept on his knees by her side, his old joints groaning, and to the end she would not name her successor.

After the execution of the Earl of Essex it became clear that the fire had gone out of the Queen. She rode, hunted, danced and travelled as she always had done with amazing vigour for her age, but now there were heavy sighs, a break in conversation, or a distracted gazing into the middle distance.

A strange story had arisen that was circulating freely in and around the Court. It was to travel down the ages and was only put into writing in 1620. It inevitably found its way to the widowed Lady Essex, living in quiet retirement on her manor of Barn Elms, down river from Hampton Court. Parts of it were known to her but its dark core was not.

Essex once told her that a ring, given to him by the Queen and which he had worn until just before his arrest, was a talisman that would always guarantee her forgiveness for any wrong if ever he sent it to her. Frances knew the ring well; it had been a part of his being for over ten years and her suspicions were roused when she saw he no longer wore it.

Legend now had it that a few days before his death he had managed to send the ring from the Tower to the Palace in the terrified hand of his page, Henry Tracy, with orders to give it to none but Lady Scrope, an old ally and a friend of the Queen. The palsied Tracy, however, had mistaken her sister, Lady Nottingham, for Lady Scrope, and given the ring into her hand with its message. Lady Nottingham was the wife of Charles Howard, the Lord High Admiral, and one of Essex's most implacable enemies. She knew exactly the significance of the ring and she had kept it securely until, on her deathbed, she confessed to the Queen what she had done. The response was terrible: "May God forgive you, Madam, for I never can".

Frances had no means of proving the truth or untruth of the story. Henry Tracy had completely disappeared. The Earl of Nottingham would certainly not speak to her and she had no contact with anyone likely to have attended the death of Lady Nottingham. After several days of agonising, she decided that for the sake of herself and her children, she would not delve further into this horrible tale. She would have to live with it and, in time, the thoughts that it raised would fade both from her mind and from the minds of those who heard it. It was all much, much too late.

One other story had come to her ears which she did not want to hear either. A Captain Thomas Lee, a supporter of Essex, was apparently arrested a few days before the execution as he kept watch outside the Queen's own chambers. His plan was to confine her and compel her to sign a warrant to release Essex. Word leaked out and he was tried and executed immediately. Frances was too far removed from the source of these rumours to be able to judge their credibility, but they left their mark on her.

Mercifully, Barn Elms wove its spell once again and she had eventually been able to pick up the fragments of her life and make of them something quietly acceptable. Now, over a year away from that morning in February, she could find a real contentment in the daily activities at home and the running of house and estate. The financial situation had been dire and, with so much debt hanging over her, she had been stringently careful. But now, with more money coming in, the home farm was thriving and she had made innovations in the dairies and in the stables and installed many more of the horses bred by her at Penshurst. This venture was proving an unqualified success and gave her great satisfaction. The line started by Philip's Andalucian stallion had become quite recognizable and was much admired and sought after.

Her little girls, so close in age, were rosy and rudely healthy, tumbling about in the gardens like puppies and Robert was beginning to lose the wary, taut look that the strain of his father's imprisonment, trial and death had stamped on his young face. He had been disinherited and remained Robert Devereux while Frances, herself, was known as Lady Essex though the title of Countess had been dropped.

Elizabeth, whose husband Roger Rutland and his two brothers had been imprisoned with Essex though later released, spent much time at Barn Elms, her small face pinched and pale; Frances put this down to intense worry over her husband.

The Queen had, however, shown more compassion than expected, perhaps because public opinion remained sharply divided on the subject of Essex's execution, or perhaps, because she did not want his children reduced to penury. Many thought he had been very harshly treated and regarded him as a wronged icon. William Camden wrote: "To this day, there are but few who thought it a capital crime." This had not improved the popularity of the old Queen.

Very soon after the Earl's death, the Queen granted Frances and her family "the fee of the extensive district of South Frith in the Lowy of Tonbridge." This was a beautiful piece of land of around six thousand, five hundred acres, to the south and east of Tonbridge in Kent, lush, clement and fertile. There were already many orchards growing there and, on one of the few hills in the area, there was a perfect site for a house. It was known as Somerhill. Frances and her children would have a good income from the estate.

This gift came betimes. Money had become extremely short, so much so that Frances was to write: "Not £40 a year is left for the maintenance of my three poor children." Large economies had been made and she had done her best to settle some of Essex's enormous debts through sale of jewelry, pictures, furniture and coaches but much due to the Crown was still outstanding. She had halved the staff at Barn Elms but refused to cut down on the upkeep of her land, stables, dairies and orchards. As with Philip, the horses were sacrosanct. She worked hard herself, often physically, and found relief in this outpouring of energy which left little time for grief. The gardens, in particular, were balm to the soul and all her father's lore came pouring back. When to plant, when to prune, where to grow and when to sow; the knowledge she had absorbed as a small child in this very garden, trailing behind Leicester and Walsingham, returned to her with the scents, the sounds and the sights.

Though not directly involved, The Queen had also been aware of and helped remove the source of one major worry for Frances. The unspeakable John Daniel, despite the fact that Essex was now dead, made another attempt to blackmail her in May 1601. She could not and would not pay his further demands and, this time, immediately contacted Robert Cecil, asking for his help. With the Queen's permission, the response was swift and savage. John Daniel was arrested, brought before Star Chamber, no less, and fined £3,000 of which £2,000 was paid to Frances. He was condemned to the Fleet Prison but not before another sentence had been carried out. He was: "to be set upon the pillory with his ears thereunto nayled, with a paper on his head "For Forgery Corrupte Cosenage and other Leude practices." He was not released until the accession of James I. Frances heard no more about the casket, but wrote a letter of deep gratitude to Robert Cecil.

With this load lifted, her spirits began to rise and the dark depression following the Earl's death slowly began to recede.

One chapter, though, had not been closed for Frances; she wished to know exactly how Essex had died and to see where he had been buried. Providence, for once, came to her rescue. Richard de Burgh had returned from Ireland in time to witness the beheading of one of his greatest friends that Ash Wednesday morning. He had seen his head and body bestowed in the nearby church of St.Peter ad Vincula immediately afterwards. A few days later, he came to Walsingham House and asked to see Frances. Perhaps he guessed that he was one of the very few people from whom she could hear what had to be told and believe it to be the unsweetened truth and he prayed that he would be able to find the right words. He had known her since he was thirteen, admired and, would now admit to himself, loved her from the time of her marriage to Essex and it seemed quite natural that he should do this for her.

She also appeared to think it natural that he was there and she did not even ask him why. She merely stood by the fireplace, looking into the glowing fire, and asked him gently to tell her everything.

She knew every detail of the trial, convoluted and dramatic as it had been. She had lived through every twist, turn, denunciation and betrayal, particularly from Francis Bacon, until the final hour when Essex and Southampton had left the chamber, the blade of the great axe carried by the Gentleman Porter turned towards them and with the foul sentence of a traitor's death ringing in their ears. Because of their rank, this was commuted to beheading and they were spared the grisly torture meted out to others. She knew that he had never asked for her, written or sent word to her or his children; that wound was a deep one. But how had he died?

Richard took her hands, fixed his eyes on her face and told her: At seven o'clock on the morning of Ash Wednesday, Essex left his room in the Tower of London and walked to the scaffold dressed in black with a black felt hat on his head. With him, in procession, walked the Lieutenant of the Tower, three priests and sixteen guards. On the green turf beside the scaffold were gathered around a hundred people including peers of the realm, knights, and gentlemen of the city. Essex mounted the scaffold, removed his hat and spoke to them, admitting his wrongs but maintaining that he had never intended to harm the Queen. He then approached the executioner and accepted the customary plea for pardon. The Earl smiled wryly at him and said "Thou art welcome to me, I forgive thee." He prayed: "Lift my soul above all earthly cogitations, and when my soul and body shall part, send Thy blessed angels to be near unto me, which may convey it to the joys of heaven." He then removed his black doublet and stood, a striking figure, in a scarlet waistcoat. He lay down on the boards before the block, stretched out his arms saying "O Lord, into thy hands I commend my spirit." It took three blows to sever his head but he did not move.

Frances's widened eyes slid away from Richard's, but he shook her hands slightly and made her look at him. It was important that no questions were left unanswered.

Essex's head and body were buried by the Earl of Arundel and the Duke of Norfolk, and the Queen personally ordered that his banner and hatchment of the Knight of the Garter remained in St.George's Chapel, Windsor.

That was all he would tell her. It was not necessary to tell her anything else or the fact that the first blow had bitten into the Earl's shoulder. Neither that Sir Walter Raleigh, having shouldered his way to the foot of the scaffold in order to make sure that Essex was aware of his gloating presence, had been told peremptorily to take himself off and that he had been obliged to watch from an upper window. His own feelings he did not mention, soldier that he was who had so often seen death, but like her, a part of him had died that morning.

He then escorted her to the Tower to see her husband's grave in the little church within the precincts of the White Tower. There was now deep snow on the ground which mercifully covered any trace of the brutal act of Ash Wednesday; there was no sign of scaffold or block. The grave, still bare earth, lay near to that of Anne Boleyn, the mother of the woman who had condemned him. Frances, shivering, moved closer to Richard. She wondered whether the

Queen would ever stand there, as she did now, and feel the irony of that proximity.

Richard had returned to Ireland soon after; he was needed increasingly there by Mountjoy who, although making headway against Tyrone, was threatened by Spanish reinforcements arriving in the south of the country.

In May 1601 his father died and he inherited the Earldom of Clanricarde. His was an old and distinguished name; the Norman French De Burgo Knights had come to Ireland with Prince John in the twelfth century and settled in the region of Loughrea with Portumna as their base. They were Lords of Connaught and Dunkellin and, in 1582, having fought the English for generations, they had agreed to serve the English crown.

Richard, then a child, had been taken to England as surety by the first Earl of Essex to be brought up with his own son. He now inherited the six baronies of Dunkellin, Kiltartan, Clare, Athenry, Loughrea and Leitrim and the old "black castle" or manor of Portumna by the river Shannon.

In December 1601, he fought with outstanding valour at the battle of Kinsale in southern Ireland and was knighted on the battlefield by Mountjoy. Thereafter he was known as Richard of Kinsale. This was the decisive battle to regain Ireland and a major triumph over both Tyrone and the Spanish invaders in the South.

At home, and in dire need of Mountjoy after Essex's death, Penelope was forced to fight her own battles and, to begin with, Frances was powerless to help her. Denounced by Essex at his trial, when at the height of another bout of religious mania, he said of her: "I must accuse one who is most nearest to me, my sister, who did continually urge me on with telling me how all my friends and followers thought me a coward and that I had lost all my valour; and thus that she must be looked to for she hath a proud spirit." He had also spoken of her love affair with Mountjoy, a double betrayal. Penelope was arrested and kept in the house of Henry Sackford, Keeper of the Privy Purse. (The Queen had not forgotten the odious letter written earlier.) She was very harshly treated there and she was obliged to ask for "a cook to dress her meat... for linen and other necessaries." Her husband, Lord Rich, ignored a request to supply these things, and had to be sharply reminded by the Privy Council that it was his duty to do so. During this time her brother was condemned to death. That Penelope emerged unscathed from her ordeal may have been due to the fact that

Mountjoy, though remaining loyal, was in a position of great power in Ireland, with total command of the army there and he would not have allowed her to be harmed. As soon as she was freed, Frances sent a coach to bring her and all her children to Barn Elms. It was a reunion of mixed emotion and relief. Frances had lost her husband and Penelope her brother but his going had, if anything, strengthened their friendship. They had not seen each other since the final departure that icy February night from Essex House, gunshot and flares around them and their last glimpse of Essex, shouting defiance from the rooftop. There was much of Lettice's resilience in Penelope and before long laughter broke out again both among the re-united children and between the two of them.

With Essex gone and nothing more to be gained from that direction, Lord Rich now abandoned Penelope completely and instigated divorce proceedings in the ecclesiastical courts.

His immortal soul under threat, Essex had done a thorough business of betrayal. Many of those comrades who might have escaped prosecution through the last minute burning of incriminating letters in Essex House, did not. His stepfather, Christopher Blount was beheaded on 5th March, followed by Sir Charles Danvers. It was unlikely that the Queen would have spared Blount, the husband of the detested Lettice. Gilly Meyrick and Henry Cuffe were hung, drawn and quartered at Tyburn. Southampton, a prime mover in the rebellion, had his death sentence commuted on the grounds of his youth, but was only released on the Accession of James 1. The Earl of Rutland was fined the enormous sum of £20,000 and lesser fines were extracted from Bedford, Mounteagle, Gorges and others. After imprisonment, all were eventually freed. They had loved and served the Earl and this was a poor reward.

Frances had moved her remaining possessions from Essex House to Barn Elms, while Lady Ursula retained Walsingham House, having inherited it from her own family. Englefield was taken over by the Crown and given to Sir John Norris, the Queen's old friend.

Lady Ursula, then with Frances at Barn Elms, suddenly fell ill and died very shortly afterwards on 18th June 1602; there was no lingering illness. She was a gallant old lady, Walsingham's "most kind and loving wife", who had sheltered her daughter throughout the turbulences of her life, always gathering children, households, friends and a variety of strangers into her house and providing for them. Anthony Bacon, crippled and heartbroken, had gone to her after the death of his beloved Earl and died in her care. He was buried in St.Olave's square little church opposite Walsingham House. She was no weakling, even Walsingham had admitted "the force of her commands", and she had spoken her mind to some of the greatest in the land. From her, Frances had inherited the iron constitution and active health without which she would never have survived. She mourned her mother deeply and Lady Ursula was buried, as were Walsingham and Philip Sidney, in St. Paul's Church.

Greville, who had reluctantly survived the move from Essex House was found, sadly dead, the following day. He was sitting snugly on a hat in Frances's dressing chamber. He must have reached a great age, having been given, fully grown, to Frances when she was fourteen and he was greatly missed by his entire family.

Frances had time now to reflect on her life and to consider her own feelings in a way she never had before. Living apace and almost from day to day for the last eleven years, Essex and her children constantly on her mind, she had seldom probed her own thoughts.

She had loved Philip with all her heart, but there had always been an element of hero worship and a slight fear of offending such a God-like figure; his early love for Penelope never quite forgotten. He had died with chivalric perfection while Essex had died with his head on a block.

Essex had been a dear friend and she had been unable to resist him physically but, as he changed, he had become very difficult to deal with. What love she had for him was eroded by his behaviour and she was appalled at some of his wilder actions and apparent lack of judgement. Something in his mind must have gone very much amiss; from sailing close to the wind, he had taken to heading for the eye of the storm and the results had been disastrous, for himself and for those who served him. But still the feckless charm of the Devereux had done its work even though she was only a part of his life; so much had been absorbed by the Queen, not to mention his mistresses. Such was his hold over her, and others, that however provoking he was, it had been enough to keep them loyal to the end.

Frances was now thirty five years old, although she appeared ten years younger, and she could not mistake what could be read in a man's eyes. She knew that Richard loved her and had, perhaps, always known but just accepted the unspoken fact. He had never married and was often a part of her life with

Essex; sometimes with them in London, sometimes campaigning abroad, and often in Ireland. Riding down to Plymouth in his charge had opened her eyes a little though never once had he shown her anything but companionship and respect. He had been at Court before, and after, Essex's banishment but found the Queen's attentions embarrassing and potentially dangerous. He was too like the Earl and Her Majesty found that extremely interesting. In Hasted's "History of Kent" it is recorded by Smollet that: "It is no wonder this lady (Frances) married him; he was a very handsome gallant young nobleman and very like the Earl of Essex. In so much that the Queen, then far advanced in years, made some advance to him, which he declined."

Having left Ireland as a child, and despite a thoroughly English upbringing and education, he still loved his own country and was deeply concerned for its future. Since inheriting his father's title and estates in May 1601, his path had been hard. The English treatment of the Irish was barbaric (he had been with Essex at the massacre of women and children at Raithlin Island) and his loyalties were severely tested then, and later, despite his admiration for Mountjoy whom he sincerely liked.

He knew that if he did not marry Frances now, he probably never would; time was not on their side and he was already thirty years old. He arranged with Mountjoy to return to England in August of 1602 and went immediately to Barn Elms.

He found Frances, having circumnavigated children beyond count, in the walled garden tying in a fan-trained apricot tree to the rosy bricks. She was perched on a high bench, her bonnet had fallen to her shoulders, her skin, contrary to fashion, was gilded to a pale shade of the ripe fruit and she was laughing at one of her many little spaniels who was worrying the branch she had just cut off and growling horribly. He took a deep breath, came up behind her and swung her off her feet into his arms. He had always thought how fragile she was and, with a sense of wonder, could not believe his load was so light.

They agreed that they would not marry until the following year. Richard was bound to return to Ireland, both for the sake of duty and his own estates and Frances would have to face real anger from the Queen yet again. First she had stolen Philip Sidney, then the treasured Essex and now it was to be someone very like him on whom her old eye had certainly lighted. Despite a lifetime of unrewarded service accepted from her father, she had always seen Frances as a vague threat. They would give Her Majesty a little longer and await events.

They went together down to Somerhill to look at the land given to Frances. It was a serenely beautiful and peaceful place with good grazing for livestock and orchards for every kind of fruit; in fact, a productive paradise. Handfast, they climbed the hill which looked down towards Tonbridge and agreed that on this site they would build a house. It was the perfect place and there, in the soft air of late summer, the swifts wheeling over their heads, they swore to love each other for the rest of their lives. Richard swept her hands behind her and, holding her against him, knew that this was the attainment of a dream he had never thought to see realised. For Frances, it was as if she were coming home after a long, difficult journey; she would be loved unconditionally and solely with no other intervening presence. The smile on her face was unshadowed and sunny as a child's.

One thing only did he ask of her; that she should consider becoming a Catholic, as he was, and this was an enormous step for her. Her upbringing was as far removed as it could be from the Roman church and her father had abominated it. But since the death of her little daughter, Penelope, she had turned more and more to the Virgin Mary for intercession, and Her protection for the remaining four children. Perhaps, with help, the transition might not be so difficult.

For the building of Somerhill they employed an architect, John Thorpe, a delightful man with Italian leanings, who produced a plan for a design based on a Palladian villa in Lisiera. For England this would be quite innovative and it was to be the future English seat of the Earls of Clanricarde. Work to clear the remains of an existing house and flatten the top of the hill began. Somerhill was close to Penshurst so they were able to stay with Robert and Barbara Sidney on the way. This was always a delight for Frances and they warmly welcomed Richard as a prospective kinsman, having known him since boyhood and appreciated his advice and work with their horses over the years.

As events turned out, Richard was free to come home by New Year 1603. Tyrone had submitted unconditionally in December 1602, having been chased from Kinsale to Ulster, and his final surrender to Mountjoy came in March 1603, a week after the death of the Queen.

Richard and Frances were married very quietly at Barn Elms as early as possible after his return, the service being acceptable to both Protestant and

Catholic. Events then moved quickly towards the Queen's death but they were man and wife before she died.

In the whole of her life, Frances could not remember being so wholeheartedly happy. Almost everything that had oppressed her was drifting away and she found an undreamed of affinity with the quiet, strong man she had married. She would not be obliged to fight her battles any more and to be so cherished and protected was something new to her.

And now England awaited the arrival of funny little James of Scotland with his wispy hair, wary expression and slight paunch. He did not resemble his beautiful mother or his tall fair father but there was nothing wrong with his intellect and his memory for people and events was outstanding. His upbringing had been the worst. Left in the care of the Earl of Mar and abandoned by his mother, Mary Queen of Scots, he was, as a child, at the mercy of the warring Scottish nobility and a succession of self-seeking regents. The last of these, his beloved Esmé Stewart, Earl of Lennox, was removed by the Calvinists who suspected a carnal association between them. James definitely preferred male company, apparent from a string of favourites, although he was devoted to his wife and children.

Advised by Robert Cecil, he and his Queen, plain Anne of Denmark, set out for London from Edinburgh on 5th April 1603 and were received with lavish hospitality and curiosity in various great houses on their way south. Among them was Belvoir Castle where the young Earl and Countess of Rutland entertained them so lavishly and well that the King was always to remember them with affection. He also remembered the various delegations led to Scotland by Walsingham, whom he had held in respect and liking. He did not forget, either, the plight of his daughter, Frances, and her family after the execution of Essex. The following year, 1604, her children were restored to their titles, Robert succeeding his father as 3rd Earl of Essex and a large part of his father's debts to the Crown being waived. Camden said of the King's relationship with Walsingham that he: "Did so much endear himself to James that he was more than happy to receive and befriend his grandchildren and his daughter."

James l, calling himself King of Great Britain and Ireland, entered London on 7th May 1603 amid scenes of genuine rejoicing and was crowned on 25th July. The streets were so packed with people that the Earl and Countess of

Clanricarde were forced to use outriders to get their coach through from Walsingham House to Westminster. The mood of the Londoners was celebratory, mingled with relief that the transition from Queen to King was both smooth and unopposed.

Based mainly at Barn Elms, Frances and Richard now took their place at the new Court, not over-enthusiastically, but to ensure the future of Frances's children and, in due course, their own. Robert and Prince Henry were the same age and were to become close companions.

Her return after so many years seemed strange to Frances but there were still old friends to greet and her enjoyment of the dancing, masques and plays was as keen as ever. Richard could not take his eyes off her or believe that with her years and many children, she could still dance the night away with supple grace and manage to look younger even than he did.

She took with her Daniel Bacheler, who had found his way back to her after the death of Essex, in order to introduce him to the new Queen as a talented musician. Anne of Denmark had a good ear for music and was immediately impressed. Very soon afterwards she appointed him a groom of her privy chamber with an excellent salary. She appreciated his genius both as a lutenist and a composer and eventually he received a manor in Suffolk. It was a delight to Frances that after all his loyalty to her family, he was given proper recognition.

Everyone who had any right, and many who did not, were at Whitehall, determined to get in on the ground floor of the new Monarch's favour.

The Devereux ladies were also back at Court in force. Penelope, Dorothy, and the unquenchable Lettice who had survived the execution of both her third husband and her son with remarkable aplomb and had moved herself back into Essex House regardless of expense or permission. She showed no surprise at Frances's re-marriage. She had done the same herself and with considerably more haste. She had a great affinity with her grandson, Robert, and since Frances's marriage, he was beginning to spend more and more time with her. Penelope, reunited with Mountjoy who had come back from Ireland in April, was beside herself with delight, particularly as King James, appreciative of his success there, created him Earl of Devonshire on 21 July, just before the coronation.

Frances was anxious for her first born and wished that Elizabeth seemed happier, but it was not a subject she could broach. Even since Roger's release, she was plainly not the contented wife she should be and Roger, together with the newly freed Earl of Southampton, seemed to be only too happy to carouse his way around London attending every theatre and certainly not attending his wife. Southampton had, in 1598, eventually married Essex's cousin, Elizabeth Vernon, after a shaky start. She became pregnant before marriage, a bad mistake for a Maid of Honour to the Queen, and her Majesty had the pair of them incarcerated briefly in the Fleet prison.

Frances's concern was increased by the lack of any heir for Rutland and was the only shadow on her own happiness. Elizabeth seemed, however, to be giving full rein to the poetic and literary side of her nature, building around her at Belvoir a court of writers and artists, playwrights and poets, just as Frances had done at Essex House. Among them were Inigo Jones, architect and designer, Ben Jonson, Shakespeare's friend and fellow playwright, and Francis Beaumont, working for Shakespeare's company, "The King's Men", and there was a close connection between Roger, these three friends, and Shakespeare himself. Ben Jonson adored Elizabeth and wrote that she "was no less in poesie" than had been her father.

Meanwhile Somerhill was rising on its mound and was one of Frances's main delights. Together, she and Richard planned every part of it; the gardens in particular were her province and she superintended their laying out and planting. She installed a physic garden within the extensive walled area and a vegetable garden where she hoped the new and exotic varieties, such as tomatoes, cucumbers and potatoes imported from the New World, would flourish. Richard's knowledge and forethought went into the planning of the stables and the home farm. It was going to be one of the largest houses in Kent and certainly one of the most beautiful.

Richard, meanwhile, had been appointed Governor of Connaught with its base in Athlone and planned now to take Frances over there on a protracted visit which would include his other Irish estates. She had never been to Ireland and was eager to see this side of his life, though loth to leave Somerhill still in its infant stages. The travelling would be rough but she was not daunted by that. Richard also warned her there would be some dismal sights along the way; Mountjoy had employed a "scorched earth" policy as an aid to subduing Tyrone and the country and its people were dirt poor and in great distress.

By March, Frances realised she was carrying a Clanricarde heir and he was born in Athlone Castle by early December 1604, another beautiful child with surprisingly fair hair and startling blue eyes. Like so many of his father's family, he was named Ulick and it was at this time that Frances converted to Catholicism. It was a far easier step to take in Ireland where it was in the bones and breath of the people, in the very air around them, and in the stick and stone of every building. She would have to face the music back in England, particularly the surprise at Court, but Richard's delight in his son and the fact that they were now of the same faith made anything else unimportant.

They visited Portumna on the shores of Lough Derg in the teeming rain with the old castle looking its grimmest, but as they rode away looking back over their shoulders, the sun cut through the gloom and the place lit up as a stage, magically beautiful, the dark woods reflected in the shining water. Grey geese came low over their heads, a fan-shaped corps de ballet, the drift of their pinions loud in the silence as they wheeled as one and settled on the water. They pulled up, laughing, and resolved, once Somerhill was done, to create something just as good here which would benefit the people and be the heart of Richard's lands in Galway. By now, he did not have to count the cost overmuch.

Frances was to bear Richard two daughters. Honora, the future Marchioness of Winchester, and Mary. All three of her Clanricarde children had long and full lives and were brought up mainly at Somerhill, finished in 1609. Like their father, they were more English than Irish, but, as with him, blood was thicker than water, and Ireland was to draw them back and keep its hold on them.

Portumna, meaning "the landing place of the oak" became the site of another original and impressive house, completed by 1618, costing over £10,000, and being both inventive and beautiful. Its form was influenced also by Italian architecture; it stood apart from the old fortified castles of Ireland, and was unequalled at the time.

Frances herself lived another fourteen years after it was finished spending more and more of her time at Somerhill, their own creation, and as much beloved as Barn Elms had been. It was entirely hers and Richard's into which they had put so much of themselves. There were many joys and some sorrows in their lives during these last years. Troubles in Ireland, to which Richard was very much committed, were endemic, and he remained closely in touch with them. James l had, from the beginning, respected and favoured him and in 1624 created him Viscount Tonbridge and Baron of Somerhill, followed, in 1628, by the titles of Earl of St.Albans, Baron of Imanney and Viscount Galway.

Frances remained mostly in her own demesne in her later years, content and energetic, surrounded by the children, dogs, horses and gardens she loved, until she died on 17th February 1631, aged sixty four, at Somerhill. She was buried in Tonbridge Church. Richard survived her by four years and died on 12th December 1635.

Even for her era she had lived an extraordinarily full life. She had survived a massacre as a child, the death of a husband, wounded in battle and tended by her through his last days, and the imprisonment, trial and beheading of a second husband. She had suffered the loss of five children and she had married again at thirty six and borne three more children. She had changed her faith from rigid Protestantism to the Roman Catholic Church quite late in life and, between them, she and her third husband had built and left to posterity two very significant houses of great beauty.

So we leave her on the brilliant stage of a vivid bygone age, a small, unsung but vital figure who had played an important role in the lives of many of the greatest Elizabethans.

EPILOGUE

Curtain Down

Although there is no exact date for her birth, Frances Walsingham must have been born on, or very near, 28th September 1567, at Appuldurcombe, the Isle of Wight estate inherited by Lady Ursula from her first husband, Sir Richard Worsley. Three circumstances support this date.

In a letter written in July 1567, Lady Ursula's brother-in-law, John Worsley, writing to Sir William More from the Isle of Wight, describes "his sister Walsingham" as being near her time. This indicates that the Walsinghams were there and that the families were visiting each other.

The second circumstance is that when her father's estates were finally proven after his death in 1590, Frances is described as being "over twenty-four on 27th September 1592 which makes it likely that she was born soon after September 27th 1567.

There was one more circumstance also. Frances was Lady Ursula's third child. She had two sons by Richard Worsley, both killed in an accidental explosion just before the arrival of Frances herself. After this tragedy, and with a birth imminent, it is most unlikely that Lady Ursula would have moved from Appuldurcombe.

The first contender for Frances's hand, John Wickerson, was indeed imprisoned by Walsingham for two years in the Marshalsea Prison and released when Frances became betrothed to Philip Sidney. His exact position in Walsingham's household is not known.

Her marriage to Sidney was probably one of convenience to begin with. Walsingham was clearly impressed by him and very keen to secure him as a son in law, paying £1,500 of his debts and housing the young couple at Walsingham House and Barn Elms, but Frances's decision to join him in the Netherlands, something she had no need to do, and the fact that she became pregnant very soon after her arrival, suggest something different. Also, her illness, long-lasting and serious, after his death confirm her deep grief at his loss.

Robert Devereux could have had his pick of the heiresses of England and a few Europeans as well, but either from fondness, friendship or chivalry, he chose Frances, the wife of his much admired Commander. She was a year younger than he was and had none of the wealth he badly needed at the time. There is nothing to prove the popular legend that Sidney, knowing he was dying, "bequeathed" Frances to Essex. It was not in Essex's nature to ally himself with any but a beautiful woman or to calculate how useful she could be to him. He must have loved her in his fashion or he would certainly have married a fortune instead.

Erudite, charming and generous, Essex had a temper like fire, over which he had little control; he wore his heart on his sleeve, but his ability to inspire and retain love and loyalty remained to the end. It has been suggested that the change in his character over his last five years may have been due to the advance of syphilis, contracted much earlier and not surprising given his way of life which included many mistresses and contact with camp followers on campaign. The tertiary stage of the disease plays havoc with the mind and character, sometimes producing indecision, depression and mood swings. It might also account for his hounding of Dr. Lopez. The Doctor was a known gossip and was said to have spread the rumour that Essex had syphilis; reason enough to dispose of him so brutally.

Richard de Burgh, recorded as an outstanding soldier, and a most attractive man in whom the Queen showed interest and whose resemblance to Essex was marked, had not married by the age of thirty. This was unusual, especially as he was heir to a huge amount of property in Ireland and needed an heir himself. He then married a woman older than he was, her husband beheaded as a traitor, with three of her children dispossessed, and in financial straits. Apart from his close connection with Essex, there was no obligatory reason for marrying Frances and it seems, therefore, fairly certain that he loved her. Also that she loved him enough to abandon her almost puritanical Protestant faith and convert to the Catholic Church. To a woman of her era, this change must have cost her a great deal. Who knows at what point they discovered their affinity. The exact date of their marriage is not known, except that it was before April 1603.

One other very endearing piece of evidence comes to light on the lead "hoppers", the decorated heads of the rainwater down pipes, at Somerhill. On some of them are the letters "RCF", Richard and Frances Clanricarde. The house is now a school but there is an aura there that whispers to those that listen of fulfilment and deep content.

Richard himself, though he does not go down in history in the same way as Sidney and Essex, must have made a great impression on James I considering the positive shower of titles and honours conferred on him after the accession. James was known for his admiration of well-favoured men.

All these circumstances point to the conclusion that Frances must have had beauty, brains and considerable charm. F.G. Waldon in "The Biographical Mirror", 3v.1795-1802, says: "The personal and mental attractions of this distinguished lady, only daughter and heiress to Sir Francis Walsingham, were the means of engaging the love of three of the most illustrious and charismatic men of the age."

Of the houses lived in by Frances, Barn Elms, when it passed out of private hands, became the Ranelagh Polo Club and is now a centre for outdoor and river sports on the Thames, the house long since gone. Englefield House eventually became the home of her daughter, Honora, and still remains magnificent today. Where Walsingham House stood in Seething Lane, there is now a Victorian office block, also named Walsingham House. Opposite it, St.Olave's Church, one of eight remaining churches which escaped the fire of London of 1666, stands over the original vault in which Anthony Bacon is buried. Of Frances's children, Elizabeth, Robert, Walter, Henry and Frances were baptised there. Penelope and Dorothy were baptised in All Hallows by the Tower. Robert's entry is on 22nd January 1590 which means that he was conceived in April 1589 and that Frances and Essex were probably married before that, rather earlier than generally supposed. The date usually given for their marriage is 1590. Most babies were baptised within days of their birth. Alternatively, the gun may have been jumped and the date of his birth altered for the benefit of posterity.

Of Frances's surviving children, only one died before she did. Elizabeth had an unhappy and childless marriage to the Earl of Rutland and the circumstances of her death were strange. Rutland had travelled in Europe in 1596 and became very ill when in Northern Italy. It was thought that whatever he suffered from resulted in impotency and that Elizabeth never lived with him as a wife but turned more and more to literary and theatrical occupations, as he did himself;

both of them very successfully. It must have been galling to see her mother effortlessly produce another three children after her marriage to Clanricarde. Elizabeth was particularly anxious to keep the Sidney line alive and there was now no chance that she could do so unless it were through a second marriage herself. Ben Jonson observed and recorded both the peculiarity of her marriage and the fact that she was very much admired. She did not accompany her husband on an embassy to King Christian IV of Denmark, but after the visit, the 1605 text of "Hamlet" was altered to include a good description of Elsinore Castle where Rutland had stayed. Inigo Jones, a friend of the Earl and Countess, was also on this visit.

In collaboration with Jones and Jonson, Elizabeth was a co-author of "The Masque of Hymenaei", a staggering production at Whitehall in 1606 to celebrate the marriage of her half-brother, Robert, 3rd Earl of Essex, aged sixteen, to Frances Howard, a member of the hated rival family. This was instigated by the King in an effort towards reconciliation. Elizabeth also danced in the Masque. Roger Rutland died in June 1612, almost immediately followed by Elizabeth in August 1612. This gave rise to a great deal of speculation. She was only twenty seven years old and was buried in St.Pauls with her father. The Earldom passed successively to two of Roger's brothers, both of whom died childless so that there may have been an inherited flaw.

Robert, 3rd Earl of Essex, also had a life of very mixed fortunes. Brought up in an around the Court and a companion of the Royal children, he turned his coat upon his future King, Charles I, and was eventually appointed, in July 1642, Captain General and Chief Commander of the Parliamentarian Army before the rise of Cromwell. His two marriages were disastrous. The first ended in a scandalous divorce from Frances Howard, following which he sat as juror at her trial for the murder of Sir Thomas Overbury, together with her lover, the Earl of Somerset, formally Robert Carr and one of the King's male favourites. They were both found guilty but the sentence was never carried out. Robert re-married, in 1630, Elizabeth Pawlett (or Paulet), a relative of the 5th Marquess of Winchester who was to take, as his second wife, none other than Honora de Burgh, the Earl's half-sister. Robert's second marriage did not last either and the only child, a son, died of plague. His Countess continued to live in Essex House, together with Lettice, his grandmother, and Robert's sister, Frances Devereux, now married to William Seymour, Marquess of Hertford, later 2nd

Duke of Somerset. The family wheels continued to turn and remain tightly interlocked.

Robert fought during the ensuing Civil War but was forced to surrender after the Battle of Lostwithiel on 2nd July 1644. He resigned his commission on 2nd April 1645 and was given Somerhill which had been sequestered by Parliament from Ulick, his half-brother. He died in September 1646, childless, and the Earldom of Essex died with him.

Dorothy Devereux, 2 months old at her father's execution, married Sir Henry Shirley of Staunton Harold on 18th May 1615, aged fifteen. Her daughter, Lettice, known as Leta, was to marry Thomas de Burgh, later 7th Earl of Clanricarde. More interlocking wheels. Dorothy divorced Henry Shirley, though both were Catholic, (Dorothy must have followed her mother's change of faith), but with three children to her name this cannot have been easy, and she is described thereafter as: "the fayrest, wittiest and newest widdowe of our time." She then married William Stafford of Blatherwyck in Northamptonshire. This was not the end of her contribution to history because, through her, her father's titles of Baron de Ferrars of Chartley, Bourchier and Lovaine were granted to her grandson, Robert of Chartley "in regard of his descent from his grandmother, Dorothy Devereux one of the sisters and heirs of Robert, Earl of Essex. He was also Baron Basset of Drayton and, by descent, created Viscount Tamworth and Earl Ferrars by Patent 3rd September 1711." Thus, some of the Essex inheritance was restored through the second Earl's youngest daughter and a great grandson of Frances inherited a good many of the titles of the Earls of Essex.

Ulick de Burgh, later fifth Earl of Clanricarde, born in Athlone Castle, was brought up and educated in England but spent a great deal of his time in Ireland. He succeeded his father on his death in 1635, inheriting Somerhill, and held the office of Governor of Galway from 1636. He was then living at Portumna. Having declared for King Charles I at the outbreak of the Irish rebellion in 1641, he was appointed Royalist Commander in Connaught and created Marquess of Clanricarde. He was not able to stop the Parliamentarian advance in Ireland, however, although he strove for unity and tolerance within the uneasy royalist-confederate alliance. After the execution of Charles I in 1649, Oliver Cromwell arrived in Dublin and the end came soon after. Portumna was besieged and fell and Ulick fought on courageously in Galway and Sligo and finally surrendered on terms, retiring to Somerhill which had been returned to him after the death of Robert, Earl of Essex, his half-brother. His Irish estates and titles were confiscated; Portumna was given to Henry Cromwell, the Lord Protector's youngest son. Ulick, Marquess of Clanricarde died in July 1657 leaving a widow, formerly Lady Anne Compton, and one daughter. Portumna was later restored to the Clanricardes.

Frances's two sons, Robert, Parliamentarian, and Ulick, Royalist, never opposed each other directly since Ulick fought only in Ireland. They might very well have done so, however, as they were both in action between 1642 and Robert's resignation in 1645, despite the fourteen years between them in age. It is interesting that Somerhill passed from Ulick to Robert and back again, though not in Frances's lifetime. There cannot have been much love lost between the two brothers.

Honora de Burgh, Frances's elder Clanricarde daughter, was married first to Garratt McCoghlan of Clonecknose in Ireland and then, on 4th October 1633, to John Paulet, 5th Marquess of Winchester. The Marquess is famous for his defence, during three sieges, of Basing House, his enormous country seat in Hampshire, against Parliamentary forces. Honora was with him during the final siege, when Basing House fell and was razed to the ground, and she joined him during his imprisonment afterwards in the Tower. (This suggests that she inherited some of her mother's gritty loyalty.) On their release they took over Englefield House in 1635. Englefield had been given by the Queen to her old friend Sir John Norris after the execution of Essex, but had been passed to others since then. Descendants of the Paulet family, evolving through the centuries, have owned the house ever since. Although Frances died in 1631, and Richard in 1635, the year his daughter moved there, their influence can, perhaps, be felt in the acquisition by Honora of this familiar place; a reward for loyalty and courage during the terrible years of the Civil War.

Mary de Burgh, the youngest of Frances's children, born when she was well over forty, also married into an Irish family. Her bridegroom was Edward Butler, a son of the 9th Earl of Ormonde, closely connected with the Clanricardes.

Among some of the slightly fictitious events recorded, the legend of Walsingham's "messengers", Nicholas Faunt and Walter Williams, carrying the memorised despatch from Paris to the Queen after the massacre of St.Bartholomew's Eve, has been told by several sources and bears a ring of truth although there is no proof that it happened.

Greville's appearance in the cast is purely fictitious, his character based on a charming parrot I often had the pleasure of looking after. He is, however, just the sort of unusual present Christopher Carleill might have given Frances. Parrots were rare and much prized. A portrait of Dorothy Devereux, married first to Sir Thomas Perrot, shows a small parrot perched on her left hand; a visual pun on her name.

Lettice, Countess of Essex, Countess of Leicester and, lastly, Lady Christopher Blount, lived to the age of ninety four and died in 1634. She had a gift for self-centred preservation which is hard to suppress and she walked a mile a day almost to the time of her death. Her grandson, Robert, remained close to her and was to spend every winter and Christmas with her at Chartley.

There is nothing recorded of Frances's association with Lady Bridget Manners, but it is more than likely that they were connected through her Uncle Roger Manners's undue interest in Frances's marriage to Sidney, Essex's close friendship with the younger Earl of Rutland, and the dates during which Brie served the Queen as Maid of Honour and Queen's Carver. Her story is historically true and she died in Rutland after a happy marriage and three children in 1604.

Neither is there any record that Richard de Burgh was with Essex during the Low Countries and Rouen campaigns, though, again, it is very likely. He had come down from Oxford and was a part of Essex's household. His ride with Frances to meet Essex at Plymouth and his presence at his execution are not recorded either.

Penelope Rich, on the other hand, is known to have been very close to Frances. It appears to have been a case of the attraction of opposites though they shared a common vitality, beauty and courage. Penelope, like Essex, hid nothing and cared nothing for public opinion and was as open and generous as he was. She and Frances made many journeys together especially to Chartley and Wanstead when Essex and Mountjoy were away and there are also several records of her visiting Barn Elms. She rose very quickly in eminence at the Court of James I, having been one of the high-ranking ladies sent to escort him from the border to Whitehall. James did not forget his friends and Penelope had been in correspondence with him before the Queen's death. In an effort to legalise her situation with Mountjoy, Penelope allowed Lord Rich to divorce her through the Ecclesiastical Courts in 1605. Unfortunately, the laws regarding re-marriage after divorce had just been tightened considerably and Penelope's marriage to her beloved Mountjoy at Wanstead, now their home, on 26th December 1605, met with rigid disapproval from the King. Penelope was, therefore, never recognised as the Countess of Devonshire, nor were her children considered legitimate. It had been a great love affair and ended very sadly. Mountjoy died of a fever on 3rd April 1606 and Penelope, heartbroken, was obliged to face most unpleasant proceedings in Star Chamber early in 1607 in order to obtain the inheritance that he had carefully arranged for her and for their offspring. This was eventually successful and much of his vast wealth passed to their five children. Penelope did not survive to enjoy the provision Charles had made for her and died on 7th July 1607, aged forty four. She is buried in All Hallows by the Tower, the resting place of most of the family; one very small entry dated 7th October 1607 reads: "A Lady Devorex." Since her marriage to Mountjoy was not recognised, society had followed the King's lead and, sadly, ostracized her.

Frances had remained close to her to the end, however. She and Richard certainly visited her at Wanstead in the early autumn of 1606.

The gifted and deadly Francis Bacon, so instrumental in sending Essex to his death, outlived his elder brother, Anthony, by many years. With the Accession of James I, his fortunes soared and he moved smoothly from appointments to Solicitor General and Attorney General, followed by Lord Chancellor in 1618. Created Baron Verulam and, later, Viscount St.Alban, he fell from grace in 1618 on charges of corruption for which he was fined £40,000 and sent to the Tower very briefly. This huge fine was commuted, but he was barred from holding any further office. He died, rather mundanely, in 1626, as a result of an experiment on refrigeration. He stuffed a chicken with snow and succumbed to pneumonia.

Robert and Barbara Sidney prospered also under King James. He had been knighted for gallantry after Zutphen but became Lord Chamberlain to Queen Anne in 1603. He was created Viscount de L'Isle in 1605 and finally succeeded his uncle as Earl of Leicester in 1615. As age took over, he and Barbara and their ten surviving children must have had much family interchange between Penshurst and nearby Somerhill. Robert Sidney, himself, was something of a poet and writer and this golden thread came to flower, as it had in Elizabeth

Sidney, in his daughter, Mary, later Lady Wroth, a renowned writer and personality.

Henry IV of France was assassinated in Paris on 14th May 1610, a just and vigorous King, much loved by his people, who had done his best to consolidate his turbulent country. Known as "Good King Henry", his declaration: "If God spares me, I will ensure that there is no working man in my kingdom who does not have the means to have a chicken in the pot every Sunday", perhaps sums up the man and his attitude.

Frances's life, as I have recorded it, is, therefore, based on all available fact and a little relevant story-telling. A great deal of the writing has been done while waiting for the small ferry connecting the islands of Luing and Seil off the coast of Scotland. This has been a great pleasure and given me ample opportunity to observe wave, wind and weather, bird and animal life in this beautiful corner of the west.

BIBLIOGRAPHY

Aikin, J: General Biographies: 1799-1815:

Baird, Henry M.: The Huguenots and Henry of Navarre

Camden, William: Annales in The History of the most Renowned and Victorious Princess Elizabeth (1675): The true and royall history of the famous Empresse Elizabeth: Camden Miscellany: "Journal of Sir Francis Walsingham from December 1570 to April 1583."

Cripps-Day. F.H.: History of the Tournament:

Daniel, John: Egerton Papers and State Trials.

Du Maurier, Daphne: Golden Lads:

Freedman, Sylvia: Poor Penelope: Lady Penelope Rich. An Elizabethan Woman:

Froude, J.A.: A History of England from the Fall of Wolsey to the Defeat of the Armada (12 Vols. 1856-1870)

Greville, Sir Fulke: The Life of the Renowned Sir Philip Sidney:

Hasted: Kent, 1999.

Hume, M.A.S: The Courtships of Queen Elizabeth (1898, 1904)

Hutton, Ronald: The Rise and Fall of Merry England. The Ritual Years: 1944

Kamen, Henry: European Society 1500-1700:

Koenigsberger, Moss & Bowler: Europe in the Sixteenth Century.

Lacey, Robert: Robert, Earl of Essex: An Elizabethan Icarus.

Lloyd, Dr.David: State Worthies During the Reigns of Henry VIII, Edward VI, Mary, Elizabeth, James I and Charles I: 2V, 1766

Nicholas, Sir Harris: Memoirs of the Life and Times of Sir Christopher Hatton. 1848. Life of William Davison, 1823.

Nicholl, Charles: The Reckoning: The murder of Christopher Marlowe:

Oglander, Sir John: Oglander Memoirs: 1660.

Oxford Dictionary of National Biography.

Read, Conyers: The Compleat Ambassador: Mr.Secretary Walsingham.Vol. 1, 2 & 3.

Robinson, J.H.: Readings in European History 2 Vols.1906

Sitwell, Edith: The Queens and the Hive:

Stewart, Alan: Philip Sidney. A Double Life.
Strachey, Lytton: Elizabeth and Essex
Strong, Sir Roy: Art and Power: 1450-1650.
Tradescant: Tradescant's Orchard:
Trevelyan, G.M: Illustrated English Social History
Waldeman, Milton: Elizabeth and Leicester:
Worsley, Richard: The History of the Isle of Wight, 1781.

PERSONAE

ALENÇON: François Duc D'Alencon. Fourth son of Henry II of France and Catherine de Medici. Suitor of Elizabeth I.

ALVA: Duke of Alva. Commander of Spanish Forces in Netherlands.

ANJOU: Henri Duc D'Anjou. Third son of Henry II of France and Catherine de Medici. Later King Henri III of France.

ARUNDEL: Henry FitzAlan, 12th Earl of Arundel. Involved in Northern Rising 1569.

AUDLEY: 8th Baron Audley. Fought in Netherlands Campaign and later in Ireland.

BABINGTON: Anthony. Instigator of the Babington Plot intended to murder the Queen and put the Queen of Scots on the throne.

BACHELER: Daniel. Composer and musician. Employed by Sir Francis Walsingham, accompanied Sir Philip Sidney to the Netherlands and remained with the Essex household. Eventually employed by Queen Anne.

BACON: Anthony, son of Nicholas Bacon, Lord Keeper. Intelligence agent to Walsingham and Essex.

BACON: Francis, brother of Anthony, Attorney General, Lord Chancellor, Baron Verulam and Viscount St.Alban.

BACON: Lady Anne. Mother of Anthony and Francis Bacon. Wife of Sir Nicholas Bacon, former Keeper of the Great Seal.

BAGOT: Robert. Servant of the Earl of Essex. Son of his agent in Staffordshire.

BEALE: Lady Edith. Wife of Robert Beale. Sister to Lady Ursula Walsingham. Mother of Margaret and Catherine.

BEALE: Robert. Brother in law to Lady Ursula Walsingham. Diplomat and Clerk of the Privy Council.

BEATON: James. Mary Queen of Scots' official ambassador in Paris.

BEAUMONT: Francis. Actor and playwright. Working with Shakespeare's Company.

BEDFORD: Countess of Bedford. Grandmother and guardian of Lady Bridget Manners.

BERKELEY: Sir Richard. The Earl of Essex's custodian on his return to Essex House in 1600.

BIZARI: Pietro. History student from Perugia. Working for Walsingham in Paris.

BLOUNT: Sir Christopher. Married to Lettice, Countess of Essex and Leicester. Executed after Essex rebellion.

BLOUNT: Mountjoy. Illegitimate son of Lady Penelope Rich and Lord Mountjoy.

BRIGHT: Timothy. Cambridge scholar involved in St.Bartholomew's Eve.

BROUNCKER: Sir Henry. Courtier.

BRUNO: Giordano. Italian priest, astronomer and agent.

BRYDGES: Mistress Elizabeth. Maid of Honour to the Queen. Daughter of Lord Chandos. Mistress of the Earl of Essex.

BRYSKETT: Lodowick. Travelling companion to Philip Sidney.

BURGHLEY: Lady Mildred. Wife of Lord Burghley.

BURGHLEY: Lord William Cecil. Secretary of State to Queen Elizabeth I.

CABRERA: Spanish historian.

CAREY: Sir John. Second husband of Joyce Denny, Walsingham's mother and brother of William Carey, husband of Mary Boleyn.

CARLEILL: Christopher. Stepson to Sir Francis Walsingham. Military and Naval Commander.

CARLEILL: Alice. Stepdaughter to Sir Francis Walsingham. Wife of Christopher Hoddeson. Mother of Ursula Hoddeson.

CARLEILL: Anne. First wife to Sir Francis Walsingham. Mother of his stepchildren, Christopher and Alice.

CARLOS: Don Carlos. Son and heir to King Philip II of Spain.

CAROSO: Fabritio. Court dancing master.

CARR: Robert. Later Earl of Somerset. Lover of Frances, wife of Robert, 3rd Earl of Essex.

CASIMIR: Johan. Ruler of part of the Electoral Palatinate. Friend of Sir Philip Sidney.

CASTELNAU: Michel de Castelnau, Seigneur de la Mauvissierre. French Ambassador in London. Agent for Mary Queen of Scots.

CECIL: Robert, Secretary of State. Son of Lord Burghley.

CHARLES IX: King of France. Succeeded his brother Francis II.

CHARLES OF AUSTRIA: Archduke Charles of Austria. Brother to Emperor Maximilian. Suitor of Elizabeth I.

CLOWES: Dr.William. Doctor to Sir Philip Sidney in the Netherlands.

COMPTON: Lady Anne. Wife of Ulick, Marquess of Clanricarde.

CONDÉ: Prince de Conde. Leader of Huguenot Party in France. Cousin of Henry of Navarre.

CONIGSBY: Thomas. Cousin of Philip Sidney.

CROMPTON: Thomas. Trustee for the Earl of Essex for Englefield House

CROMWELL: Henry. Son of the Lord Protector, Oliver Cromwell. Held Portumna until the Restoration.

CUFFE: Henry. Greek scholar and advisor to Earl of Essex.

D'ANGOULÊME: Duc d'Angouleme. Bastard brother of the Valois princes.

D'ÉSPES: Don Guerau d'Espes. Spanish Ambassador to London.

DACRE: Lord Leonard. Involved in Northern Rising.

DAKINS: Margaret. Married to Walter Devereux, brother of the Earl of Essex. Married, secondly, Thomas Sidney. Thirdly Thomas Hoby.

DANIEL: John. Husband of Jane Rehora.

DANVERS: Sir Charles. Fellow soldier of Earl of Essex and co-conspirator in Essex rebellion.

DANVERS: Sir Henry. Brother of Charles. With Earl of Essex in Irish Campaign. Co-conspirator in Essex rebellion.

De BEAUVAIS: General Francois, Sieur de Briquemault. Huguenot General killed on St.Bartholomew's Eve.

De BURGH: Honora. Elder daughter of Richard, Earl of Clanricarde and Frances Walsingham. Married first, Garratt McCoghlan. Second, John Paulet, 5th Marquess of Winchester.

De BURGH: Mary. 2nd daughter of Frances Walsingham and Richard, 4th Earl of Clanricarde. Married Edward Butler, son of 9th Earl of Ormonde.

De BURGH: Richard, 4th Earl of Clanricarde, Earl of St.Albans. Third husband of Frances Walsingham.

De BURGH: Ulick, 5th Earl of Clanricarde and later Marquess of Clanricarde. Son of Frances Walsingham and Richard, 4th Earl of Clanricarde.

De COLIGNY: Admiral Gaspard de Coligny. Leader of Huguenot Party. Murdered on St.Bartholomew's Eve 1572.

De COLIGNY: Louise, widowed Princess of Orange. Wife of William of Orange, daughter of Admiral de Coligny.

De FERIA: The Duke and Duchess de Feria. King Philip's Ambassador and his English wife, former Lady in Waiting to Queen Mary Tudor.

De MONTGOMERY: Comte de Montgomery. Huguenot leader and friend of Earl of Essex.

De NEMOURS. Madame. Friend of the Guise family.

De NEVERS: Duc de Nevers. Advisor to King Charles IX.

De SCHOMBERG: Gaspard. French Ambassador to Germany.

De THOU: Jaques-Auguste. Canon of Notre Dame. Later diplomat and historian.

DEE: Dr.John. Mathematician, astrologer, alchemist and navigator. Advisor to the Queen. Friend of Sir Frances Walsingham.

DENBIGH: Robert, Baron Denbigh. Son of Robert, Earl of Leicester and Lettice, Countess of Leicester. Died in infancy.

DENNY: Edward. Cousin of Frances Walsingham. Fellow jouster of Sir Philip Sidney.

DEVEREUX: Dorothy, later Lady Shirley and Lady Stafford. Youngest daughter of Frances Walsingham and 2nd Earl of Essex

DEVEREUX: Frances, later Duchess of Somerset. Daughter of Frances Walsingham and 2nd Earl of Essex.

DEVEREUX: Henry, died early. Son of Frances Walsingham and 2nd Earl of Essex.

DEVEREUX: Penelope, died early. Daughter of Frances Walsingham and 2nd Earl of Essex.

DEVEREUX: Lady Dorothy. Daughter of Walter, lst Earl of Essex. Married first Sir Thomas Perrot, secondly the Earl of Northumberland. Sister of Penelope Rich and the Earl of Essex.

DEVEREUX: Robert, 3rd Earl of Essex, Captain General and Chief Commander of the Parliamentarian army. Son of Frances Walsingham and 2nd Earl of Essex.

DEVEREUX: Walter, died early. Son of Frances Walsingham and 2nd Earl of Essex.

DEVEREUX: Walter. Illegitimate son of the Earl of Essex by Mistress Elizabeth Southwell.

DEVEREUX: Walter. Brother of Earl of Essex. Killed at the siege of Rouen. Married to Margaret Dakins.

DONNE: John. Poet who twice sailed with the Earl of Essex's expeditions.

DRAKE: Admiral Sir Francis: Explorer, pirate and Sea Captain.

Du PLESSIS MORNAY: Philippe. French Ambassador to England. Friend of Sir Philip Sidney.

DUDLEY: Robert. Illegitimate son of Earl of Leicester by Lady Douglas Sheffield.

DYER: Edward. Poet and playwright. Friend of Sir Philip Sidney.

EGERTON: Thomas, lst Viscount Brackley, Keeper of the Great Seal and Lord Chancellor. Custodian of Earl of Essex.

ELIZABETH I: Queen of England.

EMPEROR RUDOLF II: Holy Roman Emperor. Son of Emperor Maximilian II.

EMPEROR MAXIMILIAN II: Holy Roman Emporer.

ERIK OF SWEDEN: Prince Erik of Sweden. Suitor of Elizabeth I.

ESSEX: Robert Devereux, 2nd Earl of Essex, Baron de Ferrars of Chartley, Bourchier and Lovaine. Second husband of Frances Walsingham.

ESSEX: Walter, 1st Earl of Essex. Father of Robert Devereux, 2nd Earl of Essex. Married Lettice Knollys, cousin of the Queen.

FAUNT: Nicholas. Agent of Sir Francis Walsingham.

FISHER: John. Groom to Philip Sidney

FITZWILLIAM: George. Agent employed by Walsingham and Sir John Hawkins.

FRANCIS II: King of France. Second son of Henry II of France and Catherine de Medici. Married to Mary Stuart, later Queen of Scots.

FREDERICK III: Elector of the Palatinate.

FROBISHER: Explorer and Navigator.

GAMAGE: Barbara. Wife of Sir Robert Sidney, later Countess of Leicester.

GIFFORD: George. Leicester's chaplain attending Sir Philip Sidney at Arnhem.

GILBERT: Sir Humphrey. Sea Commander, explorer and navigator.

GORGES: Sir Ferdinand. Knighted at the siege of Rouen. Governor of the Fort at Plymouth. Follower of Essex and co-conspirator in rebellion of 1601.

GREVILLE: A small green parrot.

GREVILLE: Sir Fulke. Courtier, soldier and friend of Sir Philip Sidney.

GREY: Lord Grey. Former fellow campaigner of Essex, subsequently enemy and follower of Cecil.

GRUITHUISSENS: Madam. Widow of a judge in Arnhem. Hostess to Sir Philip Sidney when wounded at Zutphen.

GUISE: The Duc de Guise. He and his family headed the Catholic faction in France.

HAKLUYT: Explorer and Navigator.

HARDING: Mary. Companion and maid to Lady Bridget Manners.

HARVEY: Gabriel. Poet and playwright.

HATTON: Sir Christopher: Courtier and favourite of Elizabeth I. Later Vice Chamberlain and Lord Chancellor.

HAWKINS: Sir John. English Admiral and pirate. Pioneer of the Slave Trade from Africa to the West Indies.

HOBY: Edward. Son of Lady Elizabeth Russell by her first marriage.

HOBY: Thomas Posthumous: Son of Lady Russell by her first marriage. Translated Castiglione's "The Courtier" into English. Married Margaret Dakins after the death of Thomas Sidney.

HODDESON: Christopher. Husband of Alice Carleill.

HOHENLOE: Count. Netherlands Commander under William of Orange and Prince Maurice of Orange.

HOWARD: Admiral Lord Howard of Effingham. Commanding the English ships against the Spanish Armada.

HOWARD: Frances. First wife of Robert, 3rd Earl of Essex.

HOWARD: Lady Mary. Lady in Waiting to the Queen. Mistress of the Earl of Essex.

HOWARD: Lord Henry. Younger brother of Duke of Norfolk.

HOWARD: Queen Catherine. Fifth wife of Henry VIII.

HUNTINGDON: Henry, 3rd Earl of Huntingdon. Brother-in-law of Earl of Leicester. Guardian to Penelope and Dorothy Devereux.

JAMES: Dr. John: Doctor to Sir Philip Sidney in the Netherlands.

JOHN OF AUSTRIA: Don John of Austria. Half-brother of King Philip II of Spain. Regent in the Netherlands.

JONES: Inigo. Architect and artist.

JONSON: Ben. Poet and playwright.

KILLIGREW: Sir Henry. Diplomat in Paris.

KING CHARLES I: King of England. Second son of King James I.

KING CHARLES IX: King of France. Succeeded his brother, Francis II.

KING CHRISTIAN IV of Denmark: Brother of Queen Anne, wife of James I.

KING FRANCIS II. King of France. Second son of Henry II of France and Catherine de Medici. Married to Mary Stuart, later Queen of Scots.

KING HENRI III: King of France. Former Duc d'Anjou. Succeeded his brother Charles IX.

KING HENRY OF NAVARRE: Later King Henry IV of France.

KING HENRY VIII: King of England. Father of Queen Elizabeth I.

KING JAMES VI OF SCOTLAND AND I of ENGLAND. Son of Mary, Queen of Scots and Lord Henry Darnley.

KING OF PORTUGAL: Dom Antonio. Deposed by Spanish 1581.

KING PHILIP II OF SPAIN. Former husband of Mary Tudor, Queen of England. Godfather of Sir Philip Sidney.

KNOLLYS: Sir William. Uncle of 2nd Earl of Essex, later lst Earl of Banbury.

KNOLLYS: Lettice. Married first to Walter 1st Earl of Essex, second to Robert, Earl of Leicester, third to Sir Christopher Blount.

LANGUET: Hubert. Ambassador to Paris for Saxony.

LASKI: Prince Albert. Polish Diplomat.

Le MOYNE: Jacques. Artist.

LEANDER: Steward to Sir Francis Walsingham.

LECLERC: Nicholas. Secretary to Castelnau, French Ambassador in London.

LEE: Sir Henry. Queen's Champion. Founder of the Accession Day Jousts. Friend of Sir Philip Sidney.

LEE: Captain Thomas Lee. Supporter of Earl of Essex. Planned to wrest a stay of his execution from the Queen and was consequently beheaded.

LEICESTER: Robert Dudley, Earl of Leicester. Favourite of Elizabeth I. Married first to Amy Robsart. Secondly to Lettice, Countess of Essex.

LENNOX: Esmé, Earl of Lennox. Guardian of James VI of Scotland.

LINCOLN: Henry Clinton, Earl of Lincoln.

LOBBET: Jean. Protestant intellectual.

LOPEZ: Dr. Portuguese physician to Queen Elizabeth I. Executed for supposedly plotting against the Queen.

MADDOX: Griffin. Servant of Philip Sidney.

MANNERS: Lady Bridget. Eldest daughter of 3rd Earl of Rutland. Maid of Honour and Queen's Carver to Elizabeth I. Married Robert Tyrwhitt.

MANNERS: Roger. Great Uncle of Lady Bridget Manners. Courtier.

MAR: Earl of Mar. Guardian of James VI of Scotland as a boy.

MARLOWE: Christopher. Poet and playwright. Murdered in Deptford, 1593.

MAUREVERT: Hired assassin of Guise family.

MEDINA SIDONIA: The Duke of Medina Sidonia: Commander of the Spanish Armada of 1588,

MEYRICK: Sir Gilly (or Gelly). Agent to the Earl of Essex. Executed after the conspiracy and attempted uprising 1601.

MILLES: Francis. Personal Assistant to Sir Francis Walsingham.

MOFFET: Thomas. Doctor to Lady Mary Pembroke, sister of Sir Philip Sidney.

MORGAN: Thomas. Mary Queen of Scots' main agent in Paris.

MOTTE FÉNELON: Sieur de La Motte Fenelon. French Ambassador to England and Scotland.

MOUNTEAGLE: William Parker, 4th Baron Mounteagle. Co-conspirator in Essex rebellion.

MOUNTJOY: Charles, Baron Mountjoy, formerly Charles Blount, became Earl of Devonshire.

NASSAU: Prince Maurice of Nassau. Son of William of Orange.

NAVARRE: King Henry of Navarre, later King Henry IV of France.

NAVARRE: King Antione of Navarre. Father of King Henry. Leader of French Huguenots.

NAVARRE: Queen Jeanne d'Albret of Navarre. Mother of King Henry.

NEWPORT: Sir WillIam. Nephew and heir of Sir Christopher Hatton.

NORFOLK: Thomas Howard, 4th Duke of Norfolk. Involved in the Ridolphi Plot. Beheaded 1572.

NORRIS: Sir Henry. Later Lord Norris. Ambassador to France.

NORRIS: Sir John. Soldier in almost every Elizabethan campaign. Son of the Queen's old friend, Lady Norris, nicknamed her "Crow".

NORTH: Lord North. Soldier in Netherlands Campaign.

NORTHUMBERLAND: Henry Percy, 8th Duke of Northumberland. Second husband of Dorothy Devereux, sister of the Earl of Essex.

NORTHUMBERLAND: Thomas Percy, 7th Earl of Northumberland. Involved in the Northern Rising 1569

O'MALLEY: Grania or Grace. Irish lady pirate.

ORANGE: Prince Maurice of Nassau, Son of William of Orange.

ORANGE: William of Orange, Ruler of the Netherlands.

OVERBURY: Sir Thomas. Murdered by Frances, third Countess of Essex and her lover Robert Carr, Earl of Somerset.

OXFORD: Edward de Vere. Earl of Oxford. Courtier, soldier, married to Lady Anne, daughter of Lord Burghley.

PARMA: The Duke of Parma: Philip II of Spain's Governor in the Low Countries.

PAWLETT (or Paulet): Elizabeth. Second wife of Robert, 3rd Earl of Essex.

PELHAM: Sir William. Soldier and Courtier. Friend of Sir Philip Sidney.

PEMBROKE: Henry, 2nd Earl of Pembroke. Husband of Mary Sidney.

PEMBROKE: Mary, Countess of Pembroke. Sister of Sir Philip Sidney.

PEREZ: Antonio. Former member of Philip II of Spain's Court. A refugee from the Spanish Inquisition. Member of Essex household.

PERROT: Sir Thomas. First husband of Lady Dorothy Devereux, sister of Lady Penelope Rich and of the Earl of Essex.

PHELIPPES: Thomas. Employed by Sir Francis Walsingham as codebreaker and agent.

POLEY: Robert. Agent of Walsingham, Leicester and Burghley.

POOLE: Alice. Waiting woman to Lady Ursula Walsingham and nurse to Frances Walsingham.

POPE GREGORY XIII. At the time of St.Bartholomew's Eve.

POPE PIUS V: Pope in 1570. Published Papal Bull excommunicating Queen Elizabeth I.

POPHAM: Sir John, Speaker of the House of Commons, Attorney General and Lord Chief Justice

QUEEN ANNE: Anne of Denmark, wife of JAMES VI of Scotland and 1st of England. Sister of King Christian IV of Denmark.

QUEEN CATHERINE DE MEDICI: Dowager Queen of France. Wife of King Francis II of France.

QUEEN CATHERINE HOWARD: 5TH wife of King Henry VIII.

QUEEN ELIZABETH OF FRANCE: Wife to Charles IX. Daughter of Emperor Maximilian II.

QUEEN ELIZABETH I: Queen of England.

RALEIGH: Sir Walter. Courtier, Sea and Land Commander.

RAMUS: Petrus. Protestant humanist. Killed on St.Bartholomew's Eve.

REHORA: Jane. Companion and maid. Came with Frances Sidney from Netherlands. In charge of her Essex children. Later married to John Daniel.

RICH: Penelope, Lady Rich. Born Penelope Devereux, sister of 2nd Earl of Essex. Mistress and unacknowledged wife of Baron Charles Mountjoy.

RICH: Essex. Daughter of Lady Penelope and Lord Rich.

RICH: Henry: Son of Lady Penelope and Lord Rich.

RICH: Lettice. Daughter of Lady Penelope and Lord Rich

RICH: Lord Robert. Husband of Penelope Devereux.

RICH: Penelope. Illegtimate daughter of Lady Penelope Rich and her lover, Charles Blount, later Lord Mountjoy.

RICH: Robert: Son of Lady Penelope and Lord Rich

RIDOLPHI: Roberto. Agent of Pope Pius V from Florence. Instigator of "Ridolphi Plot".

ROBSART: Amy. First wife of the Earl of Leicester.

ROSS: Bishop of Ross. Mary, Queen of Scots's envoy in London.

RUSSELL: Lady Elizabeth. Formerly Lady Hoby. Mother of Edward and Thomas Hoby.

RUSSELL: Lord John. Son of the Earl of Bedford.

RUSSELL: Mistress. Maid of Honour to the Queen. Mistress of the Earl of Essex.

RUSSELL: Sir William Russell. Son of the Earl of Bedford. Fought in Netherlands Campaign with Sir Philip Sidney.

RUTLAND: Roger, 4th Earl of Rutland. Married to Elizabeth Sidney. Brother of Lady Bridget Manners.

SACKFORD: Henry. Keeper of the Privy Purse. Custodian of Lady Penelope Rich during her detention.

SANTA CRUZ: The Marquis of Santa Cruz. Commander of the Spanish Armada of 1588. Died before the event.

SCROPE: Lady Eleanor. Formerly Carey. An old friend of the Queen and of the Devereux family.

SEYMOUR: Admiral Lord Thomas: Husband of Queen Katherine Parr after the death of Henry VIII.

SEYMOUR: William. Later Duke of Somerset. Married Frances Devereux, daughter of Frances Walsingham and Robert, 2nd Earl of Essex.

SHAKESPEARE: William. Poet and playwright.

SHEFFIELD: Lady Douglas. Mistress of the Earl of Leicester and mother of his illegitimate son, Robert Dudley. Married later to Sir William Stafford.

SHIRLEY: Lettice (Leta) . Daughter of Dorothy Devereux, granddaughter of Frances Walsingham. Married Thomas de Burgh, 7th Earl of Clanricarde.

SHIRLEY: Sir Thomas. Fought in Netherlands Campaign.

SHREWSBURY: George, 6th Earl of Shrewsbury. Keeper of Mary Queen of Scots.

SIDNEY: Sir Robert. Younger brother of Sir Philip Sidney. Knighted at battle of Zutphen, Later Lord Chamberlain to Queen Anne, Viscount De L'Isle and Earl of Leicester.

SIDNEY: Elizabeth. Only surviving child of Frances Walsingham and Sir Philip Sidney. Married to Roger, 4th Earl of Rutland.

SIDNEY: Lady Mary Sidney. Mother of Sir Philip Sidney, Sister of the Earl of Leicester.

SIDNEY: Sir Henry. Father of Sir Philip Sidney, Robert, Thomas, Mary and Ambrosia Sidney. Husband of Lady Mary Dudley.

SIDNEY: Sir Philip. First husband of Frances Walsingham. Died after the battle of Zutphen in the Netherlands in 1586. Poet, Diplomat and Soldier.

SIDNEY: Thomas. Younger brother of Sir Philip and Sir Robert Sidney.

SIMIER: French courtier and marriage broker for François Duc d'Anjou.

SMITH: Sir Thomas. Diplomat in Paris.

SOUTHAMPTON: Henry Wriothesley, Earl of Southampton. Poet, playwright, actor and supporter of Earl of Essex.

SOUTHWELL: Mistress Elizabeth. Lady in Waiting to the Queen and mistress of the Earl of Essex.

SPENSER: Edmund. Poet and playwright.

STEWART: Sir Robert. Diplomat.

STUART: Mary, Queen of Scots. Formerly Queen of France, married to King Francis II. Later married Lord Darnley and then the Earl of Bothwell.

STUART: Prince Henry. Eldest son of JAMES VI of Scotland and First of England.

TALBOT: Lord. Son of the Earl of Shrewsbury.

THORPE: John. Architect and designer of Somerhill.

THROCKMORTON: Sir Nicholas. Diplomat and Politician.

THROCKMORTON: Francis. Nephew of Sir Nicholas Throckmorton. Involved in Throckmorton Plot and executed.

TINOCO: A Spanish agent employed by Dom Antonio of Portugal; executed for plotting against the Queen.

TRACEY: Henry. Page to 2nd Earl of Essex.

TSAR IVAN (The Terrible): Tsar of all the Russias.

TURENNE: Duke of Turenne. Henry IV's envoy to English Court.

TYRONE: Hugh O'Neill, Earl of Tyrone. Leader of the Irish rebellion.

TYRWHITT: Robert. Cousin and husband of Lady Bridget Manners.

VALOIS: Marguerite de Valois. Daughter of Henry II of France. Married to Henry of Navarre.

VASARI: Giorgio. Artist to Pope Gregory XIII.

VERE: Sir Francis. Friend of the Earl of Essex. Fought in the Netherlands's campaign and the Cadiz expedition.

VERNON: Elizabeth. Cousin of the Earl of Essex. Married Henry Wriothesley, Earl of Southampton.

WALSINGHAM: Lady Ursula. Wife of Sir Francis Walsingham. Former wife of Sir Richard Worsley.

WALSINGHAM: Sir Francis. Secretary of State to Queen Elizabeth I and founder of her Intelligence Service.

WALSINGHAM: Frances, Lady Sidney, Countess of Essex, Countess of Clanricarde and St.Albans.

WALSINGHAM: Joyce. Formerly Joyce Denny. Mother of Sir Francis Walsingham. Married, secondly, Sir John Carey.

WALSINGHAM: Mary. Sister of Frances Walsingham. Died aged six.

WALSINGHAM: Thomas. Cousin of Frances Walsingham. Employed by Sir Francis Walsingham. Sponsor of Christopher Marlowe.

WALSINGHAM: William. Father of Sir Francis Walsingham.

WARWICK: Earl of Warwick. Brother of Earl of Leicester.

WATSON: Thomas. Poet

WESTMORLAND: Charles Neville, 6th Earl of Westmorland. Involved in the Northern Rising 1569

WHARTON: Lord. Guest of Walsingham in Paris. Later, suitor of Lady Bridget Manners.

WHITE: Harry. Servant of Sir Philip Sidney

WHITGIFT: John, Archbishop of Canterbury.

WICKERSON: John. Employed by Sir Francis Walsingham. First suitor of Frances Walsingham.

WILLIAMS: Sir Roger. Professional soldier and friend of the Earl of Essex.

WILLIAMS: Walter. Employed by Sir Francis Walsingham.

WILLOUGHBY: Peregrine Bertie, 13th Baron Willoughby de Eresby. General of British Forces in the Netherlands following Leicester's departure. Subsequently fought for Huguenots under Henry of Navarre.

WILSON: Sir Thomas. Secretary of State with Walsingham.

WINCHESTER: 5th Marquess of Winchester. Married Honora de Burgh, daughter of Frances and Richard, Earl and Countess of Clanricarde.

WORSLEY: Sir Richard. Captain of the Isle of Wight and first husband of Lady Ursula Walsingham.

WRIGHT: Robert. Trustee for the Earl of Essex for Englefield House.

WROTH: Lady Mary. Daughter of Sir Robert Sidney. Writer and poet.

YOUNG: Bartholomew. Playwright.